Bugs Alive!

A GUIDE TO KEEPING AUSTRALIAN INVERTEBRATES

ALAN HENDERSON, DEANNA HENDERSON
AND JESSIE SINCLAIR

MUSEUMVICTORIA

Bugs alive: a guide to keeping Australian invertebrates

Published by Museums Victoria 2008

Reprinted 2012, 2014, 2017

Printed in China through Asia Pacific Offset

Museums Victoria
GPO Box 666
Melbourne VIC 3001 Australia
Telephone: + 61 3 8341 7777
http://museumvictoria.com.au

DESIGN
Toni Jolic for Design Consortium

National Library of Australia
Cataloguing-in-Publications data:

Henderson, Alan, 1970–
        Bugs alive : a guide to keeping Australian invertebrates.

        Includes index.
        ISBN 9780975837085 (pbk.).

        1. Captive invertebrates - Australia. 2. Invertebrates -
        Australia. 3. Animal culture - Australia. I. Henderson,
        Deanna, 1979- . II. Sinclair, Jessie, 1980- . III. Museum
        Victoria. IV. Title.

        592.0994

Contents

Amazing Australian bugs 4

Care guides

Ants 12
Beetles 20
Butterflies and moths 34
Cockroaches 42
Crickets and katydids 50
Grasshoppers 64
Mantids 74
Phasmids 80
True bugs 90
Wasps 96
Primitive spiders 100
Modern spiders 110
Scorpions 124
Centipedes 132
Millipedes 138
Snails and slugs 144

Reference

Housing 154
Food and water 167
Health 176
Display your invertebrates 185

Acknowledgements 193
Glossary 194
Index 197

The Splendid Gumleaf Katydid is just one of Australia's amazing bugs.

Amazing Australian bugs

From voracious mantids to pop-eyed katydids, Australia has a wealth of fascinating **invertebrates** envied by bug keepers and enthusiasts across the world. Many of Australia's invertebrates are found nowhere else in the world. We have the fastest runners, the loudest callers and the most venomous spiders on Earth. We even have a bizarre stick insect that has been dragged back from the brink of extinction. Australia also has a mind-boggling number of invertebrates; close to 100 000 species are known, and countless more exist. In fact 99% of all animal species are invertebrates! This book only covers a tiny fraction of Australian species, those that are most popular and those most suited to captivity.

Why keep bugs?

Keeping bugs can be a truly fascinating and educational experience. Anyone can keep them in the home, the classroom or in professional displays. There are many advantages to keeping bugs compared to other groups of animals.

- Bugs are small and can be kept in a limited space. Even people living in small apartments have room for them.

- They can be relatively inexpensive to acquire and maintain, as the animals and their food may come from your own garden.

- They make a great alternative to domestic pets, and are an excellent talking point in your lounge room.

- The educational benefits of keeping bugs are huge. Where else can you see a living food chain in action or an entire life cycle in a school term?

- Many bugs can be handled, and these close encounters are unforgettable experiences.

This book offers you a chance to get up close and personal with some of the world's most amazing animals and watch some truly captivating behaviour.

Bug keeping in Australia

Bug keeping has become very popular in Australia, and recently there has been a big increase in the number of species being kept. In Europe and the United States of America, bug keeping has a huge following and a long history. There are conferences and exhibitions at which invertebrate keepers get together to compare their keeping methods and to buy and sell bugs.

Many zoos and museums overseas have live bugs on display, but until recently this has not been common in Australia. In 2004 Melbourne Museum opened the world-renowned *Bugs Alive!* exhibition, which has played a part in igniting the interest in keeping invertebrates in Australia. *Bugs Alive!* currently has a comprehensive and diverse display of live invertebrates, with 50 enclosures and 90 species on display. The authors' combined experience in invertebrate keeping includes the research, development and maintenance of this exhibition. Much knowledge has been drawn from this experience, culminating in this book – the first comprehensive guide to keeping Australian invertebrates.

Where do I get bugs?

There are many ways in which to get your invertebrates.

- **Collect your own.** This can be as simple as going into the backyard, or perhaps taking a trip further afield. It is important to check with your state's or territory's environmental authority before doing so, as some species are protected in certain areas. When collecting bugs make sure you do so responsibly without damaging valuable habitats, and only take what you need.

- **Buy them from commercial suppliers.** There are a number ways you can buy bugs. Many species are available through pet shops and online. Many large, spectacular species can be purchased in this way. Unfortunately some suppliers appear to be exploiting fragile wild populations for financial gain. If you decide to purchase invertebrates,

choosing captive-bred animals will ensure that you are not contributing to this. Captive-bred invertebrates are also of a known age, and more likely to be free of diseases and parasites.

- **Trade with other bug keepers.** This is a great way to share knowledge and animals. There are many societies of bug keepers that focus on particular groups such as tarantulas, stick insects and scorpions to name a few. Being a member of these societies will put you in contact with a large number of like-minded people.

Green Jumping Spider

What are bugs?

So what are bugs? Bugs, mini beasts and creepy crawlies all refer to the same thing: a group of animals called **invertebrates**. This group includes insects, spiders, scorpions, centipedes, millipedes, snails and slugs. All invertebrates have one thing in common – no backbone. This is actually what the term *invertebrate* means.

Using the name 'bug' can be a little confusing, as, scientifically speaking, it refers to a group of insects called Hemipterans, which are often referred to as 'true bugs'. However, 'bugs' is now widely accepted as a popular name for all terrestrial invertebrates.

These animals are very different from domestic pets and the majority of zoo animals such as birds, mammals and reptiles. The main difference is that they do not have an internal skeleton; they have other unique ways to hold their bodies together. Many have a hard outer skeleton (**exoskeleton**) that supports their body from the outside. Other bugs are soft-bodied and have unique muscle structures to hold their body together.

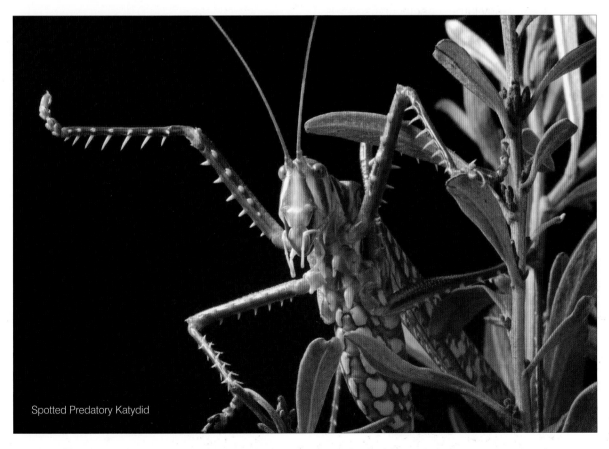

Spotted Predatory Katydid

Invertebrates' bodies come in a multitude of different shapes, forms and colours. They have some incredible features, including antennae, fangs, tentacles, stings and silk-producing organs such as spinnerets.

Grasshoppers are hemimetabolistic; this hatchling must moult a number of times to reach maturity.

Bugs with exoskeletons

Bugs with exoskeletons grow in stages. Growth is achieved by **moulting** – shedding their exoskeleton. When they emerge from the old exoskeleton these bugs are soft and expand to a new size or form before the exoskeleton hardens again.

These invertebrates have two distinct forms of development: **hemimetabolistic** and **holometabolistic**. Hemimetabolistic invertebrates begin life looking like miniature versions of their parents. They moult a number of times, getting bigger with each moult. The stages between moults are called **instars**. Moulting occurs until the bug reaches maturity (see below left).

The second form of development, holometabolistic development, is well known to many people, as it is the way in which butterflies develop.

Holometabolistic development includes an egg, **larva**, **pupa** and adult phase. The larvae also moult to grow and will go through a number of instars before pupating to change form completely and emerge as adults (below right).

Bugs with soft bodies

For soft-bodied bugs growth is a little different. These bugs do not have distinct growth stages but grow bigger steadily. They have a muscular body that holds them together and expands as they grow. Snails and slugs grow in this way. A snail will not replace its shell; instead the shell expands by continuously adding new sections to the lip as the snail grows.

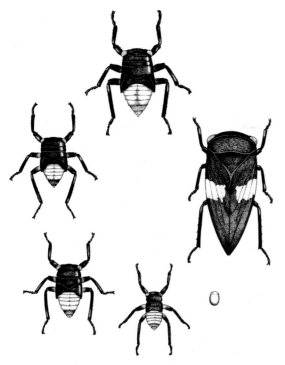

Hemimetabolistic development

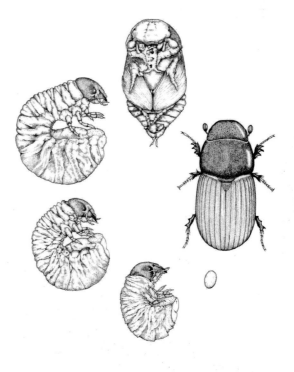

Holometabolistic development

How to use this book

This book has been designed to be an easy to follow guide to keeping a wide range of Australian invertebrates. It contains information on the care of 91 different species as well as more detailed information on invertebrate housing, food and water, health and display. Because this book has been written for a wide audience that will range from experienced keepers to young amateurs, we have tried to keep jargon to a minimum. Where we have used more specialist language, it has been in the interests of accuracy and education, and these terms can be found in the glossary.

This book contains 16 chapters that each focus on a particular group of invertebrates. Each of these chapters includes an overview and a number of care guides for individual species. The overview contains information relevant to all the species in the groups such as anatomy, diet and breeding, and many include line drawings to help you identify the body parts of your bug. Although you can go directly to the care guide pages, reading the overview will increase your knowledge and enjoyment of invertebrate keeping.

There are also four comprehensive, illustrated chapters on housing, food and water, health and display. These chapters expand on the information given in the care guides and offer a detailed guide to providing the most suitable house for your bug, feeding it and troubleshooting for common problems. The chapter on display will help you exhibit your bugs at their best, whether for the enjoyment and interest of family and friends, or for educational purposes.

This book will allow you to use the methods we have found successful. In some cases you may find that you will need to adapt a method to your own circumstances.

Care guides

The care guides contain detailed and specific information about your bug, including:

- **Common name:** the name by which the animal is widely known

- **Scientific name:** the scientific classification of the animal (always in Latin)

- **Husbandry rating 1–5:** how easy your bug is to keep; 1 for beginners through to 5 for the more advanced keeper

- ⚠ **Warning symbol:** this indicates that a bite or sting from this animal may potentially be fatal; refer to the special considerations box for more information

- **Housing:** (Refer to the chapter on housing, which starts on p.154, for details on all these elements.)

Enclosure – a guide to the type of enclosure and the minimum size each species requires as an adult; may also specify whether escape prevention is required

Substrate – material to be placed on the floor of your enclosure, the depth of substrate required and suitable moisture levels

Enclosure fit-out – items to be placed within your enclosure for your animals to use as shelter or to climb on

House as individual/pair/group/colony – whether your animal needs to be housed on its own, in a breeding pair or with others of the same species (group); a colony refers to social insects such as ants that live in a nest with lots of individuals

Temperature – the range of enclosure air temperatures suitable for your animal; a 'hotspot' is often referred to and indicates the temperature on the ground under a heat lamp

Humidity – the suitable humidity range for your animal

Lighting – the type of light and equipment required for your animal; sometimes optional or not required at all

- **Food and water:** suggested food types for your animal and how to provide water for it (refer to the chapter 'Food and water' (p.167) for more detailed information)

- **Routine care:** the regular care your animal will need

- **Sexing:** how to determine the difference between males and females

- **Breeding:** an overview of how to breed your animals

- **Lifespan:** how long your animal is likely to live

- **Captive behaviour:** the things you will see your animal doing

- **Special considerations:** special information you need to know about your animal

- **Compatibility with other species:** whether your animal can be housed with other species of invertebrates

- **Species with similar care requirements:** other invertebrates that can be cared for in the same way.

A final word: responsible bug keeping

Not all the species of bugs listed in this book are appropriate for everyone. Warning symbols are used throughout the care guides to indicate that a bite or sting from this animal has the potential to be fatal. We included these species because they will be of interest to certain bug keepers, particularly those who keep them for professional display. However, it is not advisable for children, schools or inexperienced keepers to collect these species.

Keeping invertebrates is like keeping a pet dog or cat – you must take responsibility for their care and wellbeing. This includes making sure your animals are kept under the right conditions, and not neglected because they are only bugs! Caring for invertebrates can be both rewarding and fun. We hope you find this book useful and that it allows you to enjoy keeping bugs alive.

Sugar ants have soldiers to guard their nests.

Ants Family: Formicidae

Estimated number of species in Australia: 2600

Ants may be seen as pests when they come foraging for food in the kitchen; however, they play a vital role in the Australian environment. They assist in recycling nutrients back into the soil and are a major food source for larger predators. Ants are found in all habitats across Australia, with the greatest numbers of species in the arid regions. Some, such as Green Tree Ants in the tropics, are very well known and visible, as they build nests in trees using leaves as well as silk produced by their **larvae.**

Others are known because of the stings they inflict; Jumping Jacks in Tasmania have caused deaths as a result of allergic reactions.

Ants are easily identified by their three distinct body segments – head, **thorax** and **abdomen** – and the distinct bend in each antenna.

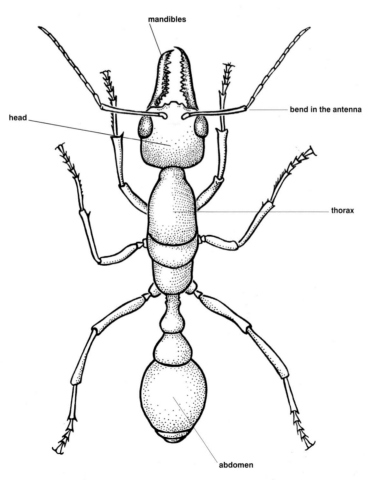

mandibles

head

bend in the antenna

thorax

abdomen

Ants are social insects; they form colonies that work together to survive. Some colonies can be small; other colonies, such as those of Meat Ants in south-eastern Australia, are extremely large, comprising thousands of individuals. Colonies are made up of a number of different types or castes of ants. Each colony will contain at least one queen, who lays the eggs and controls the colony. The most abundant caste is the worker caste. Workers are sterile females and will never reproduce. They undertake the day-to-day work in the colony, building nests, foraging for food, tending the brood and defending the nest. The brood are the eggs, larvae and pupae. Every now and then the queen will produce some fertile males and females that have wings. These winged ants leave the nest shortly after maturing and fly away and breed. A winged female that has mated will drop to the ground, chew off her wings and establish a new colony.

A queen, worker, pupa and larva bull ant

Most ants are general scavengers and predators. Adult ants feed only on liquid meals, such as sugar solutions, while the larvae (juvenile ants) will feed on animal material. One of the tasks of the workers is to bring dead insects and other animal matter into the nest to feed the larvae.

Watching ants going about their lives is fascinating, and ant farms have been popular with children for a long time. In laboratories, their social interactions and life cycles are studied and many species have been found to be easy to maintain. The main problem posed is that of preventing their escape. This can be easily overcome for most species by using an enclosure with vertical sides and a barrier of a slippery or oily substance to stop ants being able to walk out. A thin layer of vegetable oil, silicone spray or Fluon (Teflon paint) can be applied around the rim and top few centimetres of the sides of the enclosure to achieve this. (Detailed instructions are given on p.159)

Ants are fun to observe, but are not good to handle due to their ability to bite and sometimes sting. In a display situation they can be exceptional, as they are holometabolistic and all stages of the life cycle can be easily observed in a well-made enclosure.

Black House Ant *Iridomyrmex glaber*

Level of difficulty

| 1 | 2 | 3 | 4 | 5 |

beginner   advanced

Black House Ants can become a pest in our houses, coming inside in large numbers and feeding on our food. These small black ants have a distinctive acidic 'ant' smell when squashed. They also have the interesting ability to form trails to find food. They use **pheromones** (scents) to communicate with one another and can quickly recruit new workers to follow the trail. They can also be the dominant and most obvious species in natural habitats in Australia. Colonies can be very large and have many queens. The most difficult part about collecting a colony is obtaining a queen. One proven way to do this is to position an empty termite mound very close to an active ant colony. Within a month, in the warmer weather, some queens and brood will colonise the chambers in the mound, which can then be transferred directly to your enclosure.

Food and water
- Sugar solutions, dead insects
- Mist spray

Routine care
Daily: Replace sugar solutions and leave small dead insects. These insects are needed only if larvae are present in your colony. Remove any waste and ensure escape-proofing is still effective. Mist spray substrate to maintain a damp and a dry end.

Castes
Queen: Enlarged thorax and abdomen; top surface of the thorax is uneven where her wings were once attached

Males: Thin-bodied with wings

Workers: Wingless, smooth thorax

Breeding
A queen ant only needs to mate once and she will produce eggs for the rest of her life. You can start your colony either with a newly mated queen or from part of an existing colony that has been collected. In either case, maintaining it as described here should ensure an ongoing colony. Occasionally your colony will produce fertile winged males and new queens; however, in captivity they will not have the opportunity to meet fertile ants from other colonies. If you collect a single mated queen she will lay eggs and look after them until she has worker ants to look after them for her.

Lifespan
Greater than 3 years (colony); can be extended by adding queens, workers and brood from the original nest

Captive behaviour
Worker ants will be under the surface in burrows tending the brood, as well as on the surface foraging for food and defending the nest. When a worker discovers a food source it will use pheromones to communicate this to other workers and within a short period of time a large number of ants will be helping to collect the food. The queens spend their time in the burrows laying eggs.

Housing

 Enclosure: Glass tank, terrarium or custom; minimum size 30 cm H × 90 cm W × 40 cm D; escape-proofing essential (see p.159); can be open-topped

Substrate: Sand, coco-peat or mix, minimum depth 10 cm; maintain a damp and a dry end.

Enclosure fit-out: None essential

 Colony

 20–26°C

 Humidity 50–60% on surface

 Metal halide or sodium vapour

Special considerations
This species needs plenty of foraging room, and if you wish to increase this you can link one enclosure to another using plastic tubing. Ants are very good at escaping if the oily barrier around the top of the tank wears thin, so check it on a regular basis.

Compatibility with other species
Not recommended

Species with similar care requirements
Other species in the genus *Iridomyrmex*

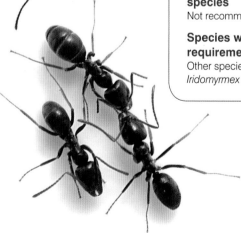

Bull ants *Myrmecia* species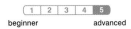

Level of difficulty (1 | 2 | 3 | 4 | **5**)

beginner   advanced

Bull ants are the largest ants in Australia (they can reach 20 mm in length) and are one of the most easily recognised because of their large **mandibles**. Bull ants have long legs and will run around quickly when disturbed. They are able to inflict a very painful sting. The sting is situated on the rear of the abdomen and can be seen with a magnifying glass. Bull ants are known as solitary predators; worker ants leave the nest by themselves and go out and hunt for food. In this way they only capture prey that they are able to kill and carry back to the nest alone.

Food and water
- Sugar solutions, dead insects such as crickets and cockroaches
- Mist spray

Routine care
Daily: Replace sugar solutions and leave small dead insects in enclosure. These insects are only needed if larvae are present in your colony. Remove any waste and ensure escape-proofing is still effective. Mist spray substrate to maintain a damp and a dry end.

Castes
Queen: Large individual, enlarged abdomen and thorax; thorax has rough upper surface where wings were once attached

Male: Thin-bodied with wings

Minor worker: Small, 10 mm

Major worker: Larger, 16 mm

Breeding
A queen ant only needs to mate once and she will produce eggs for the rest of her life. You can start your colony either with a newly mated queen or an existing colony that has been collected. In either case, maintaining it as described here should ensure an ongoing colony. Occasionally your colony will produce fertile winged males and new queens; however, in captivity they will not have the opportunity to meet fertile ants from other colonies. If you collect a single mated queen she will lay eggs and look after them until she has worker ants to look after them for her.

Lifespan
Greater than 5 years (colony)

Captive behaviour
Minor worker ants will be under the surface in burrows tending the brood, as well as on the surface foraging for food. Major workers will be defending the nest opening and foraging independently for dead insects and sugar solution. They often walk around the enclosure with waste material and dead ants, trying to find a secluded place to leave them. They often pile this waste onto the sugar dish. This is mainly to hide the sugar from any other animals that feed on nectar. The queen spends her time deep in the nest laying eggs. If the colony is well established, the brood – eggs, larvae and pupae – will be divided into different chambers.

Housing

 Enclosure: Glass tank, terrarium or custom; minimum size 30 cm H × 20 cm W × 20 cm D; escape-proofing essential (see p.159)

Substrate: Sand, coco-peat or mix, minimum depth 15 cm; maintain a damp and a dry end

Enclosure fit-out: Leaf litter

 Colony

 20–26°C

 Humidity 50–60%

 No specialised lighting required

Special considerations
The sting can be very painful, so handling is not advised. If you have a known allergy to bees, wasps or ants, it would be safer not to keep bull ants. Always use long forceps when servicing these animals.

Compatibility with other species
Not recommended

Species with similar care requirements
Jumping Jacks (*Myrmecia pilosula*)

Green Tree Ant *Oecophylla smaragdina*

Level of difficulty

| 1 | 2 | 3 | **4** | 5 |

beginner   advanced

If you have visited the tropical areas of northern Australia you would most likely have come across these ants. Green Tree Ants congregate in nests that the colony makes in trees by binding leaves together with silk produced by the larvae. Often one colony can have multiple nests reaching across a number of trees. The nests are joined together by 'highways' of ants travelling between them. Each nest can be about the size of a football. Bumping the tree they live in can disturb them, and many ants will come racing towards the disturbance. They have a good defence mechanism: they bite and then squirt acid from their abdomen into the bite site. Keeping these ants is different from keeping any other species in Australia. They tend to escape from any enclosure that is not surrounded by a water moat!

Food and water
- Sugar solutions, dead insects
- Mist spray

Routine care
Daily: Replace sugar solutions. Introduce a dead insect and either forceps feed or leave the insect in the enclosure. Water the plant and mist spray.

As required: Prune the plant so it does not extend over the moat

Castes
Queen: Large individual, enlarged abdomen

Male: Thin-bodied with wings

Minor worker: Small, 4 mm

Major worker: Larger, 10 mm

Breeding
A queen ant only needs to mate once and she will produce eggs for the rest of her life. You will most likely start your colony either with a newly mated queen or an existing colony that has been collected. In either case, maintaining it as described here should ensure an ongoing colony. Occasionally your colony will produce fertile winged males and new queens; however, in captivity they will not have the opportunity to meet fertile ants from other colonies. If you collect a single queen she will lay eggs and she look after them until she has worker ants to look after them for her.

Lifespan
2–3 years (colony)

Captive behaviour
Minor worker ants will be in the nests tending the brood, as well as occasionally outside the nest. Major workers will be positioned around the tree defending the territory and foraging for dead insects and sugar solutions. The queen spends her time inside the nest laying eggs, and will not be visible. When building a new nest the ants will grip the leaves together and pull them into place, while others carry larvae and use the silk they produce to glue the leaves together.

This species will continuously test the boundaries of the moat, so ensure it is always filled and that no plants extend over it. These ants have the ability to build ant bridges and chains where individuals will link together to hang and reach objects they otherwise would not be able to reach.

Housing
 Enclosure: Custom; minimum size 50 cm H × 50 cm W × 50 cm D; escape-proofing such as a moat essential (see p.159)

Substrate: Coco-peat or sand, minimum depth 10 cm; damp throughout

Enclosure fit-out: Plant (e.g. indoor fig such as *Ficus exotica*) preferable as it is hardy and provides enough leaves for nest formation

 Colony

 26–32°C

 Humidity 60–80%

 Metal halide or sodium vapour

Special considerations
Because this species builds bridges and chains to escape, ensure the moat is full and that no leaves or strands of grass extend over or are floating in the moat.

Compatibility with other species
Not recommended

Species with similar care requirements
None

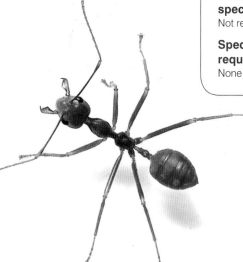

Meat Ant *Iridomyrmex purpureus*

Level of difficulty

beginner   advanced

If you have ever been out in the dry forest of Australia and seen mounds on the ground that are covered in small pebbles you would probably have been looking at a Meat Ant nest. Meat Ants are medium-sized, purple and black ants that form immense colonies that can extend widely underground. They form massive trails to find food and to move between nest sites. They use pheromones to communicate with one another and can quickly recruit new workers to follow a trail. These trails can sometimes be 'superhighways', along which all the vegetation is removed in a 5–10 cm wide strip to allow the masses of workers to move freely. These ants are voracious feeders and will quickly mass to sources of meat and sugar. Collecting a complete colony in the wild is very difficult, as the nest can extend deep underground to where the queens and brood live; however, collecting workers from the surface of the nest can be relatively simple. The following information relates to the care of the workers; the breeding section covers the requirements for other castes. The workers can make a great long-term display because of their long life and active behaviour.

Food and water

- Sugar solutions
- Mist spray

Routine care

Daily: Replace sugar solutions and remove any waste. Ensure escape-proofing is still effective. Mist spray substrate to maintain a damp and a dry end.

Castes

Queen: Enlarged thorax and abdomen; top surface of the thorax is uneven where her wings were once attached

Male: Thin-bodied with wings

Worker: Wingless, smooth thorax

Breeding

A queen Meat Ant only needs to mate once and she will produce eggs for the rest of her life. You will most likely start your colony with a newly mated queen. She will lay a first batch of eggs that she will look after herself until she has worker ants to look after them for her. Occasionally your colony will produce fertile winged males and new queens; however, in captivity they will not have the opportunity to meet fertile ants from other colonies.

Lifespan

6–12 months (workers only)

Captive behaviour

Worker ants will be under the surface in burrows tending the broods, as well as on the surface foraging for food and defending the nest. When a worker discovers a food source it will use pheromones to communicate this to other workers. In a short period of time large numbers of ants will be helping to forage.

Housing

 Enclosure: Glass tank, terrarium or custom; minimum size 25 cm H × 60 cm W × 40 cm D; escape-proofing essential (see p.159), can be open-topped

Substrate: Sand, coco-peat or mix, minimum depth 5 cm; maintain a damp and a dry end

Enclosure fit-out: Gravel or small pebbles, leaf litter

 Group

 20–26°C

 Humidity 50–60%

 Metal halide or sodium vapour, optional

Special considerations

If you add new animals from the original nest to your captive population, mist spray them thoroughly to wash away the pheromones being released. This greatly reduces the level of fighting and settles the old and new individuals quickly.

Compatibility with other species

Not recommended

Species with similar care requirements

Other species of *Iridomyrmex*

Sugar ants *Camponotus* species

Level of difficulty [1 | **2** | 3 | 4 | 5]
beginner   advanced

Sugar ants are often nicely coloured, with red, orange or yellow thoraces and abdomens, and vary in size from 2.5 mm to 14 mm. They are found throughout Australia, and are common in a wide range of habitats. There is a great deal of variation in the foraging period in species of this genus. Some will be active only during the day and some only at night, while others forage both day and night. Sugar ants have been recorded to show associations with other insect species. They 'farm' true bugs on plants and harvest the sugar secretions the bugs release. In return the ants protect the bugs from potential predators. Some also have similar associations with the caterpillars of some moths and butterflies. These ants are good to have in captivity because they cannot sting, are quite large and display well.

Food and water
- Sugar solutions, dead insects
- Mist spray

Routine care
Daily: Replace sugar solutions and leave small dead insects in enclosure. Insects are only needed if larvae are present in your colony. Remove waste. Ensure escape-proofing is still effective. Mist spray substrate to maintain a damp and a dry end.

Castes
Queen: Enlarged thorax and abdomen; top surface of the thorax is uneven where her wings were once attached

Male: Thin-bodied with wings

Soldier: Enlarged head, wingless, smooth thorax

Worker: Small head, wingless, smooth thorax

Breeding
A queen ant only needs to mate once and she will produce eggs for the rest of her life. You can start your colony either with a newly mated queen or an existing colony that has been collected. In either case, maintaining it as described here should ensure an ongoing colony. Occasionally your colony will produce fertile winged males and new queens; however, in captivity they will not have the opportunity to meet fertile ants from other colonies. If you collect a single queen she will lay eggs and look after them until she has worker ants to look after them for her.

Lifespan
Up to 20 years (colony)

Captive behaviour
Worker ants will be under the surface in burrows tending the brood, as well as on the surface foraging for food. Soldiers will be around the nest opening, defending the nest. The queen spends her time deep in the nest laying eggs. If the colony is well established, the brood will be divided into different chambers: eggs, larvae and pupae.

Housing
 Enclosure: Glass tank, terrarium or custom; minimum size 30 cm H × 20 cm W × 20 cm D; escape-proofing essential (see p.159), can be open-topped

Substrate: Sand, coco-peat or mix, minimum depth 15 cm; maintain a damp and a dry end

Enclosure fit-out: Leaf litter

 Colony

 20–26°C

 Humidity 50–60%

 No specialised lighting required

ANTS

Special considerations
There is a large number of species of sugar ants in this group, so examine the environmental conditions where you collected them and try to replicate these conditions in captivity, as this tends to produce the best results.

Compatibility with other species
Not recommended

Species with similar care requirements
Spider Ant (*Leptomyrmex* species)

Tiger Beetles have massive mandibles to catch and consume their prey.

Beetles Order: Coleoptera

Estimated number of species in Australia: 28 000

Beetles are the most diverse group of insects in Australia. They inhabit every environment from aquatic habitats to the most arid regions. They are also extremely diverse in terms of their feeding preference, which includes wood, leaves, flowers, pollen, faeces, rotting carcasses or other insects. With an estimated 28 000 described species, there are plenty to choose from to keep at home.

Beetles can be identified by their highly modified forewings, called **elytra**. The forewings are hardened to form armour over the hind wings, which are generally used for flight. When closed, the elytra meet edge-to-edge and form a straight line over the **abdomen**. Some beetles cannot fly and their elytra are permanently closed. Beetles can sometimes be mistaken for true bugs but can be identified by their chewing mouthparts; true bugs will have a sucking appendage protruding from the mouth.

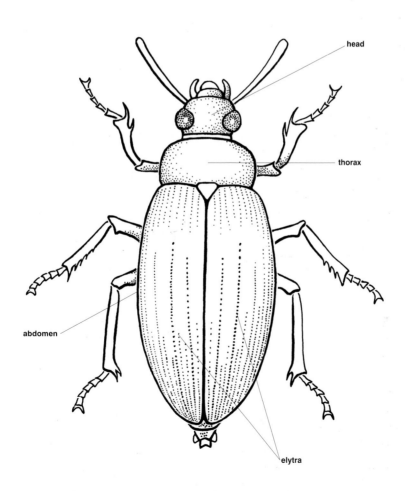

head

thorax

abdomen

elytra

Beetles are **holometabolistic**, with juveniles looking grub-like and very different from the adults. Female beetles will deposit eggs where the **larvae** will find food. Larvae hatch from the eggs and undergo a series of **moults** before pupating to adults. This process can take from a few weeks to years. The larvae of different beetles vary in appearance; some are capable of walking while others are grub-like and do not have legs. Beetle larvae can be mistaken for butterfly larvae (caterpillars). Larvae of beetles have three or fewer pairs of legs, whereas butterfly larvae have three pairs and a number of pseudo legs. When beetles pupate they can undergo **diapause**, to wait for the right environmental conditions to trigger them to emerge.

Sexing beetles can be easy for some species and almost impossible for others. It is easy for groups such as stag and rhinoceros beetles, as the males have large mandibles and horns protruding from the head. The females of many species are larger than the males because of the need to carry eggs. Often males and females need to be examined side by side or else caught in the act of mating to be sure which is which. Beetles are difficult to sex because the reproductive organs are internal and males will only invert the penis when mating.

Beetles can be great animals to keep, although patience is important because sometimes the larval stage of the life cycle can take a long time. Stag beetles are very popular as pets overseas and Australian species are prized for their size, colour and diversity. Most beetles can be held on the hand, with the exception of a few that are able to inflict a painful bite, although they pinch rather than cause severe damage. Some beetles can fly off the hand, so it is advisable to handle them in a closed room. Mixed species of **herbivorous** beetles can be housed together, as long as you provide them with their individual requirements.

Goldengreen Stag Beetles mating

Botany Bay Weevil *Chrysolopus spectabilis*

Level of difficulty

| 1 | 2 | 3 | 4 | 5 |

beginner   advanced

There are more species of weevils than any other group of beetles. They occur in almost every habitat in Australia, including many pantries. The Botany Bay Weevil was the first insect scientifically described in Australia. It was described by Joseph Banks when he landed with Captain Cook in 1770. Weevils are unique in their appearance and can be distinguished from other beetles by the pronounced snout-like rostrum in front of the eyes. The Botany Bay Weevil is relatively large (30 mm) with a black body and metallic blue-green markings; it has the ability to fly. These beetles feed exclusively on wattle and generally prefer the soft fresh foliage. Larvae develop underground and feed on the root systems of the wattles and have been known to kill the trees. These weevils are most commonly encountered around Sydney but extend north to Brisbane and south to Melbourne.

Food and water
- Wattle (*Acacia* species)
- **Adults:** Mist spray **Larvae:** Moisture in substrate

Routine care
Daily: Mist spray plant foliage (while adults are present)

As required: Water the plant for plant health and to maintain moisture in substrate for larvae and pupae. Replace plant if adults have eaten its leaves.

Sexing
Male: Smaller; will have white penis exposed from tip of abdomen when in mating mode

Female: Larger

Breeding
Males will find a female and perch on her back to mate. He will deposit sperm directly into her. Once mated, the females will drop a large number of eggs onto the substrate. When these eggs hatch the larvae will burrow into the substrate and begin feeding on the root system of the plant. Once they have grown to be as large as the adults, they will pupate. Try not to disturb them during this period, as they are very fragile at this time. If the wattle dies from overfeeding by the larvae, you will need to sort through the root system and find the larvae to transfer to a new plant. The larvae are legless with a small head, looking almost like a maggot. Once every couple of months gently sort through some of the roots and ensure they are surviving.

Lifespan
About 1 year

Captive behaviour
Adults will perch on plants and feed on the leaves and bark. If disturbed they can drop to the ground and pretend to be dead. Mating is observed regularly, with the male perched on the back of the female. They can be held on the hand, but be careful not to drop them. They are capable of flight and so should be handled in a closed room. Larvae will spend their whole time underground and are rarely seen.

Housing

 Enclosure: Terrarium, mesh or custom; minimum size 20 cm H × 30 cm W × 20 cm D

Substrate: None required

Enclosure fit-out: Potted food plant to provide perching areas

 Group

 20–26°C

 Humidity 60–80%

 No specialised lighting required

Special considerations
Try not to disturb the larvae unless necessary, checking on them could damage them or the wattle they are feeding on. If you dispose of the wattle plant, please be aware of any eggs, larvae or pupae that may be in the soil.

Compatibility with other species
Other wattle-feeding insects

Species with similar care requirements
Other weevils that feed on wattle

Chalcopterus beetles *Chalcopteroides* species

Level of difficulty 1 | 2 | 3 | 4 | 5

beginner   advanced

These beetles can often be found when searching under logs and fallen timber. They hide during the day and come out at night to forage for organic matter such as rotting vegetation. In dull light they look black but in the right lighting they have a metallic shimmer. They are not large (rarely more than 22 mm) but their colours more than make up for this, and they are able to fly. These beetles are found in the arid regions of eastern Australia. The shiny, yellow, flattened larvae have three pairs of legs and are found underground. They feed on the organic matter in soil.

Housing

Enclosure: Terrarium, glass tank or custom; minimum size 40 cm H × 30 cm W × 30 cm D

Substrate: Sand, minimum depth 10 cm; maintain a damp and a dry end

Enclosure fit-out: Wood shelters

 Group

 18–30°C, hotspot to 40°C at one end optional

 Humidity 50–70%

 None required, dichroic lamp for 4–6 hours per day optional

Food and water
- **Adults:** Orthopteran mix and rabbit and guinea pig seed **Larvae:** Pellet mix

- Water sponge, moisture in substrate

Routine care
Daily: Mist spray substrate to maintain a damp end and replace orthopteran mix

Monthly: Gently excavate the substrate to monitor how the larvae are progressing

As required: Dig a little into the substrate and leave pockets of rabbit and guinea pig seed and pellet mix (1–2 tsp). This provides food for the larvae, and the seeds will germinate, providing fresh grasses and roots for them to feed on.

Sexing
Male: Smaller; will have white penis extending from tip of abdomen when in mating mode

Female: Larger

Breeding
The male will find a female and perch on her back to mate. He will deposit sperm directly into her. Once mated, the female will lay eggs into the substrate in areas where conditions are favourable. These eggs will hatch soon after being laid and the larvae will tunnel through the sand. They will spend their time under shelter or in the substrate feeding. The juvenile beetles undergo a series of moults and will reach a length of 25 mm before pupating to maturity.

Lifespan
1–2 years

Captive behaviour
Adults will shelter during the day and emerge at night to feed. Larvae have extensive underground burrows and on rare occasions will shelter under bark.

Special considerations
Keeping the substrate damp and ensuring food is always available is essential for the survival of the larvae.

Compatibility with other species
Other arid zone herbivores

Species with similar care requirements
Darkling beetles (Tenebrionidae)

Common Spotted Ladybird *Harmonia conformis*

Level of difficulty

| 1 | 2 | **3** | 4 | 5 |

beginner   advanced

Ladybirds are one of the most well-known insects because they are so recognisable and are commonly found in our backyards. Ladybirds are great insects to have in the garden as they spend their lives feeding on aphids and other sap-suckers that eat our plants. Their tiny legs and antennae are tucked under the body and cannot be seen from above. They grow to 8 mm in length. Their wings are hidden under the elytra and are only exposed during flight. More and more people are turning to these insects as a form of natural pest control in their gardens. These ladybirds can be purchased in bulk to sprinkle on precious plants. It is not difficult to raise them yourself, as long as you have plenty of aphids on which to feed them. Common Spotted Ladybirds can be found on vegetation and lawns in southern and western Australia.

Housing

 Enclosure: Terrarium, glass tank or custom; minimum size 20 cm H × 25 cm W × 150 cm D

Substrate: Absorptive layer only (sand, coco-peat, leaf litter, newspaper)

Enclosure fit-out: Potted plant or **browse** supporting aphid colonies

 Group

 24–30°C, hotspot to 40°C optional

 Humidity 50–70%

 None required, dichroic lamp for 4–6 hours per day optional

Food and water
- Live aphids
- Mist spray

Routine care
Daily: Mist spray

Twice weekly: Replace cut browse with branches that have many aphids attached. (Rose bushes are often a good source.) It would be even better if living plants could be maintained in the enclosure to support sap-sucking colonies. Ensure that any plant material that is removed does not have eggs, larvae or pupae on it.

Sexing
Male: Smaller

Female: Larger

Breeding
The male will find the female and perch on her back to mate. He will deposit sperm directly into her. Once mated the female will lay up to 1000 eggs onto branches and leaves, close to places where aphids are congregating. These eggs are yellow and hatch soon after being laid. The tiny larvae that emerge have large mandibles and will patrol the branches searching for small aphids to eat. They will moult four times and when they are 10–12 mm long, the larvae will pupate on a leaf. They emerge as adults 8 days later.

Lifespan
6–12 months

Captive behaviour
Adults and larvae will patrol the enclosure, actively seeking food. They will feed on the sap-sucking bugs throughout the day and night. Mist spraying will increase their activity. If startled, adults can drop to the ground and pretend to be dead. Larvae do not use sight or smell to find aphids; they tend to patrol plants and bump into them.

Special considerations
Eggs and young larvae are small and hard to see, so when disposing of old branches make sure you do not throw them out. A high aphid infestation in the enclosure will increase your larvae's ability to feed.

Compatibility with other species
Not recommended

Species with similar care requirements
Other ladybirds (Coccinellidae)

Fiddler Beetle *Eupoecila australasiae*

Level of difficulty

1 2 **3** 4 5

beginner   advanced

Adult Fiddler Beetles can be found during the warmer months in eastern Australia. They are a very pretty beetle, with a glossy, black body and distinct green or yellow markings. They can grow to a length of about 30 mm. As adults they feed on the blossoms of flowering trees and shrubs. The larvae are cream coloured and grub-like, and have the ability to move on their backs by pulsing the folds of their skin. They live in the soil, feeding on rotting wood and decaying vegetation. These beetles have elytra that are modified so that they do not have to raise them fully to expose the rear wings for flight. This allows them to take off quickly.

Food and water
- **Adults:** Sugar solution **Larvae:** Pulpy wood, leaf litter and mulch
- Moisture in substrate

Routine care
Daily: Mist spray substrate and replace sugar solutions, or supply nectar-rich flowers such as eucalypt if available

As required: Add extra mulch and pulpy wood for larvae

Sexing
Male: Smaller, will have white penis exposed from tip of abdomen when in mating mode

Female: Larger

Breeding
The male will find a female and perch on her back to mate. He deposits the sperm directly into her. Once mated the female will lay eggs into the substrate in a suitable area. These eggs will hatch and the larvae that emerge will move through the substrate feeding on the organic matter. Once they have grown to a length of 50–60 mm they will pupate in a **cocoon** they build from a mixture of soil and their own secretions. This cocoon will keep them safe until they metamorphose

into adults. Try not to disturb them during this period, as they are very fragile. After pupating it will be a number of weeks before they finally emerge.

Lifespan
12–14 months

Captive behaviour
Adults either shelter during the day or are out searching for mates and sugar solutions. In warm conditions they can also be active at night. They will grip tightly to your hand when you pick them up but you can prise them off gently. Larvae will spend their whole time underground and you will see them only if you gently dig around.

Housing

Enclosure: Terrarium, glass tank or custom; minimum size 20 cm H × 25 cm W × 15 cm D

Substrate: Coco-peat, mulch and pulpy wood mix, minimum depth 15 cm; damp throughout

Enclosure fit-out: Bark shelters, leaf litter

Group

25–30°C

Humidity 60–80%

No specialised lighting required

Special considerations
Try not to disturb the larvae too much, checking them once a week is sufficient. Ensure they always have organic matter to feed on. If you do handle the larvae your hands should be clean of all chemicals (soaps etc.).

Compatibility with other species
Other herbivorous insects

Species with similar care requirements
None

BUGS ALIVE!

26

Goldengreen Stag Beetle *Lamprima latreillei*

Level of difficulty

| 1 | 2 | **3** | 4 | 5 |

beginner   advanced

Goldengreen Stag Beetles are large (25 mm) and colourful, and are a great animal to keep. They are found in rotting timber in eastern Australia. These beetles get their name from the enlarged mandibles of the males. He uses these mandibles to show off to females and to fight other males. Adults can live for a number of months and feed on sugar secretions such as sap or fruit. Larvae are soft and grub-shaped, and spend their time in wood, feeding on the rotting material and the fungi associated with it. Keeping these beetles through their entire life cycle can be difficult, as the larvae require specific conditions in which to grow, but the hard work is well worth it.

Food and water
- **Adults:** Stag beetle adult diet (p.173) or fruit **Larvae:** Stag beetle larvae food (p.173)

- Moisture in substrate

Routine care
Daily: Mist spray substrate

Every second day: Replace adult food

Monthly: Replace 50% of substrate for larvae

Sexing
Male: Enlarged mandibles (longer than head)

Female: Normal mandibles (shorter than head)

Breeding
Breeding generally takes place in late spring. Introduce a male to an enclosure with your female. The male will find the female and perch on her back to mate. He will deposit sperm directly into her. Once mated the females will lay eggs into the pulpy wood you have provided. If possible, use pulpy wood that has bracket fungus or white rot present. Once hatched the larvae will move through the wood, feeding. After a couple of months gently sort through the wood and transfer the larvae to separate jars. These jars should contain some of the wood from the female's enclosure as well as the stag beetle larvae diet (p.173) and can be three-quarters filled with the substrate mix. Larvae will grow to be as long as the adults and then pupate. Do not disturb them at this stage. Once your animals have pupated to adults they will take another 3–5 months to become sexually mature.

Lifespan
1–2 years

Captive behaviour
During the day these beetles burrow underground or beneath bark. At night they will come out and feed. If you have more than one male in the enclosure they may fight. This is interesting to see, but may lead them to damaging each other. They will grip tightly to your hand when you pick them up but you can prise them off gently. Larvae will spend their whole time underground and you will see them only if you gently dig around.

Housing

Enclosure: Terrarium, glass tank or custom; minimum size 15 cm H × 20 cm W × 10 cm D

Substrate: Coco-peat and rotting pulpy wood, minimum depth 10 cm; damp throughout

Enclosure fit-out: None required

 Individual

 20–26°C

 Humidity 70–90%

No specialised lighting required

Special considerations
If two males are housed together they will challenge each other and one may be injured. Try not to disturb the larvae too much, especially during the time they pupate. If you do handle the larvae your hands should be clean of all chemicals (soaps etc.).

Compatibility with other species
Temperate zone herbivorous invertebrates

Species with similar care requirements
Golden Stag Beetle (*Lamprima aurata*)

Green Carabid Beetle *Calosoma schayeri*

Level of difficulty | 1 | **2** | 3 | 4 | 5 |
beginner   advanced

Green Carabid Beetles are stunning and can be recognised by their sculptured shiny green elytra, strong biting mandibles and long legs designed for running. They are 30 mm in length. These beetles can often be seen in large numbers on warm nights around lights, especially in the rural areas of eastern Australia. Adults will congregate in these areas to mate. Both the adults and larvae are predators, but adults will also feed on dead animals. Larvae spend their time underground, but the adults will run around the surface at night feeding. During the day the adults will hide under timber and rocks.

Food and water
- Live and dead insects
- Water sponge, moisture in substrate

Routine care
Daily: Spray substrate to maintain humidity, and add small crickets or mealworm pupae for larvae to hunt. Moisten the water sponge.

Weekly: Leave one dead insect per animal in enclosure for adults to find.

Sexing
Male: Smaller; will have white penis exposed from tip of abdomen when in mating mode

Female: Larger, broader abdomen

Breeding
The males will find a female and perch on her back to mate. He will deposit sperm directly into her. Once mated the female will lay eggs into the substrate in areas where conditions are favourable. These eggs will hatch soon after being laid and the larvae will dig shallow burrows. The larvae are fairly small when they first emerge and need very small crickets or other small invertebrates to feed on. They seek shelter or dig burrows underground during the day, and emerge at night to feed. As they become larger the burrows will become more extensive. They moult only a few times before reaching maturity.

Lifespan
1–3 years

Captive behaviour
Adults and larvae will hide in their retreats during the day and emerge at night to forage; they are fast movers when disturbed. Larvae have extensive burrows underground and will only come to the surface to feed at night. These burrows will often run beside the glass of the tank and you may be able to see them. Cannibalism is rare in this species and individuals sharing an enclosure can even share a dead insect as a meal.

Housing

 Enclosure: Glass tank or custom; minimum size 40 cm H × 60 cm W × 20 cm D

Substrate: Sand, minimum depth 10 cm; damp throughout

Enclosure fit-out: Bark or rock shelters

 Group

 20–28°C, hotspot to 40°C at one end

 Humidity 50–60%

 Dichroic lamp for 4–6 hours per day

Special considerations
Damp substrate is essential for the larvae's survival. Minimise the amount of digging through the substrate as this may damage the developing larvae.

Compatibility with other species
Not recommended

Species with similar care requirements
Black carabid beetles (Carabidae)

Passalid beetles *Mastachilus* species

Level of difficulty

| 1 | 2 | 3 | 4 | 5 |
beginner   advanced

Passalid beetles are found living in or under rotting wood. They are flattened and have strongly grooved elytra and a distinct waist. Adults actually change colour. When they first mature they are a red-brown colour but become glossy black later in life. These are one of the few beetles that show parental care. When the eggs hatch, the adults prepare a soft wood pulp to feed to the larvae. Older siblings that have recently metamorphosed will also help care for the larvae. Passalid beetles are found Australia-wide, but are most commonly found in the tropics. This genus is the larger of the passalids and can reach a length of 60 mm. They can be easily dug up and are great to handle. These beetles are able to make a hissing sound by rubbing the elytra to the tip of the abdomen.

Food and water
- Pulpy wood
- Moisture in substrate

Routine care
Daily: Mist spray substrate to maintain humidity.

As required: Add extra substrate for larvae.

6 monthly: Replace 50% of substrate.

Sexing
Male: Smaller

Female: Larger

Breeding
These beetles should be housed in family groups. Pairs mate through direct contact of their abdomens. Once mated the female will lay eggs into the pulpy wood. The larvae that hatch move through the substrate, feeding on the organic matter and food prepared by the adults. Once they have grown to be longer than the adults, they will pupate in a cocoon they build from substrate and their own secretions. When they first emerge from the cocoon they will be a red-brown colour, which will change to black as they age.

Lifespan
12–18 months

Captive behaviour
You will rarely see your passalids out on the surface as they prefer to spend their time in the substrate.

Housing

 Enclosure: Terrarium, glass tank or custom; minimum size 20 cm H × 25 cm W × 15 cm D

Substrate: Coco-peat, mulch and pulpy wood mix, minimum depth 15 cm; damp throughout

Enclosure fit-out: None required

 Group

 25–30°C

 Humidity 60–90%

 None required, dislikes bright light

Special considerations
Try not to disturb the larvae too much; checking on them once a week is sufficient. Ensure they always have organic matter to feed on. If you do handle the larvae your hands should be clean of all chemicals (soaps etc.). When changing the substrate sift through it gently and ensure you do not dispose of any larvae.

Compatibility with other species
Other rainforest herbivores

Species with similar care requirements
Other passalid beetles (Passalidae)

Pie Dish Beetle *Helea scaphiformis*

Level of difficulty

1	2	3	4	5

beginner   advanced

These unusual beetles have large flanges on the sides of their thorax and elytra, giving them their 'pie dish' appearance. They can often be found in arid regions under logs, fallen timber or dead clumps of spinifex. They hide during the day and come out to forage for organic matter at night. They are matt black in colour and will grow to 25 mm in length. The yellow, worm-like larvae have three pairs of legs and are also found under logs and dead spinifex. They feed on the organic matter in the soil.

Housing

 Enclosure: Terrarium, glass tank or custom; minimum size 20 cm H × 25 cm W × 15 cm D

Substrate: Sand, minimum depth 15 cm; damp throughout

Enclosure fit-out: Bark or wood

 Group

 18–30°C

 Humidity 50–80%

 No specialised lighting required

Food and water

- **Adults:** Orthopteran mix **Larvae:** Rabbit and guinea pig seed and pellet mix

- **Adults:** Mist spray **Larvae:** Moisture in substrate

Routine care

Daily: Mist spray to maintain moisture in substrate and change orthopteran mix

Monthly: Gently excavate the substrate to monitor how the larvae are progressing

As required: Dig a little into the substrate and leave pockets of rabbit and guinea pig seed and pellet mix (1–2 tsp). This provides food for larvae, and the seeds will germinate providing fresh grasses and roots for them to feed on.

Sexing

Male: Smaller; will have white penis exposed from tip of abdomen when in mating mode

Female: Larger

Breeding

The male will find a female and perch on her back to mate. He will deposit sperm directly into her. Once mated the female will lay eggs into the substrate in areas where conditions are favourable. The eggs will hatch soon after being laid and the larvae will tunnel through the sand. They will spend their time under the shelter or in the substrate feeding. The larvae undergo a series of moults and will reach 30 mm before pupating to maturity.

Lifespan

10–14 months

Captive behaviour

Adults will shelter during the day and emerge at night to feed. Larvae have extensive underground burrows and on the rare occasion will shelter under wood.

Special considerations

Keeping the substrate damp and ensuring food is readily available is essential for the larvae's survival.

Compatibility with other species

Other arid zone herbivores

Species with similar care requirements

Pie Dish Beetle (*Helea castor*)

Rainbow Stag Beetle *Phalacrognathus muelleri*

Level of difficulty

| 1 | 2 | 3 | 4 | 5 |

beginner   advanced

Rainbow Stag Beetles are one of the most prized beetles in captivity, due to their large size (75 mm) and spectacular colours. They are found in the rainforests of northern Queensland, and are occasionally attracted to lights at night. Stag beetles get their name from the enlarged mandibles on the male, which they use to compete for breeding rights. In the wild these beetles will lay eggs in soft rotting wood that is lying on the forest floor. The larvae feed on the wood and fungi associated with it, and will only emerge when they are mature. Maintaining the beetle through its entire life cycle is hard work, but well worth it.

Food and water
- Stag beetle adult diet (p.173), or fruit and stag beetle larvae diet (p.173)
- Moisture in substrate

Routine care
Daily: Mist spray

Every second day: Replace adult food

Monthly: Replace 50% of food substrate for larvae

Sexing
Male: Enlarged mandibles (longer than head)

Female: Normal mandibles (shorter than head)

Breeding
Introduce a male to an enclosure with your female. The male will perch on the female's back to mate. He will deposit sperm directly into her. The female will then lay eggs into the pulpy wood you have provided. If possible use pulpy wood that has bracket fungus or white rot present. Once hatched the larvae will move through the wood, feeding. After a couple of months gently sort through the wood and transfer the larvae to separate jars. These jars should contain some of the wood from the female's enclosure as well as the stag beetle larvae diet (p.173). The jars can be three-quarters filled with the substrate mix and kept damp. Larvae will grow to be as long as the adults before they pupate. Do not disturb them at this stage. Once your animals have pupated to adults they will take another 3–5 months to become sexually mature.

Lifespan
1–2 years

Captive behaviour
During the day these beetles burrow underground or beneath bark. At night they come out and feed. If you have more than one male in the enclosure they may fight. This is interesting to see but may lead them to damaging each other. They will grip tightly to your hand when you pick them up but you can prise them off gently. Larvae will spend their whole time underground and you will see them only if you dig around carefully.

Housing
 Enclosure: Terrarium, glass tank or custom; minimum size 15 cm H × 20 cm W × 10 cm D

Substrate: Coco-peat and rotting pulpy wood, minimum depth 10 cm; damp throughout

Enclosure fit-out: Bark shelter

 Individual

 26–32°C

 Humidity 70–90%

No specialised lighting required

Special considerations
If two males are housed together they will challenge each other and one may be injured. Try not to disturb the larvae too much, especially while they are pupating. If you do handle the larvae your hands should be clean of all chemicals (soaps etc.).

Compatibility with other species
Other rainforest herbivores

Species with similar care requirements
Other tropical stag beetles

Rhinoceros Beetle *Xylotrupes ulysses*

Level of difficulty

| 1 | 2 | 3 | 4 | 5 |
beginner — advanced

Rhinoceros Beetles are one of the largest species of beetles in Australia. They are found in the moist forests from northern New South Wales to northern Queensland. They can grow to a length of 70 mm but are still able to fly. The larvae are cream coloured with a reddish head, and can be found in rotting organic matter, especially compost bins. These beetles get their name from the forked horns on the male's head. He uses these horns to show off to the females and fight other males. As scary as they look, Rhinoceros Beetles are harmless to humans. These beetles can be easily dug up and are great to handle. They are able to make a hissing sound by rubbing the elytra against the tip of the abdomen.

Housing

Enclosure: Terrarium, glass tank or custom; minimum size 20 cm H × 25 cm W × 15 cm D

Substrate: Coco-peat, mulch and pulpy wood mix, minimum depth 15 cm; damp throughout

Enclosure fit-out: Bark shelter, leaf litter

 Group

 25–30°C

 Humidity 60–90%

 No specialised lighting required

Food and water
- **Adults:** Soft fruit (especially mango and other tropical varieties) **Larvae:** Pulpy wood, leaf litter and mulch

- Moisture in substrate

Routine care
Daily: Mist spray substrate to maintain humidity, and replace fruit

As required: Add extra substrate for larvae

Sexing
Male: Horn protruding from head

Female: No horn on head

Breeding
The male will find a female and perch on her back to mate. If more than one male is in the enclosure they will challenge each other for breeding rights. Once mated the females will lay about 50 eggs into suitable places in the substrate. These eggs will hatch 1–2 weeks later. The larvae will move through the substrate feeding on the organic matter. Once they are as long as an adult they will build a cocoon with their **frass** to pupate within.

Newly emerged beetles are reddish brown and will darken over time. They can live as an adult for up to 4 months.

Lifespan
12–18 months

Captive behaviour
During the day these beetles tend to hide underground or beneath bark in the enclosure. At night you will find your beetles will come out and feed on the fruit. If you have more than one male in the enclosure they may fight. This is interesting to see but may lead them to damaging each other. They will grip tightly to your hand when you pick them up and will make a huffing noise, but you can prise them gently off the hand. Larvae will spend all their time underground and you will see them only if you gently dig around.

Special considerations
Try not to disturb the larvae too much; checking on them once a month is sufficient. Ensure that organic matter is always present. If you do handle the larvae your hands should be clean of all chemicals (soaps etc.).

Compatibility with other species
Other rainforest herbivores

Species with similar care requirements
None

Tiger Beetle *Megacephala australis*

Level of difficulty

| 1 | 2 | 3 | 4 | 5 |

beginner   advanced

Tiger beetles are some of the fastest-running insects in the world. This species can be found on saltpans and plains in the arid areas of Australia. They have fused elytra and cannot fly, so hunt at night by running down their prey. They have large mandibles, which they use to catch, kill and chew their victims. They grow to 22 mm in length, and are the largest tiger beetles in Australia. During the day these beetles will find a retreat under logs or in holes in the ground and shelter from extreme temperatures and predators. The larvae are also savage predators, ambushing their prey with their enormous mandibles from the safety of their burrows.

Food and water
- Live insects
- **Adults:** Mist spray **Larvae:** Moisture in substrate

Routine care
Daily: Spray substrate to maintain a damp end and add in small live insects if none are present for adults and larvae to hunt

Sexing
Male: Smaller; will have cream penis exposed from tip of abdomen when in mating mode

Female: Larger

Breeding
The male will find a female and perch on her back to mate. He can remain perched on her back while she runs around feeding. Once mated the females will lay eggs into the moist areas of the substrate. These eggs will hatch soon after being laid and the larvae will make shallow burrows. The larvae are fairly small when they first emerge and need hatchling crickets to feed on. As they become larger their burrows will become more extensive. They undergo only a few moults to reach maturity. You can estimate the size of the larvae by the size of the burrow opening. Young larvae will have burrow openings the size of pinpricks and older larvae nearing pupation will have burrows that are 5 mm across.

Lifespan
12–18 months

Captive behaviour
Adults spend their days in their shelter but may emerge if the enclosure is mist sprayed and the humidity increases. At night they will emerge from their shelter and run around the enclosure looking for mates or actively hunting for food. Their active behaviour means that they need plenty of live insects to feed on. Larvae have extensive underground burrows and should not be disturbed by digging them up. These burrows will often run against the glass of the tank and you may be able to see them. When in feeding mode the larvae will sit at the burrow opening and wait for food to walk past. They are very sensitive to vibrations so do not be surprised if they disappear when you approach the enclosure.

Housing

 Enclosure: Glass tank or custom; minimum size 40 cm H × 60 cm W × 30 cm D; can be open-topped

Substrate: Silty clay and sand, minimum depth 15 cm; maintain a damp and a dry end

Enclosure fit-out: Bark or rock shelters

 Group

 20–26°C, hotspot to 40°C at one end

 Humidity 40–50%

 Dichroic lamp for 4–6 hours per day

Special considerations
Keeping the substrate damp and ensuring a constant supply of food is essential for larvae survival.

Compatibility with other species
Not recommended

Species with similar care requirements
Other tiger beetles (Cicindelidae); some may be able to fly and require a lid on the enclosure

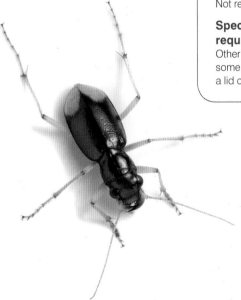

Like the larvae of many moths and butterflies, the caterpillar of the Common Eggfly Butterfly is brightly coloured and covered with spines.

Butterflies and moths Order: Lepidoptera

Estimated number of species in Australia: 20 000

Butterflies and moths are one of the most well-known groups in the invertebrate world. Their bright colours, both in caterpillar and adult form, and their gracefulness are appealing to people of all ages. Butterflies and moths differ in a number of ways. Butterflies are usually active during the day, can be more brightly coloured than moths, have knobs at the end of their antennae and, when at rest, will generally hold their wings vertically above their bodies. Moths, on the other hand, are most active at night, usually have feathery antennae and hold their wings flat when not in flight. Butterflies and moths are found all over Australia, but some species can be very specific in the areas they inhabit, as they are dependent on the types of plants their caterpillars feed on.

It is not possible to sex most species of these animals until they are mature, unless you dissect the caterpillar. Most adult butterflies and moths are very easy to sex due to the differences in their size, colour and patterning.

All butterflies and moths lay eggs. Adults will mate end to end with their **abdomens** joined. The females will then lay fertile eggs on the particular species of plant that their caterpillars feed on. This usually occurs in the warmer months of the year, as that is when the adults are active. Males of some species will compete for females, and males of other species will perform special dances to get a female's attention. The female often gets to choose the male she will mate with.

Butterflies and moths are **holometabolistic**; that is, the young hatch out of the egg looking very different from the adults. Caterpillars (**larvae**) will emerge from the eggs and begin feeding on the plant on which they hatched. They may look like they have lots of legs, but caterpillars have only six legs; a number of pseudo legs help the caterpillar to grip on plant stems. Depending on the species, caterpillars will pupate anywhere from two weeks to two years and this happens once the caterpillars have grown large enough. Butterfly caterpillars will simply find a safe resting place to **pupate**. Some moth species give themselves extra protection by building a cocoon or finding a sheltered position such as under the bark of a tree. This process varies greatly from species to species and it can take from 10 days to 10 years for the adult to emerge. Once it emerges, the adult will begin looking for a mate to start the whole process again. Butterflies and moths can experience some problems when emerging as adults. If conditions are not humid enough, the butterfly or moth can get stuck and become deformed if its body dries out before its wings have fully expanded. If kept in an open-air environment, they are also susceptible to parasitism from outside sources. Butterflies and moths can live from just a few days to up to several months as adults.

Butterflies and moths have different food preferences as their life stages progress. Caterpillars will feed on plant material and the types of plants on which they feed are very specific, depending on the species. Once the caterpillars have eaten enough, they will pupate, during which they do not feed at all.

Most butterflies and moths feed on the nectar of flowers, using a long tube-like tongue called a **proboscis**. There are some species of moths that do not have mouthparts and do not feed at all as adults. These live for only a few days. In captivity, butterflies can be fed an artificial nectar (see p.174). They need to be attracted to the nectar by bright colours. A simple way of providing food for your butterflies is described in the chapter 'Food and water'.

Butterflies and moths are most often seen in captivity in commercial butterfly houses and zoos, but there is much potential for keeping caterpillars as pets or in a classroom. Caterpillars require a lot of care, as their food plants need to be replaced as soon as they are eaten. Adult butterflies and moths can be quite easy to keep, as long as they have enough space to fly around and be active. Enclosure sizes for adults need to be very large to reduce damage to their wings. Ideally, once they have emerged, adults should be released into the wild in their natural range.

The wings of adult butterflies and moths are covered in powdery scales that fall away when touched, so handling them will usually result in their inability to fly. The more scales that are lost, the harder it is for the adult to fly. However, if a butterfly or moth lands on your hand, it will be fine. If you do need to handle your butterfly, gently pinch its wings together when they are closed. Caterpillars can generally be handled if it is done very carefully. Many species have suckers on the ends of their legs that can tear off if the caterpillar is pulled off its food plant, causing it to die. Some caterpillars have spines that can cause irritation, or they can squirt out irritating fluids, so watch out for these. Both these mechanisms are used to deter predators in the wild.

Most adult butterflies and moths can be housed with different species, but some species of butterfly will not tolerate other species. The male Common Eggfly Butterfly, for example, will often fight with males of any species for a female's attention. Caterpillars of different species can generally be housed together, but large caterpillars have been known to eat very small caterpillars living on the same food plant.

Butterflies and moths are great display animals, both as caterpillars and as adults. The upkeep of caterpillars can be a lot of work in a display sense, since they eat so much and will need many food plants, but the end result – an adult butterfly or moth – is worth the effort.

A butterfly will use its long proboscis to suck up sweet sugar solutions.

Common Eggfly Butterfly *Hypolimnas bolina nerina*

Level of difficulty

1	2	3	4	5

beginner   advanced

This butterfly species occurs in open woodland in tropical and subtropical areas of eastern Australia. They can be a common garden species around the Brisbane area. Female Common Eggfly Butterflies have a wingspan of approximately 80 mm; males are slightly smaller. Caterpillars feed on native weed-like species of plants, while adults feed on nectar. Males actively defend territories where they wait for females to come and mate. They will perch in trees and if other males (or even birds) enter their territory they will physically attack the intruder until it is chased away.

Housing

 Enclosure: Glass tank or custom; minimum size 200 cm H × 70 cm W × 70 cm D

Substrate: Absorptive layer only (sand, coco-peat, newspaper)

Enclosure fit-out: Tall plant for butterflies to perch on and caterpillars to pupate

 Group

 25–30°C

 Humidity 70–90%

 Dichroic or metal halide lamps suspended behind wire and out of reach of butterflies

Food and water
- **Adults:** Butterfly nectar **Caterpillars:** Potted plant such as Lesser Jollyweed (*Alternathera denticulata*) or Sida (*Sida rhombifolia*)
- Gravel-filled water dish

Routine care
Daily: Mist spray foliage, replace butterfly nectar, remove waste build-up, and top-up water in gravel dish

As required: Water plants. When a plant has been significantly eaten (most leaves have been chewed), swap the plant with another. When doing this ensure that all caterpillars and any eggs are transferred to the new plant. To transfer eggs, simply cut off the leaf with the eggs from the old plant and pin it to the new plant.

Sexing
Male: Jet-black wings with three pairs of white spots; the two largest spots are surrounded by a blue-purple colouration

Female: Lacks spots; upper side of wings are black-brown with white markings and an orange central colouration

Breeding
Males defend their territories aggressively, so you should have a maximum of two males in the enclosure with more females. Males will court females and lead them to a leaf where mating will occur. Females will deposit small pale-green eggs on the caterpillar food plant, generally on the underside of the leaf. Eggs will take 3–4 days to hatch. Caterpillars will begin feeding immediately, and after 3–4 weeks, or when they grow to about 55 mm long, they will pupate, a process that takes about 2 weeks. Adult females will live for about 2 weeks; adult males for about 6 months.

Lifespan
- **Male:** 6–8 months
- **Female:** 2 months

Captive behaviour
Because of the confinements of the enclosure, the flight of butterflies is reduced and they will spend extended periods of time perched on the tree rather than in flight. In the mornings or when the lights are first put on, the butterflies will perch below the light and bask to warm up. You may see the males aggressively attack each other if you have more than one male in your enclosure. Caterpillars will wander all over the food plant feeding.

Special considerations
Handling a butterfly reduces its ability to fly, so butterflies should be handled with extreme care. The lives of adult butterflies are shortened if they are kept with other butterflies. If keeping a group, ensure there are always more adult females than males in your enclosure.

Compatibility with other species
Not recommended

Species with similar care requirements
None

Emperor Gum Moth *Opodiphthera eucalypti*

Level of difficulty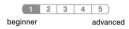

beginner   advanced

A fully grown caterpillar of the Emperor Gum Moth is a brilliant blue-green colour with a cream stripe down its side and little tufts of blue, red and yellow spines. The adult moth is large with a hairy body and wings spanning 140 mm. They range in colour from tan to pinky-brown, and have a large 'eye-spot' on each wing. These 'eye-spots' are used to startle predators. The adult moth does not feed, but relies solely on the food it ate as a caterpillar. Emperor Gum Moths are found in forests and woodlands of the Northern Territory and along the eastern states of Australia.

They are best kept as caterpillars, housed in a simple terrarium with their food plant. Adult moths need considerable space, so it is recommended that you release them in their natural range. This care guide deals with caterpillars; other life stages are covered in the breeding section.

– BUGS ALIVE!

Food and water

- Fresh foliage such as cut **browse** or potted plant; *Eucalyptus* species preferred but can also feed on Peppercorn (*Schinus molle*), Silver Birch (*Betula* species), Liquidambar (*Liquidambar* species) and Apricot trees (*Prunus* species)

- Mist spray

Routine care

Daily: Mist spray foliage and water any plants. Remove waste build up.

As required: Water plants. When a plant has been significantly eaten (most leaves have been chewed), swap the plant with another. Ensure all caterpillars are transferred to the new plant.

Sexing

Male: Large feathery antennae; generally smaller than females

Female: Thin simple antennae; generally larger than males

Note: Caterpillars do not show **morphological** sex differences, making early sexing difficult

Breeding If you have adults and wish to breed them, you will need to house them in a very large enclosure (200 cm H × 100 cm W × 100 cm D). Adult moths do not have mouthparts so cannot feed. They will mate end to end during late spring and summer before laying eggs and dying. Eggs are oval in shape, white to cream in colour, and approximately 2 mm in length. They are laid either singly or with several together in a row on the food plant. Little black caterpillars hatch after 7–10 days, and as they grow they develop spectacular colouring. When fully grown to about 80 mm long, the caterpillar will spin a silk cocoon that sets with a hard, dark-brown rough exterior. When the adult moth is ready to emerge, it will regurgitate a fluid to soften the base of the cocoon before cutting a hole in it using sharp hooks on the base of its forewings. The moth sheds these hooks and emerges to let its wings expand and dry. The moth will usually emerge from the cocoon the following year, but this can take between 4 months and 10 years to occur. Adult moths will live for 2–3 weeks.

Lifespan

1–10 years

Captive behaviour

Caterpillars are solitary and will move from leaf to leaf, feeding during the day. You may see them **moulting**. Their colours change with each moult. Adult moths are slow fliers. They come out at night and can be attracted to bright light.

Housing

 Enclosure: Terrarium, mesh or custom; minimum size 30 cm H × 20 cm W × 20 cm D

Substrate: Absorptive layer only (sand, coco-peat, newspaper)

Enclosure fit-out: Food foliage will provide climbing areas

 Group

 20–26°C

 Humidity 40–60%

 No specialised lighting required

Special Considerations

If feeding caterpillars cut browse in a jar of water, prevent access to the water as they will readily drown.

Adults will beat themselves to death in an enclosure. It is recommended that once the adult moth emerges, it is released into the wild in areas where they occur naturally.

Compatibility with other species

Eucalypt-feeding stick insects

Species with similar care requirements

Helena Gum Moth (*Opodiphthera helena*)

Hercules Moth *Coscinocera hercules*

Level of difficulty

| 1 | 2 | **3** | 4 | 5 |

beginner   advanced

Hercules Moths are the largest moths in Australia, with a massive wingspan of about 250 mm. Their colour varies over different shades of brown, and they have four small triangular 'windows' of transparent scales in each wing. The caterpillars are equally impressive. They grow to 120 mm in length and are pale blue-green with prominent yellow spikes. Hercules Moths are found in tropical rainforests of northern Queensland. The adult cannot feed, so it relies solely on the food it ate as a caterpillar. They are best kept as caterpillars, housed in a simple terrarium with their food plant. This care guide deals with caterpillars; other life stages are covered in the breeding section.

Food and water
- Fresh foliage, either cut browse or potted plant: Australian Native Bleeding Heart (*Omalanthus nutans*), Cheese Tree (*Glochidion ferdinandi*) or Queensland Apple (*Timonius rumphii*)
- Mist spray

Routine care
Daily: Mist spray foliage and remove waste products

As required: Water food plants and replace as necessary, when caterpillars have eaten them nearly bare. Ensure all caterpillars are transferred to the new plant.

Sexing
Male: Large feathery antennae and tapering, tail-like hind wings

Female: Antennae thinner, lacks tails on hind wings

Note: Caterpillars do not show morphological differences in sex

Breeding
If you have adults and wish to breed them, you will need to house them in a very large enclosure (200 cm H × 100 cm W × 100 cm D). Adult moths do not have mouthparts so cannot feed. Female moths release a powerful scent (a **pheromone**) to attract males. Pairs will mate with abdomens joined end to end. It can be difficult to mate this species, and you may have to help them by joining their abdomens together by hand. After

mating, the female will lay about 80–100 eggs either singly or in small groups. She will lay eggs continuously for her entire life as an adult moth. The first batch of eggs tends not to hatch. The reason for this is not known. Caterpillars will emerge from the eggs after about 4 days and begin feeding. After approximately 6 weeks, they will spin a double-walled cocoon that is long and slender and wrapped in leaves. Pupation times vary greatly, from a few weeks to several years. Males will emerge before females, which can make pairing difficult as adults live for only 10 days.

Lifespan
3 months to several years

Captive behaviour
Caterpillars will move from leaf to leaf, feeding both during the day and at night. You may see them moulting. Their colours change with each moult. The male adult moths are attracted to bright lights. They are active by night and rest during the day. Female moths do not fly much at all, unless they are disturbed.

Housing

 Enclosure: Terrarium, mesh or custom; minimum size 30 cm H × 35 cm W × 20 cm D

Substrate: Absorptive layer only (sand, coco-peat, newspaper)

Enclosure fit-out: Food foliage will providing climbing areas

 Group

 20–25°C

 Humidity 40–70%

 No specialised lighting required

Special considerations
If feeding caterpillars cut browse in a jar of water, access to the water must be prevented as the caterpillars will easily drown.

It is recommended that adult moths be released into the wild in areas where they occur naturally.

Compatibility with other species
Not recommended

Species with similar care requirements
None

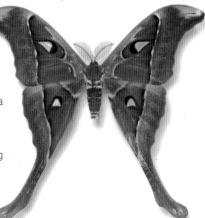

Orchard Butterfly *Papilio aegeus*

Level of difficulty

| 1 | 2 | 3 | 4 | 5 |

beginner   advanced

The Orchard Butterfly is one the easiest butterflies to raise in captivity as its food plants are easily accessible. Its caterpillars feed on citrus trees, such as lemon, and have become minor pests in some orchards. The butterfly itself is one of the largest butterflies in Australia and has a wingspan of 140 mm. When at rest this butterfly holds its wings flat. The Orchard Butterfly is found in woodland areas across eastern Australia, but it can also be found in urban backyards. The caterpillars have a unique way of avoiding predators – as small caterpillars they resemble bird droppings. When they are disturbed they can also release a pungent odour, which smells like rotting citrus fruit, from a forked red gland that protrudes from their heads.

Food and water
- **Adult:** Butterfly nectar **Caterpillars:** Potted plant or cut browse such as lemon (*Citrus limon*) or orange (*Citrus sinensis*)
- Gravel-filled water dish

Routine care
Daily: Mist spray foliage and change butterfly nectar.

As required: Water plants. When a plant has been significantly eaten (most leaves have been chewed), swap the plant with another. When doing this ensure that all caterpillars and any eggs are transferred to the new plant. To transfer the eggs, simply cut off the leaf with the eggs from the old plant and pin it to the new plant.

Sexing
Male: Forewings are mainly blue-black with white markings near tips of wings; hind wings have two red spots

Female: Forewings are mostly white with blue-black at the base; hind wings have red and blue crescents

Note: Caterpillars do not show morphological sex differences, making early sexing difficult

Breeding
Males and females will mate end to end. After mating the female will lay yellow-green eggs on the undersides of the leaves. The eggs are 1.4 mm in diameter and will hatch after 3–4 days. The newly hatched caterpillars will eat the shells of the eggs from which they emerged. When your caterpillars first hatch they resemble fresh bird droppings. As they grow, their colour becomes greener, with white markings and spikes along their body. After about 4 weeks, or when caterpillars are approximately 60 mm long, they will pupate. The pupae are often the colour of their surroundings – either green, grey or brown. The adult butterflies will emerge from the pupae after 2–4 weeks.

Lifespan
4–6 months

Captive behaviour
Adults' wings will vibrate when they are feeding. Their flight is fairly slow as they forage and lay eggs. The caterpillars will feed both day and night, and will stay on the food plant until they pupate. They may move to the top of your enclosure to pupate.

Housing

Enclosure: Glass tank or custom; minimum size 200 cm H × 70 cm W × 70 cm D

Substrate: Absorptive layer only (sand, coco-peat, newspaper)

Enclosure fit-out: Tall plant for perching and pupating

 Group

 25–30°C

 Humidity 70–90%

 Dichroic or metal halide lamps suspended behind wire and out of reach of butterflies

Special considerations
Be careful when handling the caterpillars as they can release a chemical that can be irritating. Be sure to wash your hands after handling them. The butterflies should not be handled, as the powdery scales on their wings will come off and they will lose the ability to fly.

Compatibility with other species
Other tropical zone butterflies

Species with similar care requirements
None

Wanderer Butterfly *Danaus plexippus*

Level of difficulty

| 1 | **2** | 3 | 4 | 5 |

beginner   advanced

The Wanderer Butterfly is thought to be the butterfly with the longest lifespan. The adult is bright orange-brown in colour, with a white-spotted band along the edge of its wings, while the caterpillar has black, yellow and white stripes. The pupae of Wanderer Butterflies are quite spectacular – they are pale green decorated with golden beads. The caterpillars grow to a length of about 50 mm before pupating, and the butterfly has a wingspan of 90 mm. Originally an exotic butterfly, this species has now made Australia home, and it is found in every state and territory in both temperate and tropical areas. This butterfly is renowned for its migratory nature and is able to fly across oceans and continents. The Wanderer Butterfly is poisonous but not deadly to its predators, which would experience sickness or a bad taste if they were to eat one.

Food and water
- **Adult:** Butterfly nectar **Caterpillars:** Potted plant, e.g. Milkweed (*Asclepias* species) or Moth Plant (*Araujia sericifera*)
- Gravel-filled water dish

Routine care
Daily: Mist spray foliage and replace butterfly nectar. Remove waste build-up and top-up water in gravel dish.

As required: Water plants. When a plant has been significantly eaten (most leaves have been chewed), swap the plant with another. When doing this ensure that all caterpillars and any eggs are transferred to the new plant. To transfer eggs, simply cut off the leaf with the eggs from the old plant and pin it to the new plant.

Sexing
Male: Thin wing veins; a black 'sex spot' on hind wings

Female: Thick wing veins

Note: Caterpillars do not show morphological sex differences, making early sexing difficult

Breeding
Males will congregate around the food plant, waiting for newly emerged females with which to mate. Males patrol their territory and defend it aggressively if another male enters its boundaries. For this reason, it is not recommended that a large number of males be housed in the one enclosure. Males will release a **pheromone** that is a flight arrester in females – a female that smells this scent is unable to fly and falls to the ground, where the male will mate with her.

Males and females will pair up end to end, with the male transferring sperm to the female. Females will lay small yellowish-white eggs onto the leaf of the food plant. The eggs will hatch after about 2–3 days, and the caterpillars begin feeding. The caterpillars will pupate after 3–4 weeks, or when 50 mm long. The new butterfly will emerge 10 days later. In the wild adult butterflies can live for 8–9 months, but in captivity they will live for only a few weeks.

Lifespan
9–10 months

Captive behaviour
Caterpillars will often drop off the food plant and wander around the enclosure. They will feed and moult until they are big enough to pupate. Adults will bask under lights in the early morning to warm up their flight muscles, but flight may be restricted by the size of the enclosure, and most of their time will be spent perching on plants and feeding on nectar.

Housing

 Enclosure: Glass tank or custom; minimum size 200 cm H × 70 cm W × 70 cm D

Substrate: Absorptive layer only (sand, coco-peat, newspaper)

Enclosure fit-out: Tall plant for perching and pupating

 Group

20–25°C

 Humidity 70–90%

 Dichroic or metal halide lamps suspended behind wire and out of reach of butterflies

Special considerations
This species is poisonous throughout its life cycle due to the toxins found in the caterpillars' food plant, but it is not harmful unless eaten. The lives of adult butterflies are shortened if they are kept with other butterflies. If keeping a group, ensure there are always more adult females than males.

Compatibility with other species
Not recommended

Species with similar care requirements
Lesser Wanderer Butterfly (*Danaus chrysippus*)

The colourful Mitchell's Cockroach basks in the sun's warmth

Cockroaches Order: Blattodea

Estimated number of species in Australia: 600

Who would possibly want to keep a cockroach? Just the word 'cockroach' strikes fear and loathing in many people. But Australian cockroaches are extremely colourful and can be quite beautiful – not at all the typical dull brown or black that most people expect from cockroaches. Cockroaches are often viewed as creatures that despise the light – the name 'Blatta' (from their Latin name Blattodea) actually means 'to shun the light'. But there are quite a few desert species that will actively seek out the light and bask under a heat lamp in captivity.

Cockroaches are insects that are found in almost every land habitat. They differ from other insects in that their enlarged **pronotum** forms a shield, protecting the head and **thorax** from above.

It can be quite easy to sex some species of cockroaches. In females the last segment on the underside of the abdomen has a split down the middle, to allow the egg case (called an **ootheca**) to pass through. In males the last segment is intact.

In other species, such as bark cockroaches (*Laxta* species), the mature males have wings while the females are wingless. The Giant Burrowing Cockroach (*Macropanesthia rhinoceros*) can only be differentiated in adulthood, when the pronotum over the head of the male has a more pronounced ridge than that of the female.

Cockroaches mate by joining the tips of their abdomens together. The male will transfer sperm directly into the female while they are locked together. Most Australian species breed by producing an ootheca. Different species deposit their ootheca in different ways: some bury it;

some deposit it on the substrate surface or on vegetation; others are known to attach it to the end of their abdomen until the **nymphs** hatch out.

Some cockroaches produce live young – the eggs hatch while the ootheca is still in the mother's body. Still other species do not produce an ootheca, and the young develop inside the mother's uterus and are born as live nymphs.

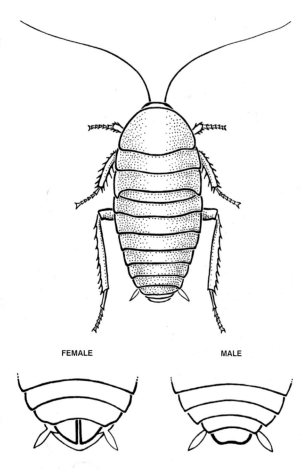

FEMALE   MALE

The end segment on the underside of some cockroaches can be used to sex them.

Cockroaches breed during the warmer time of the year, but in captivity most species can be stimulated to breed year-round if environmental conditions are right and a suitable mate is available.

Cockroaches are **hemimetabolistic**. Nymphs will undergo 2–12 **instars**, depending on the species, and can take between one and 12 months to reach maturity. Nymphs will moult their **exoskeleton** to grow. The old exoskeleton splits down the back, and the cockroach works its way free while the new exoskeleton underneath is still soft. Often the cockroach will be lighter in colour when it **moults** but will darken once the new exoskeleton hardens. The lifespan of cockroaches differs for each species – most species live for a year or two, but some species, such as the Giant Burrowing Cockroach, can live for up to 10 years.

Most cockroaches are **omnivorous** and will feed on anything from plant matter to dead insect carcasses. Some species, however, are very specific in what they eat and will feed solely on things such as dry eucalypt leaves or fungi. In captivity, a catch-all diet for most cockroaches is orthopteran mix. (See the chapter 'Food and water', p.172)

More and more people are recognising the potential of cockroaches in captivity, as they are very easy to keep. Most often seen in captivity is the Giant Burrowing Cockroach, but a lot of **diurnal** desert species are now being kept successfully.

Most Australian cockroaches are suitable to handle. Diurnal cockroaches are fairly placid and typically slow moving, and are happy to walk from hand to hand. Some burrowing species are prone to stress if handled too often. Some smaller species of cockroaches are fast moving, and are not suitable for handling due to the risk of escape. For these species, it is appropriate to use a small jar or plastic container when having a close look at them or transferring them. Some cockroaches (e.g. *Polyzosteria* species) are known for their ability to make small rasping noises when disturbed or handled roughly. They make this noise by forcing air out of small breathing pores on their sides. Some may also secrete a smelly fluid if alarmed. This fluid is usually harmless to humans, but you should wash your hands after handling your cockroaches as a precaution.

Cockroaches are able to be housed with just about any other **herbivorous** insect that has similar housing requirements.

Most cockroaches are great for display as long as their habits are taken into consideration. Diurnal desert species can be displayed by using a heat lamp to attract them to a position where they can be viewed easily. Burrowing species can also make great displays if specialised enclosures are constructed, allowing observation into burrows. (See the chapter 'Display your invertebrates' pp.185–91.)

The ootheca of a Common Shining Cockroach (*Drymaplaneta communis*)

Botany Bay Cockroach *Polyzosteria limbata*

Level of difficulty

1	2	**3**	4	5

beginner   advanced

Botany Bay Cockroaches are highly visible in captivity as they like to lounge in the vegetation with their legs hanging down, much like a leopard does in trees. These fairly large cockroaches grow to about 35 mm in length and have a dark brown to matt black body with a lighter stripe down the outside of the abdomen. These cockroaches are found in the temperate woodlands and heathlands of Victoria and New South Wales, where they are active during the day, and feed on pollen, bark and leaf material.

Housing

 Enclosure: Glass tank or custom; minimum size 25 cm H × 45 cm W × 20 cm D

Substrate: Sand, minimum deepth 2 cm; maintain a damp and a dry end

Enclosure fit-out: Low vegetation for climbing and shelter; rocks, bark or leaf litter

 Group

 20–25°C, hotspot to 40°C at one end of the enclosure

 Humidity 40–60%

UV provision, dichroic lamp for 1–2 hours per day

Food and water
- Orthopteran mix, freshly cut fruit
- Water sponge

Routine care
Daily: Change orthopteran mix and remove **frass** and food debris from substrate. Water mist substrate to maintain a damp and a dry end, and top up the water sponge.

Sexing
Male: The last segment on the underside of the abdomen is whole

Female: The last segment on the underside of the abdomen has a split down the middle

Note: These cockroaches are able be sexed as sub-adults

Breeding
Pairs will mate by joining the tips of their abdomens together, with the male transferring sperm directly into the female. The female will produce an ootheca, which she will keep attached to the end of her abdomen before depositing it onto the substrate. The nymphs that emerge after 45–65 days look like miniature adults. They grow to maturity after about 9 months.

Lifespan
12–18 months

Captive behaviour
These cockroaches will actively forage for food during the day. They will shelter in vegetation when the enclosure is cooler, and will emerge to bask in the hotspot during the day. They can often be seen perched in vegetation with their legs hanging down. These cockroaches are able to walk up vertical surfaces, and can sometimes be seen on the walls of the enclosure.

Special considerations
When alarmed these cockroaches are capable of making a hissing sound that is generated by forcing air out of small breathing pores on their sides. They will also release a strong odour. Both these traits are used for defence.

Compatibility with other species
Other herbivorous insects

Species with similar care requirements
Giant Sand Cockroach (*Polyzosteria magna*), Green Metallic Cockroach (*Megazosteria patula*)

Common Shining Cockroach *Drymaplaneta communis*

Level of difficulty

| 1 | 2 | 3 | 4 | 5 |

beginner   advanced

Common Shining Cockroaches are common throughout the eastern states of Australia, where they shelter under vegetation and debris, and usually only venture out at night. These relatively fast-moving cockroaches grow to about 25 mm in length. This wingless species is identified by the distinctive pale stripe running down either side of the pronotum. When disturbed this species exudes a strong odour to deter potential predators. These cockroaches are able to breed to large numbers in a short time, and are often found wandering inside houses searching for food. Common Shining Cockroaches are omnivores and will feed on any plant or dead animal.

Food and water
- Orthopteran mix, freshly cut fruit
- Water sponge

Routine care
Daily: Replace orthopteran mix, and remove frass and food debris from substrate. Mist spray substrate to maintain a damp and a dry end, and top up the water sponge.

Sexing
Male: The last segment on the underside of the abdomen is whole

Female: The last segment on the underside of the abdomen has a split down the middle

Note: These cockroaches are able be sexed as sub-adults

Breeding
When conditions are favourable, pairs will mate by joining the tips of their abdomens together. The male transfers sperm directly into the female. The female will produce an ootheca that she will deposit onto the substrate or, more commonly, onto vegetation.

The nymphs emerge after 1–2 months and undergo a series of moults before reaching maturity.

Lifespan
12–18 months

Captive behaviour
Common Shining Cockroaches are generally active during early morning and evening, and will spend most of the day sheltering beneath bark or rocks. More activity will be seen if these insects are kept in large numbers. This species is able to climb smooth vertical surfaces, and will often be seen sitting on the side of the enclosure.

Housing
 Enclosure: Terrarium, glass tank, custom; minimum size 20 cm H × 25 cm W × 15 cm D; escape prevention optional (see p.159)

Substrate: Sand, coco-peat or mix, minimum depth 2 cm; maintain a damp and a dry end

Enclosure fit-out: Low vegetation for climbing and shelter; rocks, bark or leaf litter

 Group

 18–24°C

 Humidity 40–60%

 No specialised lighting required

Special considerations
These cockroaches can be fast moving, so take care when opening the enclosure. Some measures should be taken to prevent escape, such as oiling the rim of the enclosure (see p. 159). This species can be handled, but again be aware of the fast movement. If handled too roughly, this cockroach will release a strong-smelling fluid, so it is best to wash your hands after handling them.

Compatibility with other species
Other herbivorous insects

Species with similar care requirements
Coulon Cockroach (*Paratemnopteryx couloniana*), black cockroach (*Platyzosteria* species), Bark Cockroach (*Laxta friedmani*)

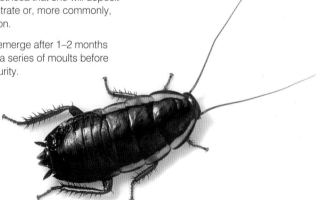

Giant Burrowing Cockroach *Macropanesthia rhinoceros*

Level of difficulty

| 1 | 2 | 3 | 4 | 5 |

beginner   advanced

Giant Burrowing Cockroaches are the world's heaviest cockroach species, with females growing to 80 mm in length and weighing 30 g. These cockroaches live underground, digging long deep burrows, and only venturing to the surface at night to feed. They are specialist feeders that will only eat brown, dry eucalypt leaves. They seldom move far from the burrow, except on humid summer nights during breeding season, when they have been mistaken for small turtles when crossing roads. These cockroaches are found in dry eucalyptus scrubland of northern Queensland, and are one of the most popular cockroaches in captivity.

Housing

 Enclosure: Terrarium, glass tank, custom; minimum size 20 cm H × 25 cm W × 15 cm D

Substrate: Coco-peat, sand or mix, minimum depth 5 cm; damp throughout

Enclosure fit-out: Bark shelter

 Pair

 18–24°C

 Humidity 60–80%

None required, dislikes bright light

Food and water

- Dried brown eucalypt leaves, freshly cut apple
- Water sponge

Routine care

Daily: Ensure the substrate is damp, add water via mist spray if required, and top-up water sponge

Twice weekly: Replace apple and check that sufficient dry eucalypt leaves are available. Add more leaves if required.

Sexing

Male: Has pronounced ridge on front of pronotum above head

Female: Larger than male; no pronounced ridge

Note: These cockroaches are able be sexed as sub-adults

Breeding

Pairs can be held together all year round, with mating usually occurring in early summer. Increasing humidity and temperature may assist with breeding in captivity. Introducing sexes just prior to the breeding season may also increase chances of mating. Mating will probably happen at night, and you may not know it has occurred.

Once mated, females can be moved to an enclosure with shallow substrate and a bark shelter. Humidity should be higher at this time. Females will give birth to about 20 live young, and should not be disturbed when young are present. They can be observed by gently lifting the bark shelter. The young will reach maturity in 2–3 years. Juveniles will remain with their mother for up to 12 months but are able to be separated from 4 months on.

Lifespan

Up to 10 years

Captive behaviour

These cockroaches will spend most of their time hidden underground (or within their shelter). They are most active at night, when they will move to the surface to feed. You will sometimes hear digging during the day. Continual digging at the base of the enclosure may indicate that the substrate is too dry. Prolonged activity on the surface during the day may be an indicator of poor heath, dehydration or stress.

Special considerations

If your cockroach seems slow and lethargic, it may be a sign that it has been handled too much; stop handling it immediately.

Compatibility with other species

Other herbivorous insects that do not directly compete for burrowing space

Species with similar care requirements

Burrowing cockroaches (*Panesthia* species and *Geoscapheus* species)

Mitchell's Cockroach *Polyzosteria mitchelli*

Level of difficulty 1 2 3 **4** 5

beginner   advanced

One of the most colourful cockroaches in Australia, Mitchell's Cockroaches are a combination of metallic green, yellow and blue. They are found in the arid parts of Australia, ranging from north-western New South Wales down into Victoria and west into South Australia and Western Australia. These cockroaches are often seen basking during the heat of the day at the tops of small shrubs. Adults will grow to about 35 mm long, and their pronotum is decorated with three small, clear 'windows' down either side. This species will forage both on the ground and in low-growing vegetation, and feed on pollen, nectar, bark and other plant matter.

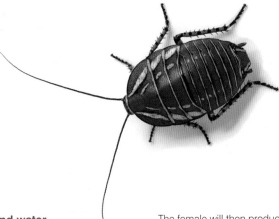

Food and water
- Orthopteran mix, freshly cut fruit, pollen
- Water sponge

Routine care
Daily: Replace orthopteran mix, and remove frass and food debris from substrate. Mist spray substrate to maintain a damp and a dry end, and top up the water sponge.

Sexing
Male: The last segment on the underside of the abdomen is whole

Female: The last segment on the underside of the abdomen has a split down the middle

Note: These cockroaches are able be sexed as sub-adults

Breeding
Pairs will mate when conditions are favourable, so ensuring that food and water are readily available will increase your chances of success. They mate by joining the tips of their abdomens together and the male transfers sperm directly into the female.

The female will then produce an ootheca that she will carry around attached to the end of her abdomen.

She will dig a shallow hole in the substrate in which she will bury her ootheca.

Nymphs will emerge after 1–2 months and undergo a series of moults before reaching maturity.

Lifespan
12–18 months

Captive behaviour
These cockroaches will actively forage for food during the day. They will shelter in vegetation when enclosure temperatures are low, and will emerge to bask in the hotspot. This species is able to climb smooth vertical surfaces, and will often be seen sitting on the walls of the enclosure.

Housing
 Enclosure: Glass tank, custom; minimum size 25 cm H × 45 cm W × 20 cm D

Substrate: Sand, minimum depth 2 cm; maintain a damp and a dry end

Enclosure fit-out: Dense vegetation for climbing and shelter; rocks, bark or leaf litter

 Group

 20–25°C, hotspot to 40°C at one end

 Humidity 40–60%

UV provision, dichroic lamp for 1–2 hours per day

Special considerations
Mitchell's Cockroaches are fantastic cockroaches for display, as they have such spectacular colours and are active during the day. This species is also good for handling as it is slow moving and content to walk from hand to hand. Be wary of cockroaches sitting around the lid or door of your enclosure as they can escape. Allowing the enclosure to cool overnight may aid with the breeding process.

Compatibility with other species
Other herbivorous insects

Species with similar care requirements
Other *Polyzosteria* species, Metallic Cockroach (*Euzosteria metallica*), Knobbly Cockroach (*Euzosteria tuberculata*)

Pandanus Cockroach *Cosmozosteria zonata*

Level of difficulty

| 1 | 2 | 3 | 4 | 5 |

beginner — advanced

Pandanus Cockroaches are commonly found sheltering between Pandanus fronds in dry scrublands of northern Queensland and the Northern Territory. They will bask in the morning and late afternoon sun, and search for food in the vegetation and leaf litter. These cockroaches often live in small groups. Females will grow to a length of 35 mm but males are slightly smaller. The entire body of a newly emerged nymph is banded. Nymphs of this species do not develop their typical three-striped appearance until the third instar. These cockroaches are highly visible, making them ideal for captivity.

Food and water
- Orthopteran mix, freshly cut fruit, pollen
- Water sponge

Routine care
Daily: Replace orthopteran mix, and remove frass and food debris from substrate. Mist spray substrate to maintain a damp and a dry end, and top up the water sponge.

Sexing
Male: The last segment on the underside of the abdomen is whole

Female: The last segment on the underside of the abdomen has a split down the middle

Note: These cockroaches are able to be sexed as sub-adults

Breeding
Pairs will mate when conditions are favourable. They mate by joining the tips of their abdomens together, and the male transfers sperm directly into the female. The female will produce an ootheca that she either buries in the substrate or attaches to vegetation or the bark shelter.

Nymphs will emerge after 6–8 weeks and grow to maturity in approximately 7 months.

Lifespan
12–18 months

Captive behaviour
These cockroaches will shelter in vegetation most of the time, but emerge to bask in a hotspot during the day. They will forage for food in the early morning and the evening. They are able to climb vertical surfaces, and may even moult their exoskeleton while perched on the side of your enclosure.

Housing

 Enclosure: Glass tank or custom; minimum size 25 cm H × 45 cm W × 20 cm D

Substrate: Coco-peat or sand, minimum depth 2 cm; maintain a damp and a dry end

Enclosure fit-out: Low vegetation for climbing and shelter; rocks, bark or leaf

 Group

 20–35°C, hotspot to 40°C at one end

 Humidity 50–80%

 UV provision, dichroic lamp for 1–2 hours per day

Special considerations
This is an ideal species of cockroach for captivity as it is able to be handled gently. If alarmed or startled, this species will release a pungent odour to deter predators. Wash your hands after handling this cockroach.

Compatibility with other species
Other herbivorous insects

Species with similar care requirements
Glorious Cockroach (*Cosmozosteria gloriosa*), Spinifex Cockroach (*Zonioploca flavocincta*), Striped Desert Cockroach (*Desmozosteria cincta*)

Katydids can be abundant in backyards, yet they are
rarely seen because they have excellent camouflage.

Crickets and katydids Suborder: Ensifera

Estimated number of species in Australia: 2300

On a warm summer's night, your backyard can come alive with the sound of these camouflaged insects. Crickets and katydids are often confused with grasshoppers. Crickets and katydids have large hind legs designed for jumping, but they also have antennae that are longer than their body. These antennae are one feature that distinguishes them from their cousins, the grasshoppers.

Crickets and katydids are found in all habitats across Australia, but have the greatest diversity in the tropics. You will often hear rather than see this group of animals, as they call at night using a technique called **stridulation**, rubbing their wings and hind legs together. This calling is generally used by the male to attract a female. Katydids will rest during the day, with their wings positioned in such a way that the katydid looks just like a leaf on the tree. Crickets, on the other hand, usually have wings that wrap around the body when not in use. They are not as colourful as katydids, generally a drab cream to brown colour, and they hide during the day in cracks in the ground or under leaf litter and rocks.

Sexing crickets and katydids is fairly easy as the females are larger than males and have an **ovipositor**. The ovipositor extends from the end of the abdomen and is used to deposit eggs into the ground, under bark or onto leaves.

Some ovipositors look like a long, thin rod, others are sabre-like, and some katydids have very short ovipositors that are hard to distinguish unless you have a male and a female side by side.

Reproduction occurs in the summer months and males will call to attract females. The male transfers a **spermatophore** to the female. A spermatophore is a mass that can sometimes be seen sitting on the female's abdomen after mating has occurred. It contains the sperm to fertilise the eggs. The spermatophore of some species will have an outer covering. This covering is a high-energy nuptial gift that will be consumed by the female and provides energy to the eggs. Females will then lay eggs singly or in small clumps in the ground or on vegetation. Some eggs may undergo **diapause** and have delayed development during the cooler weather.

Crickets and katydids are **hemimetabolistic**, and the nymphs hatching from the eggs look like small adults. The nymphs will disperse and

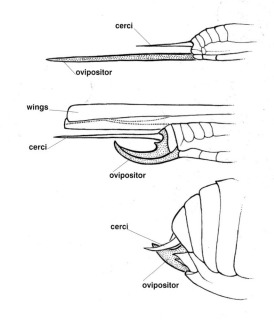

Ovipositors on female crickets and katydids come in a range of sizes and shapes. From top to bottom: long and straight, curved, and short ovipositors.

begin to feed on the same types of food as their parents. Cricket and katydid species have very varied feeding habits, and can be **omnivores**, **herbivores** or **carnivores**.

Crickets have been common in captivity as a source food for other animals, and because of this much is known about keeping them. The diversity of crickets in captivity is growing and people are now keeping them as pets rather than as the next meal for a lizard. Katydids are very diverse and many spectacular species exist in Australia. They are also becoming popular for display because of their size and their willingness to perch in trees and on branches. Some species are fairly easy to raise while others are a little more challenging.

Katydids can be held on the hand but do have the ability to fly. They do not fly very far, so handling them in an enclosed room will allow you to catch them again. Crickets, unfortunately, cannot be free handled. They jump or run off the hand very quickly and are better looked at in an enclosure. Multiple species of herbivorous crickets and katydids can generally be housed together, as long as you provide each species with its individual requirements.

This Spotted Predatory Katydid is laying eggs into the sand with her ovipositor

Black Field Cricket *Teleogryllus commodus*

Level of difficulty

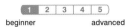

beginner   advanced

Black Field Crickets are often heard but rarely seen, as males make a loud chirping call from deep in vegetation or cracks in the soil. When you get close to them they often stop calling and will not start again until you are well away. Young crickets are jet black in colour and mature animals have dull black-brown wings and grow to about 25 mm in length. Black Field Crickets are found throughout Australia and come out at night to scavenge for decaying vegetation and dead animals as they dart around the ground moving from cover to cover. This species is a **cryptic** animal that is good at hiding within leaf litter and does not display well; however, it is useful in an educational context because its call is very distinctive.

Food and water
- Orthopteran mix and vegetables
- Water sponge

Routine care
Daily: Mist spray to maintain a damp and a dry end, and top-up the water sponge. Replace orthopteran mix and vegetables. Clean out waste material.

Sexing
Male: No ovipositor

Female: Ovipositor

Note: Juvenile females will have ovipositor developing

Breeding
When your crickets are mature, the males will call to attract females. The female will approach the male and mount him. The tip of the male's abdomen will clasp the tip of the female's and he will deposit a spermatophore. After mating the female can start to deposit eggs one by one into the substrate with her ovipositor. The eggs look like small, thin grains of rice and you can often see them through the sides of the enclosure. In captivity breeding can occur all year round. Eggs should be left in the substrate and the moisture level maintained. Eggs will hatch in 1–3 months, depending on temperature. Once the eggs have hatched, it will take 1–2 months for the juveniles to mature. If you have hatchling crickets, make sure the food dish does not have a lip in which the young can hide and accidentally be thrown out.

Lifespan
2–3 months

Captive behaviour
Your crickets will spend most of the day hidden under bark or within grass tussocks. During the night they will come out and move around the enclosure, feeding, moulting and finding a mate. They are most active at night, but they will move around a little during the day and feed. Males may also be heard calling throughout the day and night. These crickets moult on the ground, pulling themselves out of their old **exoskeleton** and often eating it immediately. If you see your cricket in the process of moulting, do not touch it; leave it to get out of its old skin and harden its new one.

Housing

 Enclosure: Terrarium, glass tank or custom; minimum size 20 cm H × 25 cm W × 15 cm D

Substrate: Sand and coco-peat mix, minimum depth 3 cm; maintain a damp and a dry end

Enclosure fit-out: Leaves and bark retreats, tussock grass optional

 Group

 20–28°C

 Humidity 40–50%

 No specialised lighting required

Special considerations
If you maintain large numbers you may experience cycles of mass births and deaths.

Compatibility with other species
Other temperate zone herbivorous invertebrates

Species with similar care requirements
Other field crickets, including Indian House Cricket (*Gryllodes sigillatus*)

53

Buchan Cave Cricket _Cavernotettix buchanensis_

Level of difficulty

1	2	**3**	4	5

beginner   advanced

These bizarre-shaped crickets have extremely long legs, a humped back, long antennae and grow to 22 mm. Buchan Cave Crickets spend their days living in the damp caves of eastern Victoria. They perch on the walls and roofs of the caves, where the temperature and humidity is steady and few predators can reach them. They leave the caves at night to forage. These scavengers will eat a wide variety of food, including dead animal and plant material. These crickets are very susceptible to low humidity levels and will not venture out of the caves if the weather is too dry. Cave crickets do not appear to disperse widely, and most cave systems have their own species. They can be kept in groups, as long as they have sufficient perching space when they need to moult.

Food and water
- Orthopteran mix
- Mist spray

Routine care
Daily: Mist spray substrate to maintain humidity. Replace orthopteran mix and remove waste material.

As required: Replace sphagnum moss if it becomes sodden or smelly. Caution: eggs may be in the moss.

Sexing
Male: Longer legs

Female: Sabre-shaped ovipositor

Note: Development of ovipositor is visible in sub-adult females

Breeding
Pairs will mate end to end with the tips of their abdomens locked together. The male will transfer a spermatophore to the female. After mating the female can start to lay eggs in the moss. It is best at this stage to provide a 3-cm deep dish of moist clay (this represents a cave floor) in which she can lay her eggs. This clay needs to be kept moist until the eggs hatch. In the wild, females will deposit the eggs into clay on the cave floor and in cracks. Eggs should be left in the enclosure and sprayed to keep damp. The hatchlings that emerge will resemble the adults. They will move into the retreat and begin to perch.

Lifespan
About 1 year

Captive behaviour
During the day, Buchan Cave Crickets sit very still in the enclosure with their rear legs folded. At night they will use their antennae to help track down food and move through the enclosure. They will perch on the walls and sides of the retreat.

Housing

 Enclosure: Terrarium, glass tank or custom; minimum size 20 cm H × 25 cm W × 15 cm D

Substrate: Sphagnum moss, minimum depth 2 cm; damp but no pooling water at bottom of enclosure

Enclosure fit-out: Create overhang with rocks or artificial materials for them to hide under

 Group

 18–24°C

 Humidity 80–95%

 None required, dislikes bright light

Special considerations
Maintaining a constant humidity and temperature is essential to keeping this species.

Compatibility with other species
Not recommended

Species with similar care requirements
Cave crickets (Rhaphidophoridae)

Common Garden Katydid *Caedicia simplex*

Level of difficulty

| 1 | **2** | 3 | 4 | 5 |

beginner   advanced

Most people in Australia will have heard these insects, even if they have not seen them. The Common Garden Katydid makes a distinct 'ttst-ttst' sound and is a widespread species found in most cities throughout Australia. This katydid spends its life in trees, shrubs and vines and has excellent **camouflage** – it looks just like a leaf and can reach 30 mm. Common Garden Katydids are herbivorous, feeding on the plants they live on. Juveniles can sometimes take on the bright colours of the flowers. Although they can be colourful as juveniles, all individuals will become green when mature. They can be kept in groups, as long as sufficient perching space is provided for them when they need to moult. This species is a good species to keep as it requires low maintenance and feeds on a wide variety of food plants.

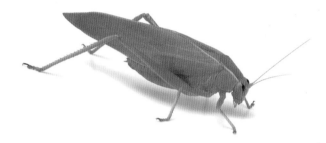

Food and water

- Orthopteran mix, fruit and cut foliage or potted plant, such as Lily Pily (*Syzygium* species), bottlebrush (*Callistemon* species), grevillea (*Grevillea* species), rose (*Rosa* species), eucalypt (*Eucalyptus* species)

- Mist spray

Routine care

Daily: Mist spray foliage to maintain humidity. Replace orthopteran mix (offer on pedestal feeder, p.172) and fruit (offer on leaves).

As required: Remove waste material from enclosure floor and water potted plants. Replace cut foliage or potted plants. Caution: foliage being removed may contain eggs.

Sexing

Male: Dark triangular area on back at the base of the wings (stridulatory mechanism)

Female: Ovipositor is very small and kidney-shaped

Breeding

They are mature when they have fully developed wings. When your katydids are mature, the male will call to the female and she will approach if she is ready to mate. The male will grasp the ovipositor at the tip of the abdomen and deposit a spermatophore. After mating the female will start to deposit eggs by pasting clusters of them to branches and leaves and covering them in a thin layer of 'glue' to hide them. The eggs look like small thin, black discs. Egg laying can happen all year round. Eggs should be left on the branches and sprayed every 1–2 days. They will generally take 3–4 weeks to hatch, although diapause can take place if the temperatures are too cold. Once hatched, it will take 2–4 months for these katydids to mature. This species has multiple generations per year.

Lifespan

3–6 months

Captive behaviour

During the day, these katydids sit very still in the enclosure, minimising movement. At night they will use their antennae to help track down food and move throughout the enclosure.

Housing

 Enclosure: Terrarium, mesh or custom; minimum size 25 cm H × 20 cm W × 15 cm D

Substrate: Absorptive layer only (sand, coco-peat, leaf litter, newspaper)

Enclosure fit-out: Food foliage will provide perching areas

 Group

 20–30°C, hotspot to 40°C at one end optional

 Humidity 60–80%

 UV provision, dichroic lamp as hotspot for 2–6 hours per day optional

Special considerations

These katydids can be easily handled and will generally sit quietly on the hand; occasionally they will jump and fly. Eggs are laid in clusters on the foliage and branches of the food plants, and when replacing potted plants or cut foliage care should be taken to ensure you do not throw any out.

Compatibility with other species

Other herbivorous invertebrates

Species with similar care requirements

Spiny-legged Katydid (*Paracaedicia serrata*) and other species from genus *Caedicia* including *C. marginata*

Gumleaf katydids *Terpandrus* species

Level of difficulty (1 2 **3** 4 5)
beginner   advanced

Gumleaf katydids are voracious hunters and there are many species of them in Australia. They are called gumleaf katydids because their forewings have the veins and colour to look just like gum leaves. They are large katydids, with the largest species, the Splendid Gumleaf Katydid (*Terpandrus splendidus*), reaching a length of 55 mm. Adults are mainly found in the canopy of eucalypts. They live in the trees and feed on other insects. Males sing on warm evenings to attract females, and their calls are loud and constant. Females will venture down onto the ground in late summer and autumn to deposit eggs into the soil. Juveniles can often be found on shrubs and small trees and move into the taller trees as they get older.

Food and water
- Orthopteran mix, fruit and live or dead insects such as crickets or cockroaches
- Mist spray

Routine care
Daily: Mist spray enclosure to maintain humidity and lightly spray katydid. Replace orthopteran mix and fruit, and clean out any waste.

Twice weekly: Introduce one live or dead insect, and either forceps feed or leave it in the enclosure

Sexing
Male: No ovipositor

Female: Long ovipositor that extends from the end of the abdomen

Note: Juvenile females will have ovipositor developing

Breeding
Male and female katydids should be housed separately until they are mature. Forceps feed the female a number of dead insects before introducing the male. Females should be set up in a large enclosure with deep substrate (minimum depth 8 cm) deeper than her ovipositor. The enclosure needs to be large so that the introduced male will have room to court the female. The male will call to the female and when he senses her approaching he will begin to call rapidly.

They will mate side by side and join their abdomens together as he transfers a spermatophore to her. After mating the female can start to deposit eggs with her ovipositor. The eggs look like small, thin grains of rice and are deposited one by one into the substrate. They should be left in the moist substrate. Egg laying generally takes place towards the end of summer and autumn. Eggs will develop over winter and hatch at the start of summer. The juveniles that hatch should be housed separately in jars. They will mature in 3–4 months.

Lifespan
About 1 year

Captive behaviour
These katydids will spend a lot of time sitting up in plants waiting for food to arrive. They are happy feeding both during the day and at night. If a juvenile does go off its food it is possibly preparing to moult, so give the substrate a good spray to increase the humidity. Katydids eat their old exoskeletons after they moult, and you will generally only know they have moulted by their increased size.

Housing
 Enclosure: Glass tank, mesh or custom; minimum size 60 cm H × 30 cm W × 30 cm D

Substrate: Absorptive layer only (sand, coco-peat, leaf litter, newspaper)

Enclosure fit-out: Branches and vegetation for perching

 Individual

 24–30°C, hotspot to 40°C

 Humidity 40–60%

 UV provision, dichroic lamp as hotspot for 4–6 hours per day

Special considerations
This species can be aggressive when handled, and bites can easily break the skin. Maintaining humidity and good perching branches for juveniles is particularly important as moulting mishaps are a common cause of death – katydids can get caught in their old exoskeleton and not dry properly.

Compatibility with other species
Not recommended

Species with similar care requirements
Species of *Terpandrus* including *T. splendidus* and *T. horridus*

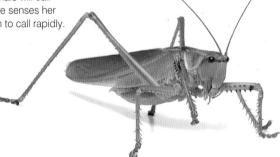

Leaf-winged katydids *Mastigaphoides* species

Level of difficulty

| 1 | 2 | **3** | 4 | 5 |

beginner   advanced

Leaf-winged katydids are spectacular animals that can grow to 35 mm. Their wings extend well above the abdomen and they are perfect mimics of the leaves on which they live. These katydids live in vines and trees around the perimeters of rainforests from northern New South Wales to far north Queensland. During the day they are almost invisible, as they position themselves motionless along the leaf vein of the plant; even their antennae follow this line. At night they are easier to see as they move through the plant, feeding. Males have a loud call; if you are patient you can easily track them down. They can be kept in groups, as long as sufficient perching space is provided for them when they need to moult.

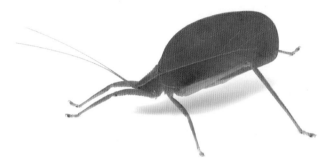

Food and water

- Orthopteran mix, fruit, fresh foliage or potted plants such as Native Gardenia (*Randia fitzalani*), Gardenia (*Gardenia* species), Weigela (*Weigela* species), Passionfruit Vine (*Passiflora* species)

- Mist spray

Routine care

Daily: Mist spray foliage to maintain humidity and replace orthopteran mix (offer on pedestal feeder, p.172) and fruit (offer on leaves)

As required: Remove waste material from enclosure floor, water potted plants and replace cut foliage or potted plants

Sexing

Male: No ovipositor

Female: Large sabre-shaped ovipositor

Note: Juvenile females will have an ovipositor developing

Breeding

This species is mature when the katydids have fully developed wings. When mature, males will call to attract females. They mate side by side and join their abdomens together as he transfers a

spermatophore to her. The sabre shape of the females ovipositor is an indicator that she deposits eggs into rotting wood. This can be replicated in the enclosure by embedding pulpy wood into a coco-peat substrate. This is ideal as it keeps the moisture levels high in the wood. The female will find the weak spots in the wood in which to leave her eggs. Another way to replicate this is by clipping together about 100 pages 5 cm × 5 cm of telephone book or newspaper. Keep these pages damp by mist spraying daily and the female should deposit eggs between the pages. Eggs should be left in the paper and sprayed every 1–2 days. It will take 2–4 months for the katydid hatchlings to mature.

Lifespan

6–12 months

Captive behaviour

During the day, leaf-winged katydids sit very still, aligned with the centre of the leaf and minimising movement. At night they will use their antennae to find their way around to move through the enclosure and feed. Chew marks on the leaves will indicate that your katydids have been feeding.

Housing

 Enclosure: Terrarium, glass tank, mesh or custom; minimum size 30 cm H × 20 cm W × 30 cm D

Substrate: Absorptive layer only (sand, coco-peat)

Enclosure fit-out: Branches and broad-leaf tropical plants (indoor varieties) for perching

 Group

 26–30°C, hotspot to 40°C at one end optional

 Humidity 70–90%

 UV provision, dichroic lamp as hotspot for 2–6 hours per day optional

Special considerations

This species can have moulting problems when maturing. Ensure the perching branches available have free space below them for the katydids to hang and moult.

Compatibility with other species

Other herbivorous rainforest invertebrates

Species with similar care requirements

None

Litter Cricket *Cardiodactylus novaeguinaea*

Level of difficulty

Litter Crickets are impressive. As juveniles they have shiny silver backs with black lines running down the sides and adult males have reddish wings with white spots. They grow to a length of about 35 mm. These crickets live in the coastal scrub and rainforest fringes of Queensland. During the day these crickets often sit exposed on understorey vegetation close to the ground, and when disturbed they will quickly drop to the ground and disappear into the leaf litter. They start moving around and calling at dusk.

Food and water
- Orthopteran mix, fruit, foliage such as Peace Lily (*Spathiphyllum* species)
- Mist spray

Routine care
Daily: Mist spray substrate and foliage and replace orthopteran mix and fruit

As required: Add new Peace Lily plants when the old ones have been eaten

Sexing
Male: Reddish markings on wings, with white dots

Female: Grey backed; ovipositor

Note: Sub-adult females will have an ovipositor developing

Breeding
When your crickets are mature, males will call to attract females. The female will approach the male and mount him. The tip of the male's abdomen will clasp the tip of the female's and he will deposit a spermatophore. In captivity breeding can occur all year round. After mating the female can start to deposit eggs one by one into the substrate with her ovipositor. The eggs look like small, thin grains of rice. They should be left in the substrate and the moisture levels maintained. Eggs will hatch in 1–3 months, depending on temperature. It can sometimes take more than 6 months for the hatchlings to mature.

Lifespan
6–12 months

Captive behaviour
Your crickets will spend most of their days perching on branches and plants. At night your they will move around the enclosure feeding, moulting and finding a mate. Crickets eat their old exoskeletons after they moult, so you will generally only know it has moulted by its increased size. These crickets moult on the ground or sitting on vertical branches, pulling themselves out of their old exoskeleton. If you do see your cricket in the process of moulting, do not touch it; leave it to get out of its old exoskeleton and for its new one to harden.

Housing

 Enclosure: Terrarium (with mesh insert into lid) or custom; minimum size 20 cm H × 25 cm W × 15 cm D

Substrate: Coco-peat, minimum depth 6 cm; damp throughout

Enclosure fit-out: Branches for perching, leaves and bark shelters

 Group

 24–30°C

 Humidity 60–90%

 UV provision

Special considerations
This species is extremely fast and the crickets can run or jump out of an enclosure if disturbed. Be aware of any animals on the door or lid before opening. If you have hatchling crickets, check the food dish before you remove it from the enclosure, as hatchlings may be hiding in it.

Compatibility with other species
Other herbivorous rainforest invertebrates

Species with similar care requirements
Spider crickets from tropical regions (*Endacusta* species)

Mountain Katydid *Acripeza reticulata*

Level of difficulty

| 1 | **2** | 3 | 4 | 5 |

beginner   advanced

Mountain Katydids are an alpine species that generally occur below the snowline along the Great Dividing Range. They are found in greatest numbers around alpine water bodies, and can be seen in large numbers around alpine bogs and in the marshy creek borders. They are not solely an alpine species, but are known to occur on the New England Tablelands and in Brisbane and Cairns. They grow to about 30 mm long. When they are disturbed these katydids raise their wings to reveal bright blue and red bands on their body that are designed to scare off potential predators. Juvenile Mountain Katydids look different from the adults; they are black with orange bands and resemble spiders or ants. This species is good for education and display because it actively forages during the day.

Food and water

- Orthopteran mix, fruit and fresh foliage such as Yarrow (*Achillea millefolium*), Alpine Daisy Bush (*Olearia* species) and Alpine Heath (*Epacris* species), which appear to be part of the wild diet

- Mist spray

Routine care

Daily: Mist spray enclosure to maintain humidity and top-up water in sphagnum moss. Replace orthopteran mix and fruit. Clean out any waste material and check eggs if they are incubating.

As required: Replace plants, but be aware that eggs may have been deposited on the stems and need to be incubated. Spray eggs if they are incubating and the humidity has dropped.

Sexing

Male: Wings extend past abdomen

Female: Wings wrap around the body

Breeding

When mature, males will perch up on a branch and call to the female. The male and female will approach one another, and the male will grasp her ovipositor at the tip of the abdomen and deposit a spermatophore. After mating the female will use her ovipositor to glue eggs onto branches and leaves. The eggs look like small, thin black discs. Mating generally happens towards the end of summer and autumn. Eggs will develop over winter and hatch around December. To aid egg development, chill the whole enclosure or just the branches containing eggs over winter. Placing eggs into the refrigerator or a cool place for about 3 months is sufficient. Check the eggs daily and mist spray if the enclosure is dry. Transfer your hatchlings to an environment with the same conditions as the adults.

Lifespan

4–5 months

Captive behaviour

They will move through the enclosure, basking under the hotspot to warm up and actively feeding on fruit, orthopteran mix and plants. They will also spend extended periods of time moving onto the sphagnum moss seeking out moisture.

Housing

Enclosure: Glass tank or custom; minimum size 40 cm H × 60 cm W × 30 cm D

Substrate: Absorptive layer only (sand, coco-peat, leaf litter)

Enclosure fit-out: Sphagnum moss in shallow dish, branches and vegetation for perching

 Group

18–24°C, hotspot to 40°C at one end

Humidity 50–70%

 Dichroic lamp for 1–2 hours per day

Special considerations
These katydids are a sub-alpine species and overheating the enclosure or dropping the humidity can sometimes cause their premature death.

Compatibility with other species
Other alpine zone herbivorous invertebrates

Species with similar care requirements
Alpine katydid (*Tinzeda* species)

Rainforest Tree Katydid *Phricta spinosa*

Level of difficulty

| 1 | 2 | **3** | 4 | 5 |

beginner   advanced

Rainforest Tree Katydids are common inhabitants of the tropical rainforests of eastern Australia. They are one of Australia's largest katydids, reaching 60 mm in length, yet they are rarely seen. They spend their lives in trees and have excellent camouflage, blending so well with tree trunks that they are almost invisible to the human eye. This katydid has large spines on the back of its thorax and legs, which helps with camouflage. It uses its powerful rear legs for defence, and if disturbed will raise both legs vertically above its body, exposing red thighs. Any further disturbance will cause the katydid to kick its attacker with both rear legs. At night these katydids move around feeding on leaves, bark and fruit, and become more noticeable.

Food and water
* Orthopteran mix and fruit, cut foliage or potted plant such as Lily Pily (*Syzygium* species), bottlebrush (*Callistemon* species), Morton Bay Fig (*Ficus macrophylla*), grevillea (*Grevillea* species), palm (*Arecaceae*)

* Mist spray

Routine care
Daily: Mist spray foliage to maintain humidity and mist spray laying tub if one is present. Replace orthopteran mix (offer on pedestal feeder, p.172) and fruit.

As required: Remove waste material from enclosure floor. Water potted plants and replace cut foliage or potted plants. Caution: Potting mix being removed may contain eggs.

Sexing
Male: No ovipositor

Female: Long ovipositor

Note: Juvenile females will have an ovipositor developing

Breeding:
They are mature when they have full wings. When mature, males will call to attract females. They will mate side by side and join their abdomens together as he transfers a spermatophore to her. From 1 to 2 weeks after mating the female will start to deposit eggs into the egg-laying tub with her ovipositor. The eggs look like brown grains of rice and are deposited one by one into the ground.

Eggs should be left in the moist laying tubs or potted plants. Egg laying can take place all year round and the eggs will generally take about 3 months to hatch. The hatched juveniles will take 2–4 months to mature.

Note: This species is known to be **parthenogenetic**, so eggs produced by unmated females may be viable.

Lifespan
1 year

Captive behaviour
During the day, they sit very still in the enclosure. At night they will use their long antennae to help locate food and move through the enclosure. Katydids eat their old exoskeletons after they moult, so you will generally only know it is has moulted by its increased size. If you do see your katydid in the process of moulting, leave it to get out of its exoskeleton and harden.

Housing
 Enclosure: Mesh or custom, mesh enclosure preferable for perching and moulting; minimum size 60 cm H × 35 cm W × 35 cm D

Substrate: Absorptive layer only (sand, coco-peat, leaf litter, newspaper)

Enclosure fit-out: Vertical and horizontal branches, egg-laying tub for females (see p.166)

 Group

 24–30°C

 Humidity 60–80%

 No specialised lighting required

Special considerations
These katydids are herbivorous, but during moulting housemates have been known to nibble each other. Moulting problems can frequently occur. Providing plenty of moisture and minimal disturbance during this time will help reduce this problem.

Compatibility with other species
Other herbivorous rainforest species

Species with similar care requirements
Other species of *Phricta*, Queensland Palm Katydid (*Segestidea queenslandica*) (requires palm as food foliage)

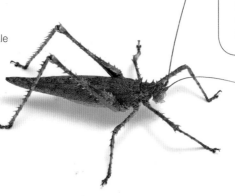

Spotted Predatory Katydid *Chlorobalius leucoviridis*

Level of difficulty

| 1 | 2 | **3** | 4 | 5 |

beginner   advanced

These insects are voracious hunters that feed on a variety of smaller invertebrates, which they catch using their spiny front legs and powerful mandibles. Spotted Predatory Katydids occur in the arid areas of Australia, with adults reaching lengths of about 50 mm. They hide during the day in the foliage of shrubs and come out at night to feed, call and find a mate. Adult individuals can flock and move through the habitat calling and feeding. This is a good species to keep as the katydids are large and do well in captivity.

Food and water
- Orthopteran mix, fruit, live or dead insects such as crickets or cockroaches
- Mist spray

Routine care
Daily: Mist spray enclosure to maintain humidity and lightly spray katydid. Replace orthopteran mix and fruit, and clean out any waste.

Twice weekly: Introduce one live or dead insect, and either forceps feed or leave it in the enclosure

Sexing
Male: No ovipositor

Female: Long ovipositor that extends from the end of the abdomen

Note: Juvenile females will have an ovipositor developing

Breeding
Male and female katydids should be housed separately until they are mature. Forceps feed the female a number of dead insects before introducing the male. The female should be set up in a large enclosure with deep substrate (minimum depth 8 cm), deeper than her ovipositor. The enclosure needs to be large so that the introduced male will have room to court the female. The male will call to the female, and when he senses the female approaching he will call rapidly. They will mate side by side and join their abdomens together as the male transfers a spermatophore to the female. After mating the female will use her ovipositor to deposit eggs one by one into the substrate.

The eggs, which look like small thin grains of rice, should be left in the moist substrate, where they may take more than 9 months to hatch. The juveniles that emerge should be housed separately in jars and fed small insects such as vinegar flies. They will take 3–4 months to mature.

Lifespan
About 1 year

Captive behaviour
This katydid will spend a lot of its time sitting up in plants waiting for food to arrive. It is happy feeding both during the day and at night. If a juvenile does go off its food it is possibly preparing to moult, so give the substrate a good spray to increase the humidity. Katydids eat their old exoskeletons after they moult and you will generally only know it has moulted by its increased size. If you do see your katydid in the process of moulting, leave it to get out of its old exoskeleton and for its new one to harden.

Housing
 Enclosure: Terrarium, glass tank, mesh or custom; minimum size 30 cm H × 20 cm W × 20 cm D

Substrate: Absorptive layer only (sand, coco-peat, leaf litter, newspaper)

Enclosure fit-out: Branches and vegetation for perching

 Individual

 24–30°C, hotspot to 40°C at one end optional

 Humidity 40–60%

 None required, dichroic lamp for 6–8 hours per day optional

Special considerations
Maintaining humidity for juveniles is particularly important as moulting mishaps are a common cause of death.

Compatibility with other species
Not recommended

Species with similar care requirements
Sluggish katydids (*Hemisaga* species)

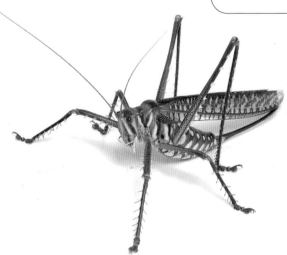

Thick-legged Raspy Cricket *Ametrus tibialis*

Level of difficulty

| 1 | **2** | 3 | 4 | 5 |

beginner   advanced

Thick-legged Raspy Crickets occur in the arid areas of Australia. They get their name from their ability to stridulate and make a 'rasping' sound when disturbed, by rubbing a leg against the body. These robust animals have stripes running across the abdomen. Two colour variations of the animal are recorded: brown and a vibrant pink. Adult body lengths can reach 35 mm. These crickets are nocturnal scavengers and they can sometimes be seen on warm nights walking across the road in large numbers to feed on 'road kill'. During the day they rest in burrows in logs or underground. The burrows are lined with silk that the crickets produce with their mouthparts. Adults of this species have very small wings and cannot fly. They do well in captivity if disturbance is kept to a minimum; constant checking of juveniles often leads to unsuccessful rearing. A way to overcome this problem is to rear them in a large enclosure with plenty of shelter.

Food and water
- Orthopteran mix, fruit, dead insects
- Water sponge

Routine care
Daily: Mist spray substrate to maintain a damp and a dry end, and top-up the water sponge. Replace orthopteran mix and fruit.

Twice weekly: Introduce dead insects (one per animal), forceps feed or leave it in the enclosure. Remove any uneaten dead insects.

Sexing
Male: No ovipositor

Female: Distinct ovipositor

Note: A juvenile female will have an ovipositor developing that is curled over her back; it straightens when she matures

Breeding
When mature, a male will seek out a female. They approach each other and the male will grasp the ovipositor at the tip of the abdomen and deposit a spermatophore. After mating the female can start to deposit eggs with her ovipositor. The eggs look like small thin grains of rice and are deposited one by one into the ground or substrate. Eggs should be left in moist substrate and will start hatching after 3 months. It will take 3–6 months for the hatchlings to mature.

Lifespan
8–12 months

Captive behaviour
These crickets will spend most of the day hidden away in the burrow. At night they will move around the enclosure foraging, moulting and mating, and will go back to their same burrow at the end of a night's foraging. Raspy Crickets eat their old exoskeletons after moulting, so you will generally only know it has moulted by its increased size. If you do see your Raspy Cricket in the process of moulting, leave it to get out of its exoskeleton and for its new exoskeleton to harden.

Housing
 Enclosure: Terrarium or custom; minimum size 20 cm H × 25 cm W × 15 cm D

Substrate: Sand, minimum depth 5 cm; maintain a damp and a dry end

Enclosure fit-out: Branches for juveniles to moult; leaves and log shelters

 Group

 24–30°C

 Humidity 40–60%

 No specialised lighting required

Special considerations
Minimising daytime disturbance seems to assist with the survival of juveniles.

Compatibility with other species
Desert cockroaches

Species with similar care requirements
Other arid area raspy crickets (*Hadrogryllacris* species)

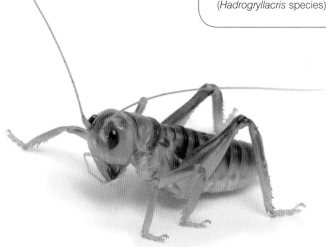

White-kneed King Cricket *Penalva flavocalceata*

Level of difficulty

1	2	3	4	5

beginner   advanced

White-kneed King Crickets are unmistakable, with their large hind legs and bright white knees. They are common inhabitants of the tropical rainforests of eastern Australia, but are rarely seen during the day because they hide in burrows in the soil and close over their openings with a leaf. At night these crickets will emerge and forage on the forest floor, where they scavenge and feed on fruit, nuts, leaves and dead animals. They are extremely large and they can grow to 50 mm long and weigh as much as 10 g. White-kneed King Crickets lack wings so cannot fly, but they are excellent jumpers and can jump more than a metre in a single bound.

Housing

 Enclosure: Terrarium, glass tank or custom; minimum size 25 cm H × 35 cm W × 20 cm D

Substrate: Coco-peat, minimum depth 10 cm; maintain damp throughout

Enclosure fit-out: Pulpy wood embedded into substrate, large dried leaves on top as shelters

 Group

 24–30°C

 Humidity 60–80%

 No specialised lighting required

Food and water
- Orthopteran mix, fruit, dead insects
- Moisture in substrate

Routine care
Daily: Mist spray substrate and replace orthopteran mix and fruit.

Weekly: Introduce dead insects (one per animal), and either forceps feed or leave in enclosure.

As required: Add additional dried leaves.

Sexing
Male: No ovipositor

Female: Large sabre-shaped ovipositor

Note: Juvenile females will have an ovipositor developing

Breeding
White-kneed King Crickets can be reared in groups in large tanks with deep substrate. Providing your crickets with plenty of room in which to shelter is sufficient to keep the individuals out of each other's paths. When your crickets are mature, the male will seek out a female. The male will approach the female, grasp the ovipositor at the tip of the abdomen and deposit a spermatophore. After mating the female can start to deposit eggs into the substrate with her ovipositor. The eggs look like grains of rice and are deposited one by one into the ground. Egg laying can take place at any time of the year. The eggs should be left in the damp substrate and will generally hatch 4–6 weeks after being laid. Once hatched, it will take 16–24 months for these crickets to mature.

Lifespan
3–5 years

Captive behaviour
Your crickets will spend most of their days hidden away in their burrows or under leaves. At night they will come out and move around the enclosure to feed. These crickets moult underground and eat their old exoskeletons, so you will generally only know they have moulted by their increased size.

Special considerations
This species has large mandibles, so holding adults in your hand is not recommended. If the density of your group is too high you may find that they nibble on each other. Your crickets need more space if this is happening.

Compatibility with other species
Other rainforest herbivores that do not compete directly for space

Species with similar care requirements
King crickets (*Australostoma* species)

The Blistered Pyrgomorph is peppered with colourful
spots that advertise its foul taste to potential predators.

Grasshoppers Suborder: Caelifera

Estimated number of species in Australia: 700

Most people encounter grasshoppers when there is a sudden movement beside them as a grasshopper is disturbed and jumps away. Grasshoppers are a well-recognised group because they can occur throughout Australia and are often found around our homes and on agricultural land in large numbers. They are generally long-bodied with large hind legs for jumping. Grasshoppers are related to crickets and katydids but can be distinguished by their short antennae; the antennae are shorter than their total body length. Most grasshoppers use **camouflage** to hide from predators, although some species such as the Blistered Pyrgomorph (*Monistria pustulifera*) are very brightly coloured, and advertise themselves as being distasteful to predators.

Sexing grasshoppers can be fairly difficult if you do not have the adult male and female side by side. Females are generally larger, with a bigger **abdomen** due to their need to carry eggs. Another way of sexing grasshoppers is to closely examine the tip of the abdomen. Males have a single upward facing point that forms a covering over the reproductive organs. The females have small structures coming off the end of the abdomen that they use to dig into the soil and deposit eggs.

In the wild, grasshoppers usually breed in the summer, but in captivity they may breed all year round. Males can often be seen perching on the female's back mating with her or guarding her from other males. A mated female will generally lay an egg mass underground by burying her whole abdomen into the substrate and depositing eggs in a foamy egg mass. You may see holes in the substrate where the female has buried her abdomen; if the holes have not been filled in it means that eggs were not deposited. Females will move around the enclosure digging these 'test holes' until they find a spot that has the right environmental conditions for egg development. Grasshopper eggs can be very good at withstanding drought periods and they can remain in **diapause** until the right conditions trigger them to hatch. Not all eggs from a single egg mass will hatch at the same time.

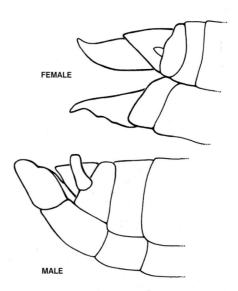

The tip of the abdomen of male and female grasshoppers.

Grasshoppers are **hemimetabolistic**, and the **nymphs** that hatch from the eggs look like small adults. These hatchlings will disperse and begin to feed immediately. Grasshoppers are **herbivores**, feeding on plant material their whole life. Some are fussy and will only feed on certain plant types, while others may be generalists and feed on a wide variety of plants. Grasshoppers are active during the day and like to bask in the sun, so enclosures should be set up to take this into account.

These insects are becoming a popular group for display, as they are active during the day, a large size and can demonstrate many concepts that are covered in educational facilities. Unlike many other invertebrates, it is possible to house multiple species of grasshoppers together, as long as you provide them with their individual requirements.

Handling grasshoppers is possible. Most can be restrained by pinching them lightly on the upper thorax, as this stops their powerful hind legs flicking into your hand. Some can also be gently encouraged onto the open palm and will sit there comfortably unless disturbed. Be aware that some of the larger species of grasshoppers have powerful and spiny legs that cause powerful and painful kicks.

Grasshoppers can be maintained in quite large numbers, and groups do make impressive displays. Large numbers can build up quickly with successful egg incubation and the subsequent mass emergence of hatchlings. Although it is great to have lots of animals they do have the tendency to eat everything – even **frass** and dead house-mates. Because of this, a build up of diseases in your enclosure can rapidly occur as individuals pass infection through consuming others wastes. Indications of a build up of diseases can be:

- reduced lifespans, with females dying before they deposit eggs; and

- hatchlings emerging from the egg and then dying in large numbers soon after.

Maintaining high levels of hygiene by cleaning out frass, removing any dead individuals promptly and regularly changing the substrate will improve your success in maintaining healthy groups of grasshoppers.

Large grasshoppers can be handled easily by pinning the hind legs between your fingers.

Baby grasshoppers often emerge in large numbers after hatching from eggs laid underground.

Common Toadhoppers are inquisitive grasshoppers and are great to keep.

Blistered Pyrgomorph *Monistria pustulifera*

Level of difficulty

| 1 | 2 | 3 | 4 | 5 |

beginner   advanced

This peculiar grasshopper is covered in red, yellow and white spots, much like an Aboriginal dot painting. Most adults only develop tiny flap-like wings that are used for defence and cannot fly, although, strangely, a small proportion of grasshoppers will develop full wings. When the grasshoppers are disturbed their wing flaps flare out, exposing the bright red colouration of the inner wings and warning potential predators that they are foul tasting and should not be eaten. Their taste comes from the strongly aromatic plants they eat. Blistered Pyrgomorphs are found in the arid inland areas of Australia.

Food and water
- Fresh **browse** including Abelia (*Abelia grandiflora*) species from the Prostanthera group, Coastal Rosemary (*Westringia fruiticosa*) and species from the Eremophila group, orthopteran mix

- Mist spray

Routine care
Daily: Replace orthopteran mix and mist spray substrate to maintain a damp and a dry end

As required: Replace browse

Sexing
Male: Up to 25 mm long

Female: Up to 40 mm long

Note: Because they only have wing flaps, careful examination will be needed to confirm they are adult

Breeding
The male will mount the female's back for mating and may ride there for long periods of time. The female will deposit foam-covered clusters of eggs underground by burying most of her abdomen in the moist substrate. Nymphs will generally hatch after 2–4 months, but you may have new hatchlings emerge much later.

Lifespan
About 6–12 months

Captive behaviour
They are a fairly sluggish grasshopper and will walk rather than jump. They will either be perched up in food plants or spend their time on the substrate surface.

Housing
 Enclosure: Glass tank or custom; minimum size 40 cm H × 60 cm W × 30 cm D

Substrate: Sand, minimum depth 10 cm; maintain a damp and a dry end

Enclosure fit-out: Food foliage will provide perching areas

 Group

 23–35°C, hotspot to 40°C at one end

 Humidity 50–70%

 Dichroic lamp for for 4–6 hours per day

Special considerations
Ensure that the pot in which you provide fresh foliage is covered to prevent your animals drowning. This species has a tendency to fall into the water and drown.

Compatibility with other species
Other herbivorous insects, especially grasshoppers

Species with similar care requirements
Other species of *Monistria*

Common Toadhopper *Buforania crassa*

Level of difficulty

| 1 | 2 | **3** | 4 | 5 |
beginner   advanced

Common Toadhoppers are well-camouflaged grasshoppers that resemble the small rocks of central Australia, on which in the wild they sit motionless and simply 'disappear' into the background. Their habitat ranges through the arid regions of mainland Australia, where they live in the open red sands and gibber rocks. Toadhoppers forage on and around low-growing shrubs, feeding on the vegetation. Eggs are adapted to dry conditions and have the ability to hatch over several years in the wild. Adults are generally a deep red colour, but if raised on a light sand substrate they will become lighter shades of red, orange and yellow.

Housing

 Enclosure: Glass tank or custom; minimum size 40 cm H × 60 cm W × 30 cm D

Substrate: Sand, minimum depth 8 cm; maintain a damp and a dry end

Enclosure fit-out: Vegetation and branches, flat rock positioned where hotspot hits substrate

 Group

 23–35°C, hotspot to 40°C at one end

 Humidity 50–70%

 Dichroic lamp for 4–6 hours per day

Food and water
- Orthopteran mix, pollen granules, fresh grass; vegetation optional, including paper daisies (*Bracteantha* species), banksia flowers (*Banksia* species), emu bush (*Eremophila* species), Abelia (*Abelia grandiflora*)

- Water sponge

Routine care
Daily: Replace orthopteran mix, mist spray substrate to maintain a damp and a dry end, and dampen water sponge

Weekly: Replace pollen

As required: Replace vegetation and grass

Sexing
Male: 40 mm long, wings extend past tip of abdomen

Female: 60 mm long, wings barely extend past tip of abdomen

Note: The body shape can help with sexing juveniles, as young females are more robust and thicker around the abdomen

Breeding
This species will breed all year round in captivity. The male will mount the female's back for mating. The female will deposit foam-covered clusters of eggs into the substrate by burying most of her abdomen into the moist substrate. Nymphs will generally hatch 1–3 months later, although you may have hatchlings 1–2 years after having this animal in the enclosure. Nymphs that emerge are quite large and will climb the walls of your enclosure and settle. They need to be fed soft grass immediately.

Lifespan
1–2 years

Captive behaviour
Common Toadhoppers alternate their time foraging for food and basking under the hotspot. They are an active animal during the day and can be seen feeding and interacting with other individuals. They rarely jump, preferring to walk around. Although they look bulky, they have the ability to climb vegetation quite well.

Special considerations
If the population in your enclosure becomes too high, individuals have a tendency to chew and damage other Common Toadhoppers while they are moulting.

Compatibility with other species
Other arid zone herbivorous insects

Species with similar care requirements
Living Stones (*Raniliella testudo*)

Giant grasshoppers *Valanga* species

Level of difficulty `1 2 3 4 5`
beginner   advanced

Giant grasshoppers are Australia's largest grasshoppers, with adults reaching close to 90 mm in length. They occur in coastal and inland areas of northern and eastern Australia and are a pest in coffee plantations and other agricultural crops. These grasshoppers can also be found in low numbers in suburban backyards. Over winter you will generally only find the adults, as the eggs will undergo diapause until spring. During spring you will often see lots of small juveniles on 'weedy' plants in the undergrowth. Giant grasshoppers are easy to keep due to their ability to feed on many commonly grown plants.

Housing

 Enclosure: Glass tank or custom; minimum size 40 cm H × 60 cm W × 30 cm D

Substrate: Sand, minimum depth 10 cm; maintain a damp and a dry end

Enclosure fit-out: Branches

 Group

 22–30°C, hotspot to 40°C at one end optional

 Humidity 60–80%

None essential, dichroic lamp for 4–6 hours per day optional

Food and water
- Fresh browse such as New Zealand Mirror Bush (*Coprosma*), Abelia (*Abelia grandiflora*), citrus such as lemon (*Citrus* species), rose (*Rosa* species); orthopteran mix, grass shoots if juveniles present

- Mist spray

Routine care
Daily: Replace orthopteran mix and mist spray substrate to maintain a damp and a dry end

As required: Replace browse, and replace grass if juveniles present

Sexing
Male: Up to 65 mm long, tip of abdomen tapered with a sharp point

Female: Up to 90 mm long, tip of abdomen has digging structures

Breeding
The male will mount the female's back for mating and will guard her from other males. The female will deposit foam-covered clusters of eggs underground by burying most of her abdomen into the moist substrate. Juveniles will generally hatch 3–4 months later, although diapause can occur if conditions are too dry or cool. Juveniles are pale green and will begin to feed almost immediately, so fresh soft grass should be provided. The juveniles undergo seven **instars** before adulthood is reached.

Lifespan
About 1 year

Captive behaviour
Your grasshoppers will spend a lot of time sitting motionless in the foliage and branches. They will move around more after a spray and if fresh green food is added to the enclosure. If startled they may jump powerfully or fly in any direction, so it is recommended that you have a container handy to catch them if they escape.

Special considerations
These grasshoppers have very powerful, spiny legs and can jump and fly a long way if disturbed. They can also use their spines and kick quite hard as a defensive response.

Compatibility with other species
Other tropical and subtropical zone herbivorous insects

Species with similar care requirements
Spur-throated Grasshopper (*Austracris guttulosa*)

Giant Green Slantface *Acrida conica*

Level of difficulty

1 **2** 3 4 5

beginner   advanced

These slender grasshoppers have a distinct slant to the face and look like blades of grass when motionless. If examined closely, it can be seen that even the antennae are flattened to help this camouflage. The Giant Green Slantface is widespread across mainland Australia, and appears to favour habitats close to humans that have abundant grasses growing. In some seasons populations of this grasshopper have been known to increase to large numbers. During the day these grasshoppers are easily startled and will fly away, which makes them difficult to approach. At night, however, they are more relaxed and can be collected easily.

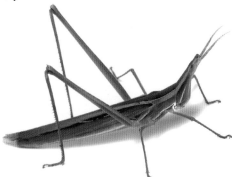

Food and water
- Fresh grass, orthopteran mix
- Mist spray

Routine care
Daily: Replace orthopteran mix and mist spray substrate to maintain a damp and a dry end

As required: Replace grass

Sexing
Male: Up to 55 mm long, tip of abdomen tapered with a sharp point

Female: Up to 85 mm long, tip of abdomen has digging structures

Breeding
Individuals are mature when they have full wings. The male will mount the female's back for mating and may ride there for some time. The female will deposit foam-covered clusters of eggs underground by burying most of her abdomen into the moist substrate. Nymphs will hatch 2–4 months later, although this could be longer if conditions are too dry or cool. Nymphs will begin to feed almost immediately, and fresh soft grass should be provided for them.

Lifespan
Up to 12 months

Captive behaviour
Your grasshoppers will spend extended periods of time sitting still in the enclosure. They will move around much more after a spray and if fresh grass is added. If you startle them they are likely to jump and fly in any direction, so it is recommended that you have a container handy to catch them if they escape.

Housing
 Enclosure: Glass tank or custom; minimum size 40 cm H × 60 cm W × 30 cm D

Substrate: Sand, minimum depth 10 cm; maintain a damp and a dry end

Enclosure fit-out: Branches and dry grasses

 Group

 22–30°C, hotspot to 40°C at one end

 Humidity 50–70%

Dichroic lamp for hotspot for 2–4 hours per day

Special considerations
This species is a big eater and maintaining sufficient grass for them to eat is the main difficulty in keeping them.

Compatibility with other species
Other herbivorous insects, especially other grasshoppers

Species with similar care requirements
Australian Grass Pyrgomorph (*Atractomorpha australis*)

Gumleaf Grasshopper *Goniaea australasiae*

Level of difficulty

1	2	3	4	5

beginner   advanced

Gumleaf Grasshoppers are incredibly well camouflaged and look exactly like dead gum leaves. As their name suggests, they are associated with eucalypt trees, although under peppercorn trees is another good place to look for them. These grasshoppers are often found hiding and feeding among the dried leaves at the base of trees. They are found Australia-wide and every stage of the life cycle can be found all year round. If startled during the day, the juveniles will jump a short distance and then drop into the dried gum leaves and freeze, literally disappearing as they blend into the background. Adults, on the other hand, have wings and will fly a reasonable distance (5–10 metres) before landing and sitting motionless. At night they travel up into the trees to feed on the green leaves.

Housing

Enclosure: Glass tank or custom; minimum size 40 cm H × 60 cm W × 30 cm D

Substrate: Sand, coco-peat or mix, minimum depth 6 cm; maintain a damp and a dry end

Enclosure fit-out: Vegetation and branches

Group

23–35°C, hotspot to 40°C at one end

Humidity 50–70%

Dichroic lamp for 4–6 hours per day

Food and water

- Dried brown and fresh eucalypt leaves, orthopteran mix

- Mist spray

Routine care

Daily: Replace orthopteran mix and mist spray substrate to maintain a damp and a dry end

As required: Replace browse. This may need to be replaced often if small nymphs are present, as new soft tips are required. Add dried, brown eucalypt leaves.

Sexing

Male: Up to 35 mm long

Female: Up to 50 mm long, large crest on upper side of thorax

Breeding

Individuals are mature when they have full wings. A male will mount the female's back for mating and may ride there for some time. The female will deposit foam-covered clusters of eggs underground by burying most of her abdomen into the moist substrate. Nymphs will hatch in about 3 months, although this could be longer if conditions are too dry or cool. Nymphs will begin to feed almost immediately, and fresh soft browse should be provided.

Lifespan

About 1 year

Captive behaviour

Your grasshoppers will spend a lot of time sitting fairly still in the enclosure during the day. They will start to move more after a spray and if fresh gum leaves are added to the enclosure. When the dichroic lamp is first turned on they will cluster around the hotspot, basking to raise their body temperature. At night there is more activity as they move through the enclosure to feed. If you startle them, they are likely to jump and fly in any direction, so it is recommended that you have a container ready to catch them if they escape.

Special considerations

When using hot dichroic lamps ensure sticks, branches and leaves are far enough away that they will not pose a fire threat. Positioning a rock under this lamp will maximise the heat being provided.

Compatibility with other species

Other herbivorous insects, especially grasshoppers

Species with similar care requirements

Other gumleaf grasshoppers (*Goniaea* species), bark mimicking grasshoppers (*Coryphistes* species)

Lesser Mountain Spotted Grasshopper *Yeelana pavonina*

Level of difficulty | 1 | 2 | **3** | 4 | 5 |
beginner   advanced

These flightless grasshoppers are quite distinctive, with small, white spotted markings. They can be found under eucalypts in the granite country of sub-alpine areas. Their colour and patterning is used to warn potential predators that they are foul tasting and should not be eaten. Their bad taste comes from the strongly aromatic species of plants they eat.

Housing

 Enclosure: Glass tank, terrarium or custom; minimum size 40 cm H × 60 cm W × 30 cm D

Substrate: Coco-peat and sand mix, minimum depth 6 cm; maintain a damp and a dry end

Enclosure fit-out: Vegetation and branches

 Group

 18–26°C, hotspot to 40°C at one end optional

 Humidity 50–70%

 None essential, dichroic lamp for 1–2 hours per day optional

Food and water
- Fresh browse including species from the Prostanthera group and Coastal Rosemary (*Westringia fruticosa*); orthopteran mix
- Mist spray

Routine care
Daily: Replace orthopteran mix and mist spray substrate to maintain a damp and a dry end

As required: Replace browse

Sexing
Male: Up to 20 mm long, tip of abdomen tapered with a sharp point

Female: Up to 45 mm long, tip of abdomen has digging structures

Note: Because they do not have fully developed wings, they will need to be examined carefully to confirm they are adult.

Breeding
These grasshoppers can be housed together in groups, and if artificial conditions are stable they can breed all year round. The male will mount the female's back for mating. The male can remain there for extended periods, 'mate guarding' the female from other males. The female will deposit foam-covered clusters of eggs underground by burying most of her abdomen into the moist substrate. Cooling the eggs to below 15°C within the substrate over a period of several months and then warming them again will aid egg development. The eggs will generally hatch after 3–6 months and the nymphs will commence feeding almost immediately, so fresh soft browse is recommended for these younger animals.

Lifespan
6–12 months

Captive behaviour
These grasshoppers are fairly relaxed and are not startled easily. They will be either perched on food plants or sitting on the substrate. If you use a hotspot in the enclosure they will cluster around it, basking to raise their body temperature.

Special considerations
This is a sub-alpine zone species and overheating or dropping the humidity of the enclosure can sometimes cause premature death.

Compatibility with other species
Other herbivorous sub-alpine zone invertebrates

Species with similar care requirements
None

Mantids have extraordinary eyesight. Their eyes have black dots called pseudo-pupils which give the appearance that the mantid is always looking at you.

Mantids   Order: Mantodea

Estimated number of species in Australia: 160

Mantids are predators to be feared in the invertebrate world, as they have excellent eyesight and powerful raptorial legs. Mantids are found in most land habitats across Australia and are common in suburban backyards. Most mantids inhabit trees and shrubs, camouflaging into the foliage, although some have adapted to more unusual habitats such as living on termite mounds in northern Australia (*Gyromantis* species). Mantids are well known and easily recognised by the 'praying' posture in which they hold their front legs. These raptorial front legs have one or two rows of spines that are used to catch and hold prey while they eat it. Perhaps the most engaging features of mantids are their large **compound eyes** and their triangular-shaped head.

Sexing mantids is fairly easy; males generally have full wings that extend past the tip of their **abdomen**, whereas females have shorter wings. A far more precise method of sexing is to count the number of segments on the abdomen. Males of any species of mantid will have a greater number of segments than the female of that species.

Reproduction occurs in the warmer months of the year and males will fly to find females. Mating sometimes leads to the male being eaten by the female and, as odd as this may seem, it is beneficial for him to be eaten to give the female energy to produce lots of eggs. Females will then lay an **ootheca** on vegetation, in cracks in wood or on windowsills. The ootheca is wafer-like, with a 'seam' on one side , and it may contain up to 400 eggs.

Mantids are **hemimetabolistic** and the **nymphs** look like small adults. The hatchlings will disperse and begin to feed immediately. To hunt, mantids sit very still with their raptorial legs in a praying-like pose, waiting to ambush the insects and spiders that make up their diet. They will catch and hold their prey in their raptorial legs while they eat it alive. Mantids have powerful chewing mouthparts, and can eat even the hardest parts of their prey.

Handling mantids is more appropriate with the larger species, although the males can be a little flighty. The smaller species are fast movers and need to be contained.

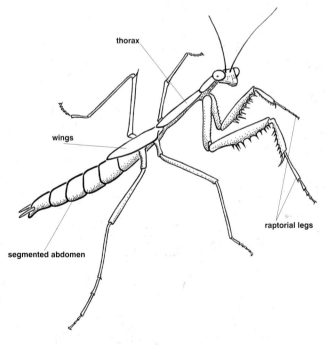

thorax

wings

raptorial legs

segmented abdomen

Common Green Mantid *Orthodera ministralis*

Level of difficulty | 1 | 2 | 3 | 4 | 5 |
beginner   advanced

These compact little mantids are a common garden species and are a good species for beginners to keep. Common Green Mantids occur Australia-wide. They feed on insects and spiders and adults reach a length of about 40 mm. They are green in colour and have a bright blue to purple spot on their inner forelegs. Adults are always green but younger individuals can vary in colour from green to brown and pink. Checking vines and bushes at night with a torch during the warmer months is a good time to spot this species. They can be distinguished from other mantids by having forelegs that tuck tightly against the thorax.

Food and water
- Live insects such as crickets, mealworms and cockroaches
- Mist spray

Routine care
Daily: Mist spray branches and sticks and lightly spray mantis

Twice weekly: Forceps feed or leave one or two live insects in the enclosure. Remove any dead or uneaten insect.

Sexing
Male: eight abdominal segments

Female: seven abdominal segments

Note: Juveniles can be sexed by counting the number of abdominal segments

Breeding
Your mantids are ready to be mated about a week after reaching maturity. For a few days before pairing, feed both individuals well, to reduce their appetite for each other. Introduce the male into the female's enclosure while she is eating, and place him at the other end of the enclosure so that he does not disturb her. The male may take hours or even days to mate, so be patient. He will dart around the enclosure and may approach the female a number of times. In time he will quickly mount the female's back and start mating. There is a chance with this species that the female will eat the male during mating. In the following weeks the female will lay multiple oothecae, suspended under a branch or on the side of the enclosure. Remove her from the enclosure before the eggs hatch or she will eat the hatchlings. Eggs generally hatch 1–4 months after being laid, and this large variation depends on

temperature. You may have as few as 10 to as many as 100 hatchlings. If hatchling numbers are too high for you to manage, leave them together and their first meals can be each other. Otherwise separate them into easy-feeders described on p.158. Mantids can spend their first 2–3 **instars** in these and then be separated into individual enclosures.

Lifespan
6–9 months

Captive behaviour
Your mantis will spend a lot of its time motionless waiting for food. It feeds during the day and at night. If a juvenile is very plump and stops eating, remove all food and give the enclosure a good spray as it may be about to **moult**. You will know if it has moulted by the old **exoskeleton** that has been left behind and because your mantis will have grown noticeably. If you see your mantis moulting, do not touch it; leave it to get out of its exoskeleton and dry. This species is a little flighty and will move around very quickly when disturbed, so be conscious of this when handling.

Housing
 Enclosure: Terrarium or custom; minimum size 20 cm H × 15 cm W × 10 cm D

Substrate: Absorptive layer only (sand, coco-peat, leaf litter, newspaper)

Enclosure fit-out: Branches and sticks for perching

 Individual

 20–26°C

 Humidity 40–70%

 No specialised lighting required

Special considerations
Ensure your juveniles have sufficient live insect food during this critical growing phase.

Compatibility with other species
Ground-dwelling invertebrates, as there is little interaction

Species with similar care requirements
False Garden Mantis (*Pseudomantis albofimbriata*)

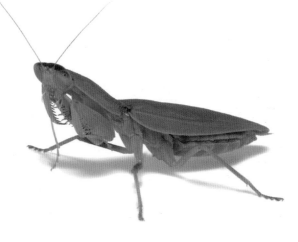

Giant Green Mantid *Hierodula majuscula*

Level of difficulty

1	2	3	4	5

beginner   advanced

This species is Australia's largest (up to 70 mm long) and most powerfully built mantid. It occurs in north Queensland's coastal and rainforest areas, and can be common in gardens. It is an excellent species to keep because of its large size and good survival rate. It is a pale green colour with orange and black inner forelegs. It feeds on a range of insects and spiders, and in the wild has even been recorded catching and eating vertebrates such as lizards, frogs and birds.

Food and water
- Live insects such as crickets and cockroaches
- Mist spray

Routine care
Daily: Mist spray branches and sticks, and lightly spray mantis

Twice weekly: Forceps feed or leave one or two live insects in the enclosure. Remove any dead or uneaten insects.

Sexing
Male: Wings extend past the tip of abdomen, seven abdominal segments

Female: Wings are slightly shorter than abdomen, six abdominal segments

Note: Juveniles can be sexed by counting the number of abdominal segments

Breeding
You can begin mating your mantids about a week after they have moulted to maturity. For a few days before pairing, feed both individuals well (especially the female) to reduce their appetite for each other. Introduce the male into the female's enclosure while she is eating and place him at the other end of the enclosure so he does not disturb her. The male may take hours or even days to mate, so be patient. When he does mate, he will sneak up and climb onto her back. There is a high chance that the female will eat her mate during mating, but he is able to mate without a head! The female will lay an ootheca 20–40 days after mating. She will attach the ootheca to a branch or the walls of the enclosure, and she may guard it for a number of days. Remove her from the enclosure before the eggs hatch or she will eat the hatchlings. Eggs hatch 40–60 days after being laid, and you may have as few as four or as many

as 400 hatchlings. If hatchling numbers are too high for you to manage, leave them together and their initial meals can be each other. Otherwise separate them into easy-feeders described on p.158. Mantids can spend their first 2–3 instars in these and then be separated into individual enclosures and fed larger meals.

Lifespan
9–12 months

Captive behaviour
Your mantid will spend a lot of time sitting on plants waiting for food to arrive; it will feed during the day and at night. If a juvenile stops eating, remove all food and give the enclosure a good spray, as your mantid may be about to moult. If this occurs the old exoskeleton will be left behind and your mantid will be larger. If you see your mantid in the process of moulting, do not touch it; leave it to get out of its exoskeleton and to harden.

Housing

 Enclosure: Terrarium or custom; minimum size 30 cm H × 15 cm W × 15 cm D

Substrate: Absorptive layer only (sand, coco-peat, leaf litter, newspaper)

Enclosure fit-out: Branches and sticks for perching

 Individual

 24–30°C, hotspot to 40°C optional

 Humidity 60–90%

 Not essential, dichroic lamp optional

Special considerations
Maintaining high humidity for juveniles is essential as moulting mishaps are a common cause of death; mantids can get caught in their old exoskeleton and not dry properly.

Compatibility with other species
Large rainforest snails are one of the few invertebrates this voracious feeder will ignore

Species with similar care requirements
Hooded Horror (*Hierodula atricoxis*)

Grass Mantis *Archimantis latistyla*

Level of difficulty

| 1 | 2 | 3 | 4 | 5 |

beginner   advanced

These mantids look like blades of grass and are the longest in Australia, growing to a length of 90 mm. They occur in all states and territories of Australia except Tasmania. They are common in the arid regions and live in trees, shrubs and long grass, where they feed on insects and spiders. They range in colour from pastel green to brown and purple. This variation in colour is the result of the type of habitat in which the mantis lives. Nymphs can be recognised by their skinny appearance and the white stripe that runs down their back.

Food and water
- Live insects such as crickets, mealworms and cockroaches
- Mist spray

Routine care
Daily: Mist spray branches and sticks, lightly spray mantis

Twice weekly: Forceps feed or leave one or two live insects in the enclosure. Remove any dead or uneaten insects.

Sexing
Male: Wings extend past the tip of abdomen, seven abdominal segments

Female: Wings are short (about 1 cm), six abdominal segments

Note: Juveniles can be sexed by counting the number of abdominal segments

Breeding
These mantids can be mated about a week after moulting to maturity. For a few days before pairing, feed both individuals well to reduce their appetite for each other. Introduce the male into the female's enclosure while she is eating, and place him at the other end of the enclosure so he does not disturb her. The male may take hours or even days to mate. When he does mate, he will sneak up and climb onto her back. There is a chance that the female will eat her mate during mating, but he is able to mate without a head! The female will lay an ootheca 14–20 days after mating. She will attach the ootheca to a branch or the wall of the enclosure, and she may guard it for a number of days. Remove her from the enclosure before the eggs hatch or she will begin to eat the hatchlings. Eggs hatch 1–2 months after being laid, and you may have as few as 10 or as many as 300 hatchlings. Leave hatchlings together if

numbers are too high for you to manage and their first meals can be each other. Otherwise separate them into easy-feeders described on p.158. Mantids can spend their first 2–3 instars in these and then be separated into individual enclosures. Males have six moults to reach maturity, females have seven.

Lifespan
9–12 months

Captive behaviour
Your mantis will spend a lot of its time sitting on branches waiting for food to arrive, and it will feed during the day and at night. If a juvenile stops eating, remove all food, give the enclosure a good spray as it may be about to moult. You will know if it has moulted by the old exoskeleton that is left behind and because your mantis has grown. If you see your mantis in the process of moulting, do not touch it; leave it to get out of its exoskeleton and dry.

Housing

 Enclosure: Terrarium or custom; minimum size 30 cm H × 15 cm W × 15 cm D

Substrate: Absorptive layer only (sand, coco-peat, leaf litter, newspaper)

Enclosure fit-out: Branches and sticks for perching

 Individual

 24–30°C

 Humidity 60–80%

 No specialised lighting required

Special considerations
Make sure there is sufficient room for your animal to moult as this species is prone to moulting problems if kept in cramped conditions.

Compatibility with other species
Not recommended

Species with similar care requirements
Purple Winged Mantis (*Tenodera australasiae*), Mallee Mantis (*Coenomantis kraussiana*)

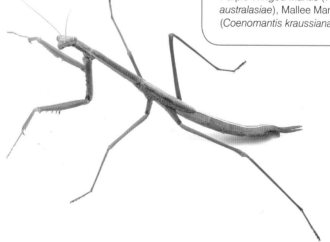

Netwinged Mantid *Neomantis australis*

Level of difficulty

| 1 | 2 | **3** | 4 | 5 |

beginner   advanced

Netwinged Mantids are masters of camouflage, and with their leaf-like wings they become invisible in their natural environment. They are found in northern Australia's open woodland and rainforest areas. They can be encountered if you have a good eye and plenty of patience, as they often hide on the underside of leaves and are quite small (20 mm). They feed on a range of invertebrates, especially small flies. This delicate species can be fairly challenging to keep because of the small-sized food they require, but are fascinating to watch.

Food and water
- Live insects such as crickets, cockroaches, flies
- Mist spray

Routine care
Daily: Mist spray branches and leaves, and lightly spray mantis

Twice weekly: Forceps feed or leave one or two live insects in the enclosure. Remove any dead or uneaten insects.

Sexing
Male: White bulge on underside end of abdomen

Female: A more full-bodied abdomen

Note: This species is hard to sex, and a magnifying glass can assist

Breeding
You can pair your mantids about a week after they have moulted to maturity. Before pairing, feed both individuals well to reduce their appetite for each other. Introduce the male into the female's enclosure while she is eating and place him at the other end of the enclosure so he does not disturb her. The male may take hours or even days to mate, so be patient. He will climb onto her

back to mate. There is a chance that the female will eat him during mating. If this happens there is nothing you should do. After mating expect the female to lay a small ootheca that she will attach to the underside of a leaf or the side of the enclosure. Transfer her away from the eggs before they hatch, as she will eat the hatchlings. Eggs hatch about 16 days after being laid, and you may have as few as four to as many as 50 hatchlings to care for. If numbers are too high for you to manage, leave them together and their first few meals can be each other. Otherwise separate them out to easy-feeders described on p.158. These mantids can spend their entire life in these easy-feeders, but it is better to transfer them to their own enclosures when they are sub-adults so that they can feed on larger food items.

Lifespan
4–6 months

Captive behaviour
Your mantis will spend a lot of time sitting up under leaves waiting for food to arrive. It feeds during the day and at night and ambushes insects coming near it. If startled your mantis will run in quick bursts to escape.

Housing
 Enclosure: Terrarium or custom; minimum size 10 cm H × 5 cm W × 5 cm D

Substrate: Absorptive layer only (sand, coco-peat, leaf litter, newspaper)

Enclosure fit-out: Branches with leaves that are larger than your mantid

 Individual

 24–30°C, hotspot to 40°C optional

 Humidity 60–90%

 Not essential, dichroic lamp optional

Special considerations
Maintaining high humidity is particularly important for juveniles, as moulting mishaps can be a cause of death. These mantids are very fast runners, so care must be taken when opening and closing the enclosure.

Compatibility with other species
Ground-dwelling herbivorous invertebrates are great because there is little interaction

Species with similar care requirements
Bark mantid (*Gyromantis* species), forest mantid (*Ciulfina* species)

Phasmids are masters of camouflage; this Spiny Leaf Insect resembles a dead leaf.

Phasmids Order: Phasmatodea

Estimated number of species in Australia: 150

Phasmids are stick and leaf insects. They are more common in the wild than you might think. Many people tend to overlook them because of their excellent **camouflage**. Occasionally they will fall from trees during windy weather, making them easier to find. This order contains the longest insects in Australia. The Titan Stick Insect (*Acrophylla titan*), for example, can be a whopping 250 mm long. Plasmids come in a range of sizes and shapes, from fat and flightless to slender and capable of flight.

Phasmids spend their days motionless and looking just like sticks or leaves. They are generally solitary animals, although on rare occasions some species have been known to mass and defoliate trees. This solitary nature helps to reduce their detection by potential predators. Winged species also have another form of protection. If a predator comes too close, the phasmid will raise its hind wings, exposing brightly coloured or patterned wings that are designed to startle the predator. Some phasmids can release strongly scented chemicals to deter predators. The Peppermint Stick Insect (*Megacrania batesii*) can squirt a white peppermint scented liquid from behind its head at potential predators. Most phasmid defences rely entirely on bluff, as they are harmless; they do not bite or sting and are not poisonous.

Sexing phasmids can be fairly simple in the sub-adult and adult form. Females are generally larger due to their need to carry eggs and have a broader abdomen. In some species both sexes are capable of flight as adults and have fully developed wings. In other species neither sex is capable of flight, as they only have wing

buds. In larger species it is generally the male that is able to fly, as the female is simply too heavy. In species such as the Spiny Leaf Insect (*Extatosoma tiaratum*) the sexes can look very different. A more precise method of sexing for all phasmids is to examine the tip of the **abdomen**. Males have a swelling on the underside just before the tip; in this bulge are claspers that are used to hold the female while he transfers a **spermatophore** to her. The tip of the abdomen in females is tapered to a point, with a scoop on the underside that she uses to bury, drop or flick eggs.

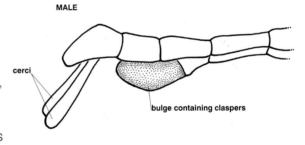

MALE

cerci

bulge containing claspers

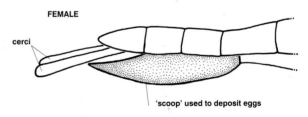

FEMALE

cerci

'scoop' used to deposit eggs

The tip of the abdomen of male and female phasmids

An interesting feature of phasmids is **parthenogenesis**: the ability of the females of some species to produce viable eggs and offspring without mating with a male. When a male is present he will track down a female and perch on her back to mate. You can see the tips of the abdomen joined when mating is occurring. The male transfers a spermatophore to the female, and it is sometimes obvious on the tip of the female's abdomen.

Most phasmids will drop eggs to the forest floor, although a few species will bury eggs or 'glue' them to plants. The eggs can be better mimics than the adults, with many looking like seeds or bits of bark. The eggs can take anywhere from a couple of months to a few years to hatch. **Nymphs** will emerge and begin to feed immediately. Phasmids are **hemimetabolistic**, and as they grow they moult their **exoskeleton** a number of times until they are mature. After they moult they will eat their old exoskeleton so you may not realise they have moulted.

Children's Stick Insect (*Tropidoderus childreni*)

Goliath Stick Insect (*Eurycnema goliath*)

Margin-winged Stick Insect (*Ctenomorpha marginipennis*)

Lord Howe Island Stick Insect (*Dryococelus australis*)

Pepperment Stick Insect (*Megacrania batesii*)

Spiny Leaf Insect (*Extatosoma tiaratum*)

Phasmid eggs can come in all shapes and sizes.

Phasmids are strictly **herbivores**. Some species feed only on particular plants, but most phasmids typically kept in captivity are generalist feeders and can be fed a variety of plants. Nymphs need to be fed the soft tips of plants, as their mouthparts are not strong enough to crush the harder foliage. They get moisture from the leaves they eat, or by drinking droplets of water from foliage. This can be imitated in captivity by mist spraying your phasmids.

Phasmids should always be handled with care. They have the ability to drop limbs if handled roughly. This limb loss is called **autotomy**. Fortunately, they also have the ability to regenerate these lost limbs if the loss occurs before the phasmid is mature. With each successive moult the new limb will increase in size until it looks almost the same as the others. Phasmids should be gently coaxed onto the hand when handled. Very small nymphs can be moved using a leaf for them to grip to. Adults will sit calmly on the hand, although if startled they may display wings or press leg spines into your hand. This will only cause mild discomfort.

Phasmids are popular for display and as pets in the home, as they are easy to care for and because they can be maintained in groups. Different species can be kept in the same enclosure as long as you provide for the individual requirements of each species. Because of their popularity, more and more species are being brought into captivity from the wild.

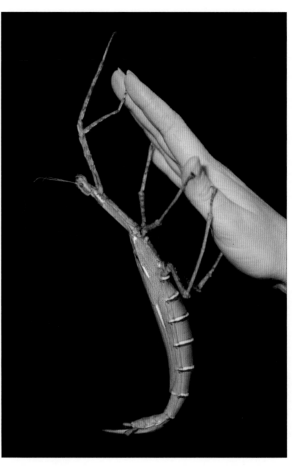

Large phasmids such as this Goliath Stick Insect prefer to hang while being handled.

Children's Stick Insect *Tropidoderus childrenii*

Level of difficulty `1` `2` `3` `4` `5`
beginner   advanced

This stick insect is a good phasmid for beginners to keep. They are hardy and lack the large spines that some of the larger species possess. They are generally a rich pastel green colour but cream and pink forms can occur. Females can reach a length of 140 mm, while males are thinner and slightly smaller. They have full-length wings that will flare up and display bright warning colours when disturbed. In the wild they feed on eucalypts, and this diet is suitable in captivity.

Food and water
- Fresh foliage such as eucalypt (*Eucalyptus* species), Peppercorn (*Schinus molle*)
- Mist spray

Routine care
Daily: Mist spray foliage and check incubating eggs if present

Twice weekly: Change foliage; soft foliage may need to be changed sooner if small nymphs are present. Lightly spray incubating eggs if present.

Weekly: Clean out **frass** and collect eggs from enclosure floor.

Sexing
Male: Slender-bodied; bulge on underside of abdomen, near the end where claspers are located

Female: Robust animal with enlarged abdomen and obvious scoop located at tip; wide flanges on legs

Note: Juveniles can be sexed from third **instar**, as the bulge at the claspers is obvious in males, and females are developing flanges on legs

Breeding
These phasmids can be housed together in groups. The male will hang from the female's back soon after she has matured. He deposits a spermatophore, a small white ball that can be visible around the tip of the female's abdomen. About 2 weeks later the female will begin to 'flick' eggs around the enclosure. These eggs look like grains of pinkish rice but have a knob on one end. The eggs need to be collected and put into a well-ventilated container with a bed of sand or coco-peat. Keep the eggs in a warm room (about 25°C), spray once or twice a week and check daily. The eggs can take from 2 months to 1 year to hatch. Small (35 mm), delicate, bright green nymphs will emerge and actively move around the container. Transfer them to the main enclosure and provide fresh soft tips of plants.

Note: This species is known to be parthenogenetic so eggs produced by unmated females may be viable.

Lifespan
9–12 months

Captive behaviour
These insects will spend most of the day hanging motionless from branches. They hang rather than sit upright, due to their large size and as it provides better camouflage. From time to time they will rock from side to side to mimic a leaf in the wind. When misted with water they will drink from the droplets if they are thirsty. Most of the feeding, mating and moulting will occur at night. If you observe a juvenile moulting, do not disturb it; allow it to get out of its old exoskeleton and harden before handling.

Housing
 Enclosure: Terrarium, mesh or custom; minimum size 35 cm H × 30 cm W × 30 cm D; mesh roof provides extra perching and moulting space

Substrate: Absorptive layer only (sand, coco-peat, leaf litter, newspaper)

Enclosure fit-out: Food foliage will provide perching areas

 Group

 18–26°C

 Humidity 40–70%

 No specialised lighting required

Special considerations
Provide foliage with thickened branches for larger individuals to hang from. Do not fill the enclosure with leaves, as the phasmids need space to hang and successfully moult.

Compatibility with other species
Other phasmids

Species with similar care requirements
Spur-legged Phasmid (*Didymuria violecens*), ringbarker phasmid (*Podocanthus* species)

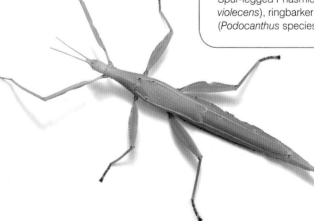

Goliath Stick Insect *Eurycnema goliath*

Level of difficulty

| 1 | 2 | 3 | 4 | 5 |

beginner　　　　　　advanced

Rarely do you see a more spectacular insect than the Goliath Stick Insect. These insects are a large (200 mm) species with an intense green body featuring yellow and pink markings. Males and females look similar, although males are much thinner. In the wild they are found in southern Queensland and northern New South Wales where they feed mainly on wattle trees. In captivity they are generally fed on eucalypt. When disturbed they will raise their wings in defence to show bright pink warning colours.

Food and water
- Fresh foliage such as eucalypt (*Eucalyptus* species), wattle (*Acacia* species), Peppercorn (*Schinus molle*) or rose (*Rosa* species)
- Mist spray

Routine care
Daily: Mist spray foliage and check incubating eggs if present

Twice weekly: Change foliage. Young foliage, where it is provided, may need to be changed often if small nymphs are present. Lightly spray incubating eggs if present.

Weekly: Clean out frass and collect eggs from the enclosure floor

Sexing
Male: Bulge on underside of abdomen, near the end where claspers are located; slender-bodied with functional wings (capable of flight)

Female: Robust animal with enlarged abdomen; fully developed wings (incapable of flight)

Note: You can sex individuals before they mature by looking at the tip of the abdomen

Breeding
These phasmids can be housed together in groups. The male will mount the female's back soon after she has matured and deposit a spermatophore. The female will become very plump around the abdomen where the eggs are being carried. The female will start to 'flick' eggs around the enclosure a couple of weeks after mating. The eggs look like small pieces of frass but have a knob on one end. These eggs need to be collected and put into a container with sand or coco-peat and ventilation holes in the lid.

Keep the eggs warm (about 25°C) and spray once or twice a week, but check daily. The eggs can take from 2 months to 1 year to hatch. Nymphs (40 mm) that look like small brown twigs with legs will emerge and move around the container. Transfer them to the main enclosure and provide fresh soft tips of plants.

Lifespan
12–16 months

Captive behaviour
These insects spend most of the day hanging from branches and the roof of the enclosure. They will also rock from side to side to make themselves look like a leaf in the wind. Most of the feeding, mating and moulting will occur at night. If you observe a juvenile moulting, do not disturb it. Allow it to get out of its old exoskeleton and its new exoskeleton to harden before handling.

Housing

Enclosure: Mesh or custom; minimum size 60 cm H × 35 cm W × 35 cm D; mesh roof preferable for perching and moulting

Substrate: Absorptive layer only (sand, coco-peat, leaf litter, newspaper)

Enclosure fit-out: Food foliage will provide perching areas

 Group

 18–26°C

 Humidity 50–60%

No specialised lighting required

Special considerations
Provide foliage that has thickened branches for support for larger individuals to hang from. Ensure the branches reach the top of the enclosure. Do not fill the enclosure with leaves, as these phasmids need free space to hang and moult successfully. If juveniles are regularly losing limbs it may be due to insufficient space and individuals disturbing each other during moulting.

Compatibility with other species
Other phasmids

Species with similar care requirements
Northern Goliath Stick Insect (*Eurycnema osiris*), Titan Stick Insect (*Acrophylla titan*) and Wuelfing's Stick Insect (*Acrophylla wuelfingi*)

Lord Howe Island Stick Insect *Dryococelus australis*

Level of difficulty

This stick insect is one of the few animals in history to have been rediscovered after having been declared extinct. In 2001 the Lord Howe Island Stick Insect was found on a tiny island near Lord Howe Island called Ball's Pyramid. It is the only known wild colony still in existence. Since then an intensive breeding program has been undertaken by staff at Melbourne Zoo to make the population stable in captivity. These phasmids are like no other in Australia: they are glossy black or brown and spend their days hiding in tree hollows or under logs. Although much is known about the history of this species in captivity, little is known of its behaviour in the wild.

Food and water
- Fresh foliage: bottlebrush (*Callistemon* species), Morton Bay Fig (*Ficus macrophylla*), Tree Lucerne (*Chamaecytisus palmensis*), Lord Howe Island Melaleuca (*Melaleuca howeana*)
- Mist spray

Routine care
Daily: Mist spray foliage and check incubating eggs if they are present

Twice weekly: Change foliage. Lightly spray incubating eggs if present

Weekly: Remove frass and clean out hide boxes, and collect eggs from enclosure laying trays (p.166)

Sexing
Male: Bulge on underside tip of abdomen where claspers are located; spur on rear leg

Female: Obvious pointed scoop located at tip of abdomen, used to bury eggs

Note: Juveniles can be sexed before reaching maturity, as the bulge at the claspers is obvious in males

Breeding
These phasmids can be housed together in groups of one male to a number of females. The male perches on the female's back once she has matured and deposits a spermatophore into her. You will know mating is taking place when he wraps the tip of his abdomen around to come in line with the base of hers. The female will bury eggs in the substrate or in the frass in the hide box. The eggs are like large rounded grains of rice. They need to be collected and placed into a container with sand or peat and plenty of air holes in the lid. Place the eggs 1–2 cm underground with the knob facing up. Keep the eggs in a warm and humid room and spray once or twice a week but check daily. Small (20 mm) bright green nymphs will emerge and move to the lid of the container. Transfer them to the main enclosure and provide fresh soft foliage.

Lifespan
18–24 months

Captive behaviour
Nymphs will cluster together during the day around the top of the enclosure and move onto the branches at night to feed. Sub-adults and adults (individuals that have gone brown-black) will seek shelter together at ground level during the day and travel up into the plants at night to feed. They move around the enclosure during the night and have been observed chewing on enclosure structures, although there is no evidence that they are actually feeding on these objects.

Housing

 Enclosure: Mesh or custom; minimum size 70 cm H × 70 cm W × 70 cm D

Substrate: Absorptive layer only (newspaper)

Enclosure fit-out: Food foliage will provide perching areas; hide box at ground level, and laying tray with sand (p.166)

 Group

 24–27°C

 Humidity 80–95%

 Not essential for adults and sub-adults; UV provision for 4–8 hours per day for nymphs

Special considerations
Ensure the temperature and humidity are maintained, and fresh foliage is supplied, as these are the most important factors in maintaining this species.

Compatibility with other species
Not recommended

Species with similar care requirements
None

BUGS ALIVE!

Margin-winged Stick Insect *Ctenomorpha marginipennis*

Level of difficulty 1 **2** 3 4 5
beginner   advanced

Although the Margin-winged Stick Insect does not have the spectacular colour or body structure of other species, it does have the amazing ability to look just like a stick. These insects can be common in woodlands of New South Wales and Victoria; they may even be found in metropolitan areas. The juveniles are green but they become a dark olive green or brown as they mature. This stick-like species can reach 175 mm but the males are shorter, slender and have smaller cerci. In the wild they feed on eucalypts, and this diet is typically replicated in captivity.

Food and water
- Fresh foliage such as eucalypt (*Eucalyptus* species), Peppercorn (*Schinus molle*)
- Mist spray

Routine care
Daily: Mist spray foliage and check incubating eggs if present

Twice weekly: Change foliage. Soft foliage may need to be changed often if small nymphs present. Lightly spray incubating eggs if present.

Weekly: Clean out frass and collect eggs from the floor of the enclosure

Sexing
Male: Bulge on underside of abdomen, towards the end where claspers are located; slender-bodied

Female: Scoop at tip of abdomen; thicker body

Note: You can sex individuals before they mature by looking at the tip of the abdomen

Breeding
These phasmids can be housed together in groups. The male will hang from the female's back soon after she has matured. He deposits a spermatophore, a small white ball that can be visible around the tip of her abdomen. After mating the female will 'flick' eggs around the enclosure. The eggs look like very small brown pieces of frass but have a knob on one end. These eggs need to be collected and put into a container with sand or coco-peat and a well-ventilated lid. The eggs should be kept in a warm room (about 25°C) and sprayed once or twice a week and checked daily.

The eggs can take from 2 months to 1 year to hatch. Small, delicate, bright green nymphs will emerge and move around the container. Transfer them to the main enclosure and provide the nymphs with the fresh soft tips of plants. These nymphs will undergo successive moults until they grow to maturity.

Note: This species is known to be parthenogenetic so eggs produced by unmated females may be viable.

Lifespan
12–14 months

Captive behaviour
These insects spend most of the day hanging motionless from branches. When misted with water they will drink the droplets. Most of the feeding, mating and moulting will occur at night. If you observe a juvenile moulting, do not disturb it. Allow it to get out of its old exoskeleton and its new exoskeleton to harden before handling.

Housing
 Enclosure: Mesh or custom; minimum size 50 cm H × 30 cm W × 30 cm D

Substrate: Absorptive layer only (sand, coco-peat, leaf litter, newspaper)

Enclosure fit-out: Food foliage will provide perching areas

 Group

 18–26°C

 Humidity 40–50%

No specialised lighting required

Special considerations
Provide foliage that has thickened branches to support larger individuals. Do not pack the enclosure with leaves, as these phasmids need free space to hang and moult. The hatchlings from this species are very delicate and small, so handle them very gently and provide a constant supply of fresh very soft leaves. You can even break the leaves a little to help the juveniles get past the hard edge of the leaf.

Compatibility with other species
Other phasmids

Species with similar care requirements
Pink winged stick insects (*Sipyloidea* species); Tessellated Phasmid (*Ctenomorphodes tessulata*)

PHASMIDS

Peppermint Stick Insect *Megacrania batesi*

Level of difficulty

| 1 | 2 | 3 | **4** | 5 |

beginner   advanced

These insects are named for the peppermint-smelling secretions they release as a defensive response to predators. They can squirt this substance from a gland behind the head over a distance of more than 50 cm. They only feed on Screw Pines and are found around coastal areas of northern Queensland. The colour of this species is incredible – it can range from lime green to sky blue. These insects grow to a length of about 100 mm. Males are thinner than females, and neither sex is capable of flight. Peppermint Stick Insects are closely associated with the Screw Pine and will hide motionless in its fronds during the day.

Food and water
- Screw pine (*Pandanus tectorius*)
- Mist spray

Routine care
Daily: Mist spray foliage and check incubating eggs if they are present

Weekly: Collect any eggs that have fallen to the ground and incubate them in a container

As required: Water plant or swap plant over. Resting plants that have been eaten should ensure they recover and can be reused.

Sexing
Male: Bulge on underside of abdomen near the end, where claspers are located

Female: Scoop located at tip of abdomen, used to drop eggs

Note: Juveniles can be sexed before maturing, as the bulge at the claspers is obvious in males

Breeding
If conditions are warm enough these insects can breed all year round. The male will mount the female's back soon after she has matured. He deposits a spermatophore, a small white ball that can be visible on the tip of her abdomen. The female will become very plump around the abdomen where the eggs are developing. The female will 'drop' eggs, which look like small pebbles with a knob on one end, around the enclosure. Most eggs will fall into the gap between the fronds of the plant and can incubate there. Those that fall onto the ground need to be collected and either placed between the fronds or put into a container with sand or coco-peat, and with ventilation holes in the lid. The eggs

should be kept in a warm room (about 27°C) and sprayed once or twice a week but checked daily. The eggs can hatch about 4 months after being laid. Small nymphs will emerge and move around the container. Transfer them to the main enclosure. These nymphs will undergo successive moults to reach maturity.

Note: This species is known to be parthenogenetic, so eggs produced by unmated females may be viable.

Lifespan
12–14 months

Captive behaviour
During the day these insects will remain motionless, lying flat against the fronds of the Screw Pine. If disturbed they will move deeper into the centre of the plant for better protection. At night they will move around the plant feeding on the fronds. You can recognise fresh chew marks because the edges are green, old chew damage will develop a brown tinge to the edges. If you observe a juvenile moulting, do not disturb it.

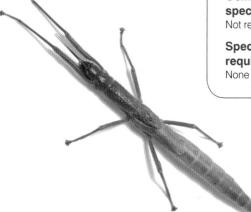

Housing
 Enclosure: Mesh or custom; minimum size 70 cm H × 70 cm W × 70 cm D; enclosure size needs to be able to fit a potted Screw Pine

Substrate: Absorptive layer only (sand, coco-peat, leaf litter, newspaper)

Enclosure fit-out: Potted plant provides perching areas

 Group

 24–28°C

 Humidity 60–80%

 No specialised lighting required

Special considerations
Be careful that they do not squirt their secretions into your eye. Some varieties of *Pandanus* that can be purchased in plant nurseries are not the correct food source. If possible, try to source wild varieties rather than a cultivar. Be aware of eggs incubating in the resting plants and maintain them in appropriate conditions.

Compatibility with other species
Not recommended

Species with similar care requirements
None

Spiny Leaf Insect *Extatosoma tiaratum*

Level of difficulty

 1 | 2 | 3 | 4 | 5
beginner advanced

The Spiny Leaf Insect is found in forests along the Queensland and New South Wales coasts. It is currently one of the most commonly kept species of phasmids in Australia, due to its large size (150 mm) and ease of keeping. Males and females look so different that they were originally described as two species. Most specimens are cream or brown, but if fed certain plants such as Native Mulberry (*Pipturus argunteus*) they may become green.

Food and water

- Fresh foliage such as eucalypt (*Eucalyptus* species), wattle (*Acacia* species), rose (*Rosa* species) or Blackberry (*Rubus fruticosus*)

- Mist spray

Routine care

Daily: Mist spray foliage and check incubating eggs if present

Twice weekly: Change foliage. Soft foliage may need to be replaced more often if small nymphs present. Lightly spray incubating eggs if they are present.

Weekly: Clean out frass and collect eggs from the enclosure floor

Sexing

Male: Brown and slender, with fully developed wings, which when extended are patterned cream and brown

Female: Small non-functional wings; robust animal with enlarged abdomen that when at rest will curl like a scorpion's tail

Note: Nymphs can be sexed after their first moult. Females will have a double row of spines coming off the upper surface of the abdomen, males will be smooth.

Breeding

If conditions are warm these phasmids can breed all year round. The male will mount the female's back soon after she has matured. He deposits a spermatophore, a small white ball that can be visible on the tip of her abdomen. The female will become very plump around the abdomen where the eggs are being carried. She will 'flick' eggs around the enclosure. The eggs look like white and brown smooth balls with a knob on one end. These eggs need to be collected and put on a bed of moist coco-peat or

sand in a container with ventilation holes in the lid. Keep the eggs in a warm room (about 25°C) and spray once or twice a week but check daily. The eggs can take from 2 months to 3 years to hatch. Small black nymphs with a red head will emerge and actively move around the container. Transfer them to the main enclosure and provide fresh young foliage. Males will moult five times and females six times to reach maturity.

Note: This species is known to be parthenogenetic so eggs produced by unmated females may be viable.

Lifespan

12–16 months

Captive behaviour

These insects spend most of the day hanging from branches and the roof of the enclosure. They hang rather than sit upright, due to their large size and because it provides better camouflage. They will also rock from side to side in a breeze to make themselves look like a leaf in the wind. Most of the feeding, mating and moulting will occur at night. If you observe a juvenile moulting, do not disturb it.

Housing

 Enclosure: Terrarium, mesh or custom; minimum size 35 cm H × 30 cm W × 30 cm D; a mesh roof maximises hanging and moulting room

Substrate: Absorptive layer only (sand, coco-peat, leaf litter, newspaper)

Enclosure fit-out: Food foliage will provide perching areas

 Group

 18–26°C

 Humidity 50–60%

No specialised lighting required

Special considerations
Provide foliage that has thickened branches for adults to hang from. Do not fill the enclosure with leaves, as they need space to hang and moult.

Compatibility with other species
Other phasmids

Species with similar care requirements
Spiny Leaf Insect (*Extatosoma bufonium*)

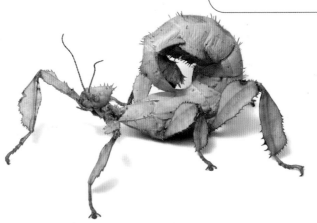

A Crusader Bug pierces a plant stem with its proboscis to

True bugs   Order: Hemiptera

Estimated number of species in Australia: 6000

Imagine having to suck all your food through a straw! This is exactly what true bugs need to do. They have a mouthpart that is modified for piercing and sucking, which is called a **proboscis**. True bugs can be sapsuckers that feed on plants, predators that feed on other **invertebrates**, or bloodsuckers that feed on birds or mammals. These bugs live in a variety of habitats, both in water and on land. This chapter describes some species that live on land.

True bugs are in the order Hemiptera, which means 'half wing'. They have two pairs of wings, and in some species the base of the forewing is hardened to help protect the hind wing. True bugs are **hemimetabolistic** and the **nymphs** resemble the adults. Most species will lay eggs, but some give birth to live young. Nymphs are wingless and colours and markings may vary from those of the adult form. They will **moult** up to six times before they mature, depending on the species. Most species will complete their life cycle in a year and some can produce three or four generations in this time. True bugs generally breed in the warmer months of the year, but in captivity it is possible to breed them all year round if warm conditions are maintained. True bugs do not display sexual differences until they are adults. The adult female is generally larger than the male, and in most species both adult individuals are winged.

Some species such as the Cotton Harlequin Bug (*Tectocoris diophthalmus*) have been kept in captivity for many years for their bright metallic colours. The predatory Assassin Bugs (Reduviidae) are also becoming popular in captivity perhaps due to interest in watching them hunt down or ambush their prey.

Most true bugs can be handled safely, but some species can release a foul-smelling odour or liquid to repel predators. They may also do this if they are startled while being handled. Some species such as the Assassin Bug (*Gminatus australis*) can bite if handled roughly. This can be painful, as the Assassin Bug will inject the enzyme-filled saliva it uses to dissolve its prey. The result is some localised and sometimes burning pain followed by a small itchy lump that lasts for a few days.

Most sap-sucking bugs are able to be housed in groups or with any other non-predatory invertebrates. However, the predatory bugs should ideally be housed individually, although it may be possible to house them with large snails or large cockroaches that would not be looked on as prey.

True bugs make fascinating displays both for their bright colouration and tendency to group together in large numbers. They are also interesting for the unique way in which they feed – the plant-feeding species pierce the leaves and stems of plants to drink the juices, and the predatory species hunt their prey. Displaying true bugs is generally very easy, as they do not require highly specialised enclosures.

Assassin Bug *Gminatus australis*

Level of difficulty

beginner · · · · · · advanced

Assassin Bugs are just as their name describes them – assassins that prey upon other insects. They have an incredible proboscis that pierces their prey and injects saliva into them. The saliva contains an enzyme that immobilises and dissolves the prey. The juices are then sucked out and the hollow body of the victim is discarded. Assassin Bugs have been known to prey upon caterpillars, snails, bees and many other invertebrates. Adult Assassin Bugs have an orange-red body with black legs and black wings. They grow to about 17 mm in length and can capture prey their own size. Assassin Bugs either actively hunt down their prey, or lie in wait to ambush passing insects.

Housing

 Enclosure: Terrarium, jar or custom; minimum size 15 cm H × 10 cm W × 10 cm D

Substrate: Absorptive layer only (coco-peat, sand, newspaper)

Enclosure fit-out: Sticks or branches for perching, leaves for shelter

 Individual

 20–28°C

 Humidity 60–80%

 No specialised lighting required

Food and water
- Live insects
- Mist spray

Routine care
Daily: Remove waste products and uneaten food, and mist spray branches

Twice weekly: Either forceps feed with small or medium-sized crickets or leave them in the enclosure

Sexing
Male: Smaller, body slender

Female: Larger, body more rounded

Note: Sexes are very hard to distinguish as size can change after feeding

Breeding
The male should be introduced to the female after both individuals have been fed, to avoid cannibalism. The male will mount the female's back to mate. After mating, the male should be removed from the enclosure. The female will lay a cluster of about 40–80 eggs on plant material or the side of the enclosure. Nymphs will hatch out after 14–16 days. They look similar to hatchling spiders, although they have six legs, not eight. They are actually a small version of the adult, but are

black and without wings. These nymph Assassin Bugs should be separated and housed in an easy-feeder or individual vials (see p.158). They will moult six times before maturing, and as they moult they develop their orange colouration.

Lifespan
10–14 months

Captive behaviour
Once a food item is placed in the enclosure, the Assassin Bug will either actively hunt or lie in wait to ambush it. Assassin Bugs spend most of their time sitting still in one position on branches or on the walls of the enclosure.

Special considerations
Assassin Bugs are usually not aggressive to humans, but if handled roughly they can bite in self-defence. A bite from an Assassin Bug may be very painful, as it will inject the saliva usually used to dissolve its prey. You may feel a burning sensation at the bite site, which may develop into a small lump that can itch and last for a few days. It is best to use a jar or vial when moving these animals.

Compatibility with other species
Not recommended

Species with similar care requirements
Red Assassin Bug (*Gminatus wallengreni*), Bee Killer Assassin Bug (*Pristhesancus plagipennis*)

Cotton Harlequin Bug *Tectocoris diophthalmus*

Level of difficulty

| 1 | 2 | **3** | 4 | 5 |

beginner   advanced

Cotton Harlequin Bugs are an eye-catching species with bright metallic colours and a tendency to cluster in groups. They are found in northern Australia and are common in urban as well as agricultural areas, particularly through the warmer months. Cotton Harlequin Bugs are quite large, growing to around 20 mm. They have a long sucking proboscis that is used to pierce plants and feed on the liquid nutrients, and they are particularly fond of flower buds.

Housing

 Enclosure: Glass tank or custom; minimum size 25 cm H × 20 cm W × 15 cm D

Substrate: Absorptive layer only (coco-peat, sand, newspaper)

Enclosure fit-out: Food foliage will provide perching areas

 Group

 18–26°C, hotspot to 40°C at one end

 Humidity 50–70%

 UV provision, dichroic lamp for 1–2 hours per day

Food and water
- Fresh foliage: potted plant or cut browse such as hibiscus (*Hibiscus* species) or Cotton (*Gossypium hirsutum*) plants
- Mist spray

Routine care
Daily: Mist spray enclosure

As required: Water potted plant. Change over potted plant or replace cut browse at first sign of wilting. Be sure to remove any leaves or branches with eggs on them and pin them to the new plant.

Sexing
Male: Metallic blue colour with red patches; smaller than females

Female: Orange with patches of metallic blue; larger than males

Note: Nymphs cannot be sexed until they are mature.

Breeding
Pairs will mate by joining the tips of their abdomens together. After mating, the female will lay a cluster of pale pink eggs around the stem of the food plant. Females exhibit maternal care and will tend their eggs to ward off potential parasites. They do not feed during this time. Nymphs emerge looking like miniature versions of the adults, except that they are metallic blue and have no patterning.

Lifespan
About 1 year

Captive behaviour
Cotton Harlequin Bugs will actively feed on live plants during the day. They prefer young shoots and unopened flower buds. Nymphs will group together, while adults are more solitary. They are able to walk up smooth vertical surfaces and will climb the walls of your enclosure.

Special considerations
If startled, Cotton Harlequin Bugs will release an offensive odour from a specialised gland to ward off potential predators. This is not harmful to humans and they are safe to be handled.

Compatibility with other species
Other subtropical zone herbivorous invertebrates

Species with similar care requirements
None

Crusader Bug *Mictis profana*

Level of difficulty

1 | **2** | 3 | 4 | 5
beginner — advanced

These bold bugs will sit out in full view of predators with little fear, as their defensive smell and taste is enough to turn most predators off. Found throughout Australia, except in Tasmania, Crusader Bugs are easily recognisable by a diagonal yellow cross on their back. They are commonly found in both eucalypt forests and urban backyards. Crusader Bugs release a strong odour when alarmed, to ward off predators. Adults grow to about 25 mm in length and feed using a proboscis to suck the juices from a wide variety of native and introduced plants.

Food and water

- Fresh foliage such as potted plant or cut browse of wattle (*Acacia* species), citrus (*Citrus* species) or Happy Wanderer (*Hardenbergia* species)

- Mist spray

Routine care

Daily: Mist spray the enclosure. Remove waste products

As required: Water potted plant. Change over potted plant or replace cut browse at first sign of wilting. Be sure to remove any leaves or branches with eggs on them and pin the leaves to the new plant.

Sexing

Male: Rear legs enlarged, the underside of **abdomen** is red and has two pointed **pheromone** glands; abdomen is concave in profile

Female: Underside of abdomen is brown and lacks pheromone glands; abdomen is convex in profile

Note: Juveniles have no wings and no cross, but have two yellow spots on the abdomen. They cannot be sexed until they are adults.

Breeding

Mating should occur as long as both sexes are present and temperatures are warm. Crusader Bugs can produce three or four generations per year. After mating, eggs are laid in a chain or a cluster on the leaves. The female will lay a new chain of eggs every 5 days or so. The eggs are large, elongated and pearly brown with a rounded lid. After 6–10 days the eggs will hatch and small juveniles will emerge. Nymphs will moult six times and take about 30 days to reach maturity.

Lifespan

2–4 months

Captive behaviour

Crusader Bugs will spend most of their time perched on the foliage and feeding at their leisure. Young nymphs will feed in groups on new leaves, and if disturbed will jump or drop off the food plant. Older nymphs and adults are solitary feeders and will feed on both new and mature leaves and shoots. You will see them hanging from the foliage to moult. You should not disturb them at this time. Crusader Bugs can walk up vertical surfaces and you will see them on the sides of their enclosure.

Housing

 Enclosure: Glass tank, mesh or custom; minimum size 20 cm H × 14 cm W × 10 cm D

Substrate: Absorptive layer only (coco-peat, sand, newspaper)

Enclosure fit-out: Food foliage will provide perching areas

 Group

 18–26°C, hotspot to 40°C at one end optional

 Humidity 50–70%

 No specialised lighting required, dichroic lamp optional

Special considerations

Crusader Bugs release a strong repellent odour, from a small gland just above the second pair of legs, if they are disturbed. This is not harmful to humans, and Crusader Bugs are safe to be handled. These bugs require high humidity to moult to ensure they do not get stuck in their old exoskeleton.

Compatibility with other species

Other herbivorous invertebrates

Species with similar care requirements

Shield bug (*Poecilometis* species)

Harlequin Bug _Dindymus versicolor_

Level of difficulty

1	2	3	4	5

beginner   advanced

These common backyard bugs are regularly seen mating end to end, with the female dragging the male wherever she goes. They often occur in large numbers and can be spotted easily due to their bright orange-red and black markings. These markings warn predators of their extremely bad taste. They are found in southern Australia and grow to 12 mm.

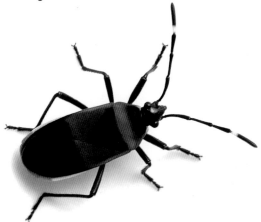

Food and water

- Fresh foliage such as potted plant or cut browse of soft fruit plants such as Fig (_Ficus carica_), grape (_Vitis_ species) and stone fruits (_Prunus_ species); will also feed on strawberry plants and common garden vegetables, fresh fruit and dead insects such as crickets

- Mist spray

Routine care

Daily: Mist spray, replace fruit and remove waste products

Weekly: Leave freshly dead insects in the enclosure

As required: Water potted plant. Change over potted plant or replace cut browse at first sign of wilting. Be sure to remove any leaves or branches with eggs and pin the leaves to the new plant.

Sexing

Male: Smaller, abdomen rounded

Female: Larger, abdomen elongated

Note: Nymphs do not have wings

Breeding

Mating should occur as long as both sexes are present and temperatures are warm. Pairs will mate facing in opposite directions and joined at the tip of the abdomen. As females are larger, they tend to pull the male behind them as they walk. After mating, females will lay clusters of eggs on the food plant. Young bugs will hatch and begin to feed on the new plant growth.

Lifespan

6–12 months

Captive behaviour

Harlequin Bugs will congregate together to feed if kept in large numbers. They will wander around the entire enclosure, and can often be found at the top of an enclosure, so be watchful for escapees.

Housing

 Enclosure: Glass tank, mesh or custom; minimum size 20 cm H × 14 cm W × 10 cm D

Substrate: Absorptive layer only (coco-peat, sand, newspaper)

Enclosure fit-out: Food foliage will provide perching areas

 Group

 18–26°C, hotspot to 40°C at one end optional

 Humidity 50–70%

 No specialised lighting required, dichroic lamp

Special considerations

These invertebrates are harmless to humans and can be handled. They have been known to feed on anything from dead animals to dog droppings, so you may like to trial different foods when keeping them.

Compatibility with other species

Other temperate zone herbivorous invertebrates

Species with similar care requirements

Metallic Shield Bug (_Scutiphora pedicellata_)

As sunset approaches, a female velvet ant comes out to track down the larvae of bees, ants and other wasps to parasitise.

Wasps Order: Hymenoptera

Estimated number of species in Australia: 12 000

Wasps are a large and diverse group. They contain some of the smallest insects found in Australia, barely distinguishable with the naked eye, as well as some of the most feared. The European Wasp was introduced to Australia in about 1959 and is now considered a dangerous pest. These wasps live around our homes and can deliver a very painful sting. But, in general, wasps are beneficial to the Australian environment. Many pollinate flowers and some parasitic wasps can play an important role in controlling the populations of many **invertebrate** species.

Wasps are found in all habitats across Australia. They are closely related to ants and have some characteristics that are similar, such as three distinct body segments and a distinct waist between the **thorax** and **abdomen**. The easiest feature by which wasps can be distinguished from ants is their antennae, which can curve but do not have a distinct bend. In some groups of wasps, the egg-laying appendage, the **ovipositor**, has evolved to form a sting.

In general, adult wasps feed on nectar and pollen, but they will capture other insects to provide food for the **larvae**. Adult wasps will either capture prey and carry it to the larvae to feed them, or if they are parasitic, they will lay eggs on or near invertebrates. When the eggs hatch the larvae will live off the invertebrate host until they mature. The larvae are grub-like but have mouthparts with **mandibles** designed for feeding on the host. Some Australian wasps such as the paper wasp are social insects, but most others are solitary.

The wasps discussed in this chapter are solitary and parasitic, and come together only to mate.

They have been chosen for inclusion in this book because of the relative ease with which they can be kept, and their long lifespan. They are specific parasites looking for hosts on which to lay eggs. Females are wingless and fairly noticeable at certain times of the year, when they move around the ground and trees looking for invertebrate hosts. Some have modified legs for digging up the host.

It is not common for people to keep wasps in captivity, as their life cycles can be complex and hard to replicate. Some species require specific hosts on which to lay their eggs. Although maintaining the entire life cycle is difficult, keeping females for extended periods in captivity is relatively simple. The most important factor to consider is not getting stung, so they should not be handled! Wasps in a display can be exceptional as they can be very colourful and patterned, and are active during the day.

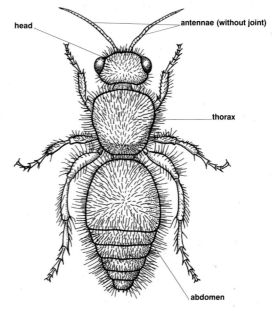

head — antennae (without joint) — thorax — abdomen

Blue Ant *Diamma bicolor*

Level of difficulty 1 2 3 4 **5**

beginner   advanced

Blue Ants are actually wasps, not ants as their name suggests. They are called an 'ant' because females are wingless and move around the ground, looking like ants. Upon closer inspection you will see that the antennae are curved not bent, indicating they are wasps. Blue Ants are a species of flower wasp. The females are bright blue-green with red legs and grow to a length of about 25 mm. They are found in the south-eastern areas of Australia, often in open woodland. The following information relates to the care of the adult females. However, the breeding section covers the requirements for males and juveniles. The female can make a great long-term display because of her long life and active behaviour.

Food and water
- Sugar solutions
- Mist spray

Routine care
Daily: Replace sugar solution (especially diluted honey), and mist spray to maintain a damp and a dry end.

Sexing
Male: Winged, slim black with white spots on abdomen, 15 mm

Females: Wingless, blue-green body with red legs, 25 mm

Breeding
Breeding of this group has not been achieved in captivity, but the following is an outline of the theory of completing it and the problems you will have to overcome. Males can be found around flowering plants, feeding on the nectar. They will track down the female and mate. You will need a secure enclosure for this part of the life cycle so that the male does not fly away with the female. Branches will give the male space to perch. The male will hold the female from above and fly her to a food source such as a flower to mate. The mated female will only parasitise mole crickets, and this is the most difficult period of breeding in captivity. Mole crickets will need to be captured and introduced to the enclosure. The female will seek out these crickets to lay her eggs. The female wasp is capable of digging and will track down the cricket in its burrow. She will paralyse the cricket and lay a single egg on it. The larva that hatches will feed on the cricket until it pupates.

Lifespan
About 2 years

Captive behaviour
The female will move around the enclosure in a jerky manner. She appears to be constantly using her antennae to track down crickets in their burrows. When not moving around the enclosure she will rest in a covered area. She will burrow under the substrate for extended periods of time, and if you do not see her for a few days gently dig through the substrate to check on her.

Housing

 Enclosure: Glass tank or custom; minimum size 20 cm H × 30 cm W × 30 cm D; escape-proofing essential (p.159)

Substrate: Sand and coco-peat mix, minimum depth 2 cm; maintain a damp and a dry end

Enclosure fit-out: None essential

 Group or individual

 18–25°C, dichroic hotspot to 40°C at one end

 Humidity 40–50%

Dichroic lamp for 1–2 hours per day

Special considerations
The sting can be very painful, so handling is not advised. If you have a known allergy to wasps, ants or bees, it would be safer not to keep them.

Compatibility with other species
Other temperate zone herbivores

Species with similar care requirements
Wingless flower wasps (*Hemithynnus* species)

Velvet ants Mutillidae

Level of difficulty 1 | 2 | 3 | 4 | **5**
beginner   advanced

Velvet ants are wasps not ants, so their common name can be very confusing. This name has arisen because females are wingless and move around the ground looking like ants. You will see, upon closer inspection, that their antennae are not bent, indicating they are wasps. These wasps have a hairy thorax and abdomen, making them look velvety. They range in colour from red to brown and black, often with white spotted markings, and can grow to about 25 mm in length. Velvet ants can be locally abundant in warm weather just before sunset, often around areas of high ant numbers. They are found Australia-wide, but the species covered in this guide are found only in arid regions. The following information relates to the care of the adult females, however, the breeding section covers the requirements for males and juveniles. The female can make a great long-term display because of her long life and active behaviour.

Housing

 Enclosure: Glass tank or custom; minimum size 20 cm H × 30 cm W × 30 cm D; escape-proofing essential (p.159)

Substrate: Sand, minimum depth 1 cm; maintain a damp and a dry end

Enclosure fit-out: None essential, leaves and bark optional

 Group

 22–28°C, hotspot to 40°C at one end

 Humidity 40–50%

 Dichroic lamp for 2–3 hours per day

WASPS

Food and water
- Sugar solutions
- Mist spray

Routine care
Daily: Replace sugar solutions (especially diluted honey), and mist spray to maintain a damp and a dry end

Sexing
Male: Winged

Female: Wingless

Breeding
Breeding of this group has not been achieved in captivity but the following is an outline on the theory of completing it and the problems you will have to overcome. The male of this species is winged and smaller than the female. Males can be found around flowering plants, feeding on the nectar. They will track down the female to mate. You will need a secure enclosure for this part of the life cycle to ensure that he does not fly away. Branches in the enclosure will give the male space to perch. Once mated, place the female in an enclosure with the specific host invertebrate for your velvet ant to parasitise. Most velvet ants parasitise bee and wasp larvae, but this will be dependent on the species you are keeping. This is the hardest part of keeping these wasps, as so little is known about these specific requirements. The female wasp will paralyse the host and lay eggs on it. The larvae will hatch and feed on the host until they pupate. For this period of the life cycle provide deeper substrate (greater than 5 cm), as the host and larvae will inhabit an underground chamber.

Lifespan
Greater than 2 years

Captive behaviour
The female moves around the enclosure in a frantic manner with her abdomen raised to mimic an ant. She appears to be constantly using her antennae to track down burrows of the invertebrate host. When not moving around the enclosure she will rest in a sheltered area. The female velvet ant will burrow under the substrate for extended periods of time, so if you do not see her for a few days gently dig through the substrate to check on her.

Special considerations
The sting from these wasps can be very painful so handling is not advised. If you have a known allergy to wasps, ants or bees, it would be safer not to keep them.

Compatibility with other species
Other arid zone invertebrates that do not feed on smaller insects

Species with similar care requirements
Wingless wasps from arid areas

The downward-facing fangs on this female Sydney Funnelweb are typical of primitive spiders.

Primitive spiders   Suborder: Mygalomorphae

Estimated number of species in Australia: 500

Primitive spiders are similar in many ways to the prehistoric spiders that roamed the Earth before the time of the dinosaurs. One obvious feature that sets these spiders apart is their large downward pointing fangs, which are parallel to one another and work in a 'pick-axe' fashion. This group contains a number of well-known spiders such as the funnelweb, trapdoor and mouse spiders, as well as the large tarantulas.

Many of these spiders live underground, and all rely on a humid habitat for survival, whether it is in the confinement of a burrow or a humid rainforest. Humidity is important because they have primitive lungs known as **book lungs**, which work best in these moist environments. Primitive spiders have two pairs of book lungs located under the abdomen. Most spiders in this group have long **spinnerets** that produce sheet-like silk, rather than the fine cable silk of many of the modern spiders.

Sexing primitive spiders is quite simple, but only after they have reached maturity. Mature males have obvious enlarged ends on their **pedipalps**. These act as sperm pumps during mating. Males are more lightly built, and often have a slender abdomen that is smaller than their **cephalothorax**. As a general rule females are the larger sex. The females are powerfully built spiders, and usually have an **abdomen** that is larger than their cephalothorax.

To prepare for mating, a male spider must first transfer sperm from his sexual organs in the abdomen to his pedipalps. To do this he makes a small silk pad called a **sperm web**. Males then find females by using their sense of smell, tracking the chemicals with their pedipalps. The male identifies himself by tapping his legs on the ground, and touching and stroking the female, ultimately relaxing her into a mating position.

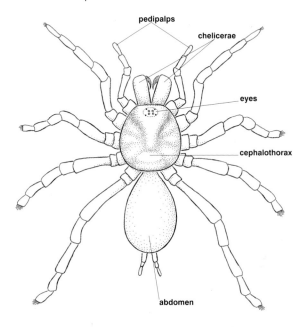

pedipalps
chelicerae
eyes
cephalothorax
abdomen

DORSAL VIEW

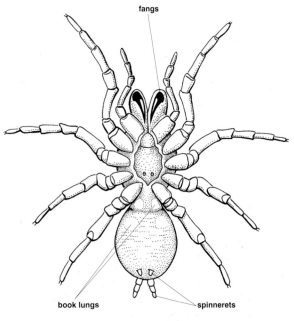

fangs
book lungs
spinnerets

VENTRAL VIEW

A male primitive spider must reach under the female to place his pedipalp against her genital opening to transfer the sperm. He often does this by encouraging the female to lift up the front half of her body, and then leans under her fangs. This is a risky business, as one bite could spell his death. Males of some species have special spurs on their legs (known as **tibial spurs**) that they use to hold the female during the dangerous mating period. To pair these spiders in captivity you need to give the males space and time. If a male is forced to approach a female too quickly he will not identify himself as a mate and most likely will be eaten!

Primitive spiders lay eggs, which usually number in the hundreds. The eggs are protected in a silken wrapping called an **egg sac**. The egg sacs range in shape from round to disc-like, and are woven from papery, white silk. Females guard the egg sacs within their silken retreats or burrows, and are often very aggressive during this time.

Young spiderlings are miniature replicas of the parents. Spiderlings of most species will cluster around their mother for some weeks after hatching, before moving off to start life on their own. Primitive spiders grow by **moulting** their **exoskeletons**, and their first moult takes place within their egg sac. Male primitive spiders will moult several times before reaching maturity at 2–5 years of age. Males do not live as long as females. They will often stop eating when they reach breeding age and die soon after mating. Females will continue to moult for all of their lives, which, in some species, may be longer than 15 years. Most of these spiders will moult while lying on their back or side, and this normally takes place in a safe area such as a burrow.

Primitive spiders are ambush hunters, and most will sit still for long periods of time waiting for prey. They are very sensitive to both air and ground vibrations, and can even feel the footsteps of small insects. They usually feed on **invertebrates**; however, in the wild the largest species are also likely to feed on small vertebrates. Insects are the best food source for these spiders in captivity.

Primitive spiders cannot eat solid food; it must be sucked through their filter-type mouthparts in liquid form. Their **venom** plays an important role in this process. As well as killing the prey, the chemicals in the venom help to break down many parts of the animal into an edible juice that can be sucked up. These spiders salivate continuously onto the prey as they mash and squeeze it using their **chelicerae**. The parts that cannot be eaten are discarded.

These animals are cannibalistic and cannot be housed together. In most cases they cannot be housed with other invertebrate groups either, due to their aggressive predatory behaviour.

One group of primitive spiders – Australian tarantulas – are becoming very popular in captivity. There are many species of Australian tarantulas, and it appears quite a few are yet to be identified. These spiders are close relatives of the tarantulas overseas, but do not grow as large. Australian tarantulas are often sold as 'bird-eating spiders', which is quite misleading.

Handling Australia's primitive spiders is not recommended. Most are quite defensive and will bite if alarmed. If you do need to move your primitive spiders, it is best to use a padded tool and usher them into a jar or container.

A padded tool is best used to move spiders to avoid injuring them.

Spiders are delicate animals and need to be treated gently. Damage to their exoskeleton often will not heal, and any wound to the main body parts (cephalothorax or abdomen) will usually cause the spider to bleed to death. A spider can deal with a leg wound by the process of **autotomy**. The injured leg can come off at the point where it meets the body, with the release point closing up rapidly to stop blood loss. Spiders may also lose legs in this way to free themselves from the grip of a predator, so never restrain your spider by its limbs! Spiders will regrow lost limbs between moults, with the new leg appearing at the next moult – an amazing process.

When keeping these spiders, there may be long periods of time when they are not seen. On occasions it is important to check on them by carefully exposing the burrow or retreat. This should be done infrequently and with extreme care to avoid injuring them.

Many primitive spiders will make interesting displays, as long as the displays take the habits of the species into consideration. With most species, the display enclosure requires some form of artificial burrow or retreat that allows viewing into it. This needs to take into account the requirement for humidity. Red light may be used to view these spiders, as it does not seem to disturb them.

Australian tarantulas mating in an artificial burrow.

Australian tarantulas are one of the most popular groups
of invertebrates being kept.

Australian tarantulas *Phlogius* species

Level of difficulty

| 1 | 2 | 3 | **4** | 5 |

beginner   advanced

There are many species of Australian tarantulas, and most are found in the warm northern parts of Australia. These large spiders, some growing to more than 50 mm in body length, are capable of making a sound if they are alarmed. They do this by a process called **stridulation**, in which the spider rubs tiny peg-like surfaces around its mouthparts together. Australian tarantulas live in burrows and ambush small animals that pass by. Unfortunately large numbers are being collected from the wild and sold to commercial dealers, and this is having an impact on some wild populations. Therefore, it is wise to choose captive-bred specimens, to ensure you are not contributing to this problem.

Food and water
- Live insects and dead 'pinky' mice
- Water sponge

Routine care
Daily: Mist spray one end of the enclosure's substrate with water to keep it damp. Ensure the water sponge is moist.

Weekly: Introduce live insects into the enclosure (more than one may be consumed per feed) or forceps feed your tarantula a dead 'pinky' mouse. Remove any dead or uneaten insects and other wastes. This species may not eat every time food is offered.

Sexing
Male: Noticeably enlarged ends on the pedipalps; slender body and long legs

Female: Robust body, with the abdomen usually larger than the cephalothorax

Breeding
Ensure the female is set-up in a large enclosure. This allows the male to be introduced well away from her, and to approach her in his own time. Ensure the female is well fed, as this will decrease the chances of her eating the male. Closely watch your spiders – the male should approach the female while tapping and drumming the ground with his legs and pedipalps. If he doesn't do this, it would be wise to remove him and try again later. If things go well, he will entice the female out of her retreat and engage in mating. Sometimes he will follow her into the retreat. Remove the male after they have separated. The female will produce an egg sac inside the retreat and may become aggressive while she guards it. Do not to disturb her during this period as she may destroy the eggs. Up

to several hundred spiderlings will hatch and cluster in the shelter with their mother, but they should be separated and housed independently when they emerge from their retreat. Spiderlings can be housed in vials or small jars, and can be fed on small insects.

Lifespan
- **Male:** 3–5 years
- **Female:** up to 15 years

Captive behaviour
These spiders are usually inactive during the day. At night (or in subdued light) they will move to the entrance of their retreat ready to ambush prey, or will actively hunt around their enclosure. It is best to feed your spider when this is observed. They may stop eating for several weeks before they moult, and will often seal up the entrance to their retreat with silk, or mound up the substrate to protect them during this vulnerable period.

Housing

Enclosure: Terrarium, glass tank or custom; minimum size 30 cm H × 40 cm W × 30 cm D

Substrate: Coco-peat or sphagnum moss, minimum depth 10 cm; maintain a damp and a dry end

Enclosure fit-out: A retreat such as hollow log nestled within the substrate or a burrow

 Individual

 22–28°C

 Humidity 60–80%

 None required, dislikes bright light

Special considerations
These spiders have very large fangs and are capable of inflicting a painful bite. They should be treated with care! They are capable of climbing smooth surfaces such as glass, so a secure enclosure lid is required.

Compatibility with other species
Not recommended

Species with similar care requirements
Other tropical zone Australian tarantulas (Theraphosidae)

PRIMITIVE SPIDERS

Red-headed Mouse Spider *Missulena occatoria*

Level of difficulty | 1 | 2 | 3 | 4 | **5** |

beginner   advanced

Red-headed Mouse Spiders are solid-looking burrowing spiders, growing to 27 mm in length. Females are black and powerfully built, and males have a red head and bluish abdomen. They are found in the arid regions of southern and central Australia. Males are more commonly seen because they wander in search of mates. Their name comes from a mistaken belief that they live in long, winding tunnels like mice, which they do not. Their burrows usually go down to a depth of about 30 cm and have a silken lid that the spider can close. The burrows also have a small side chamber with its own little door. This chamber is used to hide from predators and as a safe place for the egg sac. They hunt by ambushing invertebrates that pass the burrow entrance. Red-headed Mouse Spiders have large fangs that curve inwards, much more so than those of others in this group, and they are the only primitive spiders whose spiderlings are known to disperse by aerial ballooning.

Food and water

- Live insects

- Moisture in substrate

Routine care

Daily: Mist the substrate with water so that it is always damp, but not wet

Weekly: Introduce one live insect into the enclosure. Remove any dead or uneaten insects and other wastes. This species may not eat every time food is offered.

Sexing

Male: Obvious enlarged ends on the pedipalps, chelicerae and front half of the cephalothorax is bright red

Female: All black, with a robust rounded body and short stumpy legs

Breeding

Pairs should be kept separate until you are ready to breed them to avoid cannibalism. Males that are ready to mate will wander around their enclosure; this may be in autumn or early winter. The female should be placed in a large enclosure so that when the male is introduced he has space to court her. An eager male will seek out the female using his pedipalps to follow her chemical scent (**pheromone**). He will lure her to the top of her burrow by tapping it with his legs and pedipalps, and if she is receptive he will follow her back down to mate. Remove the male as soon as they have separated; however, males usually die naturally soon after the mating season. In the burrow the female will produce an egg sac that contains several hundred eggs.

Tiny spiderlings will come out of the burrow when they are ready to live independently, and should be housed separately in vials or a toolbox set-up (see p.158).

Lifespan

- **Male:** 2–4 years

- **Female:** longer than 10 years

Captive behaviour

These spiders prefer to spend their entire lives in a burrow, except for adult males in the breeding season. If they are hungry, they will move towards the top of the burrow at night and wait for prey to pass by. They cannot climb smooth surfaces, and females in particular are quite cumbersome if moving outside their silk-lined burrows. Both sexes are extremely aggressive and will rear up with their fangs exposed at the slightest disturbance. This species can be encouraged to burrow against glass by starting to dig the burrow yourself.

Housing

 Enclosure: Jar or terrarium; minimum size 15 cm H × 10 cm W × 10 cm D

Substrate: Sand, coco-peat or mix, minimum depth 5 cm; damp throughout

Enclosure fit-out: Burrow (p.166)

 Individual

 18–24°C

 Humidity 60–80%

 None required, dislikes bright light

Special considerations

These spiders are not suitable for classrooms or children. The venom of this species is considered potentially dangerous, with some studies comparing it to the venom of the Sydney Funnelweb. There have been very few reported bites and no fatalities, but be extremely cautious when keeping these spiders.

Compatibility with other species

Not recommended

Species with similar care requirements

Other mouse spiders (*Missulena* species)

BUGS ALIVE!

Sydney Funnelweb *Atrax robustus*

Level of difficulty 1 2 3 4 **5**

beginner   advanced

These spiders are one of the world's most feared animals due to their extremely toxic venom. They live in the ground, either burrowing or building a retreat in gaps beneath rocks or logs. Their retreat is a silk-lined tube, often with several openings at ground level. Each opening has radiating trip lines for detecting prey. The silk openings are not actually funnel-like in appearance; they are more like flattened silk 'socks' that the spider opens when it passes through. Sydney Funnelwebs are most common in cool gully areas within forests, parks and gardens, and are confined to a radius of about 160 km around Sydney, New South Wales. They grow to 40 mm in body length.

Food and water
- Live insects
- Moisture in substrate; water sponge optional

Routine care
Daily: Ensure that the substrate remains damp (not wet) by misting with water

Weekly: Introduce one live insect into enclosure and remove any dead or uneaten insects and other wastes. This species may not eat every time food is offered.

Sexing
Male: Slender body with obvious enlarged ends on pedipalps and tibial spurs on the second pair of legs

Female: Larger robust spider, abdomen usually larger than cephalothorax

Breeding
Mating takes place from late summer to early autumn. Pairs should be kept separate until this time to avoid cannibalism. Males will often wander above ground in their enclosure when they are ready to mate. The female should be set up in a large enclosure so that when the male is introduced he has space to court her without the risk of being eaten immediately. An eager male will seek out the female and approach her making tapping motions with his legs. Mating may take place out of sight in the female's retreat or burrow. Remove the male once they have separated. The female will produce a round, pillow-shaped egg sac within her retreat. The eggs will hatch several weeks later. Spiderlings will emerge when they are ready to live independently. They may be housed individually in vials or using the toolbox method (see p.158) and fed tiny crickets.

Lifespan
- **Male:** 3–4 years
- **Female:** up to 10 years

Captive behaviour
These spiders will spend most of their time hidden in their burrows. When hungry they will either sit at the entrance to their burrow or emerge quickly when they detect the vibrations of live food. A wandering individual (other than a mature male in breeding season) may indicate that housing conditions are not suitable. This spider will occasionally climb in captivity, but cannot climb smooth surfaces such as glass or plastic. However, because of the dangerous nature of this species it is critical that the enclosure remains securely sealed.

Housing

 Enclosure: Jar or terrarium; minimum size 15 cm H × 10 cm W × 10 cm D

Substrate: Coco-peat, sand or mix, minimum depth 8 cm; damp throughout

Enclosure fit-out: Stable rock to burrow beneath, leaf litter optional

 Individual

 16–24°C

 Humidity 60–80%

None required, dislikes bright light

Special considerations
This spider is not suitable for classrooms or children. The venom of the male of this species is extremely toxic and caused 13 human deaths before antivenom was developed in 1980. The female is potentially lethal, but lacks the significant venom component that makes the male so dangerous. Both sexes are extremely aggressive and will bite readily, so great care should be taken when keeping them. If bitten, medical assistance should be sought immediately. Check the availability of antivenom in your city before acquiring this species.

Compatibility with other species
Not recommended

Species with similar care requirements
Other funnelweb spiders (*Hadronyche* species)

Trapdoor spiders *Stanwellia* species

Level of difficulty

1	**2**	3	4	5

beginner   advanced

These burrowing spiders can grow to 22 mm in body length. They are very common throughout eastern Australia and many people have hundreds in their gardens and lawns and do not even realise it. Despite their name, these spiders do not make a lid or 'trapdoor' to their burrow. The entrance is usually a perfectly round hole up to the size of a 10 cent piece, which may have silk surrounding it. The burrow is lined with silk and often ends at a slightly wider chamber up to 30 cm below the ground. Trapdoor spiders hunt at night, coming to the mouth of the burrow to wait for passing insects, which they sense by vibrations on the ground and through silk trip-lines. When an unsuspecting insect walks by, the spider rushes out of the burrow and impales it with its fangs, and then drags it back down the hole.

Food and water
- Live insects
- Moisture in substrate

Routine care
Daily: Ensure that the substrate remains damp (not wet) by misting with water

Weekly: Introduce one live insect into the enclosure. Remove any dead or uneaten insects and other wastes. This species may not eat every time food is offered.

Sexing
Male: Obvious bulbous ends on pedipalps, slender body and long thin legs

Female: Larger, more robust; abdomen usually larger than cephalothorax

Breeding
These spiders usually breed from late summer through till early autumn. Pairs should be kept separate until this time to ensure the female does not consume the male. Males will often leave their burrow and start wandering above ground in their enclosure when they are ready to mate. Set up the female in a large enclosure so that when the male is introduced he has space to court her without blundering straight over her burrow and being eaten. An eager male will seek out the female and approach her retreat by tapping the ground with his legs. The spiders may mate out of sight in the female's burrow. Remove the male as soon as they separate. The female will produce an egg sac within the burrow a few weeks after mating, and hatching will occur 1–2 months later, depending on the temperature. Spiderlings will emerge from the burrow when they are ready to live independently, and should be housed separately. They can be housed in vials or in a toolbox set-up (see p.158).

Lifespan
- **Male:** 2–3 years
- **Female:** 5–10 years

Captive behaviour
Trapdoor spiders will spend most of their time deep within their burrows, but will move to the burrow entrance with their legs out when they are hunting. They are very sensitive to vibrations, so don't be surprised if they disappear when you open the enclosure to feed them. Have patience and you will see them return and ambush their food. At times they will cover the entrance to their burrow with silk or substrate. This can sometimes indicate that the substrate is too dry, and they are trying to conserve water. It can also be a sign that they are preparing to moult, and are protecting themselves from intruders while they are vulnerable.

Housing

 Enclosure: Jar or terrarium; minimum size 15 cm H × 10 cm W × 10 cm D

Substrate: Coco-peat or soil, minimum depth 5 cm; damp throughout

Enclosure fit-out: Burrow (p.166)

 Individual

 16–24°C

 Humidity 60–70%

 None required, dislikes bright light

Special considerations
Although the venom of these spiders is not considered dangerous, they do have large fangs and care should be taken when keeping them. They are quite sensitive to dehydration, so always ensure their substrate is kept damp, but not sodden.

Compatibility with other species
Not recommended

Species with similar care requirements
Other species of trapdoor spiders

Wishbone spiders *Aname* species

Level of difficulty

| 1 | 2 | **3** | 4 | 5 |

beginner   advanced

These spiders grow to about 24 mm in length and are found in the arid inland areas of Australia, where they live in burrows in the ground. They get their name from their unique wishbone-shaped burrows, which have a side shaft off the main shaft, leading back up towards the surface–forming a 'Y'. There are two apparent reasons for this. The first is to avoid predators. When a predator such as a centipede comes into the tunnel, the spider rushes up the side shaft, its entrance concealed with debris, leaving the predator to think that nobody is home. The second benefit is that it helps the spider to avoid drowning if the main tunnel floods, as the second shaft doesn't actually go all the way to the surface, so it forms an air pocket for the spider to shelter in.

Food and water
- Live insects
- Moisture in substrate

Routine care
Daily: Ensure that the substrate remains damp (not wet) by misting with water

Weekly: Offer food by introducing live insects into enclosure (one per feed). Remove any dead or uneaten insects and other wastes. This species will not eat every time food is offered.

Sexing
Male: Obvious large ends on pedipalps; slender, with long, thin legs and tibial spurs on the first pair of legs

Female: Larger, more robust; abdomen usually larger than cephalothorax

Breeding
Wishbone spiders usually breed in summer in the wild, with the males wandering after rains. These conditions can be mimicked in captivity by raising the humidity in the enclosures of both your male and female spiders prior to introducing them. If the male is above ground wandering around his enclosure it is a good sign he is ready to mate. Set up the female in a large enclosure so that when the male is introduced he has space to court her without wandering straight over her burrow. An interested male will seek out the female and approach her burrow, tapping the ground with his legs. The spiders may mate at the entrance to the burrow or inside the burrow. When they separate it is best to remove the male. The female will produce an egg sac within the retreat

a few weeks after mating. The eggs will hatch 1–2 months later, depending on the temperature. Spiderlings will emerge from the burrow when they are ready to live independently. They should be housed separately in vials or in a toolbox set-up (see p.158) and fed on tiny insects such as hatchling crickets.

Lifespan
- **Male:** 2–3 years
- **Female:** 5–10 years

Captive behaviour
Wishbone spiders will spend most of their time within their burrows, but they will move to the entrance with their legs sticking out of the doorway when they are hunting. They are very sensitive to vibrations, so do not be surprised if they disappear when you open the enclosure to feed them. Have patience and you will see them return and ambush their insect food. At times they will cover the entrance to their burrow with silk or substrate. This can indicate that the substrate is too dry, and they are trying to conserve water, or that they are preparing to moult, and are protecting themselves from intruders while they are vulnerable.

Housing

 Enclosure: Jar or terrarium, minimum size 15 cm H × 10 cm W × 10 cm D

Substrate: Sand, coco-peat or mix; minimum depth 10 cm; damp throughout

Enclosure fit-out: Burrow (p.166)

 Individual

 18–24°C

 Humidity 60–70%

 None required, dislikes bright light

Special considerations
Although the venom of these spiders is not considered dangerous, they do have large fangs and care should be taken when keeping them. They are quite sensitive to dehydration, so always ensure that their substrate is kept damp, but not sodden.

Compatibility with other species
Not recommended

Species with similar care requirements
Other wishbone spiders (*Aname* species)

Wolf Spiders have incredible eyesight for hunting.

Modern spiders Suborder: Araneomorphae

Estimated number of species in Australia: 9500

Modern spiders come in all shapes, colours and sizes. This group includes the most commonly encountered species, such as Wolf spiders, Huntsmen and Orb-weavers. Several features set them apart from primitive spiders, including horizontally directed pincer-like fangs, only one pair of **book lungs** and **spiracles**. Having spiracles is a more efficient way to breathe, and these spiders are far more active than their primitive relatives. Modern spiders are found Australia-wide in almost all habitat types. Most are nocturnal and all have the capacity to produce silk, although not all species use it to capture their prey. Although at first glance many spiders in the group appear very different from one another, they all have the same basic features outlined below.

Sexing spiders is relatively simple when they are mature, but juvenile males and females are quite similar. The **pedipalps** of adult males have enlarged ends that act as sperm pumps during mating. These look a little like boxing gloves. Males often have longer legs and a smaller **abdomen** than females and are more lightly built. Females of most species are the larger sex because they need to develop and hold eggs in their bodies.

To prepare for mating a male spider must first transfer sperm from his sexual organs in the abdomen to his pedipalps. The male spider makes a small silk pad called a **sperm web** for this purpose. Reproduction in spiders is a tricky business because of their appetite for each another. Their courtship is fascinating, and the male must first introduce himself to the female as a mate rather than dinner. Males can do this in many ways, including waving their legs, vibrating the web, and tapping and stroking the female.

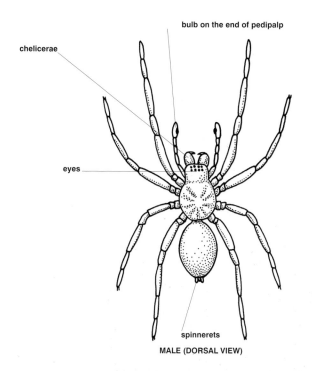

MALE (DORSAL VIEW)

chelicerae
bulb on the end of pedipalp
eyes
spinnerets

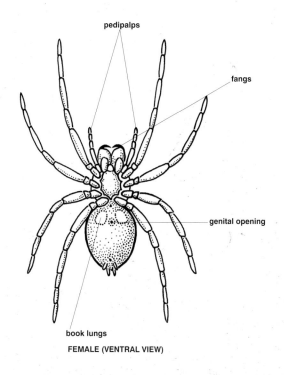

FEMALE (VENTRAL VIEW)

pedipalps
fangs
genital opening
book lungs

To do this properly male spiders need some space and time. Never place two spiders in a confined space and expect immediate mating – you'll be left with only one!

Mating involves the male placing one pedipalp at a time against the female's genital opening. This can be either a very quick or a drawn out process, depending on the species. In some species it is natural for the female to eat the male after mating.

Banded Huntsman spiders mating; the male has one of his pedipalps placed against the underside of the female's abdomen.

The life cycles of modern spiders vary quite a bit in their detail, but the basics are the same. All lay eggs that are protected in a silken wrapping called an **egg sac**. These sacs come in many shapes, colours and sizes, depending on the species, but all serve the same protective function for the eggs within. The number of eggs can vary from four to 600, again depending on the species. Egg incubation times vary a great deal even within a species, as temperature affects the rate of development.

Modern spiders will **moult** to grow, and will do so many times before reaching maturity. The first of these moults occurs within the egg sac prior to the spiderling emerging. Spiderlings are miniature replicas of their parents, and the spiderlings of some species will cluster around

their mother for weeks after hatching. They will moult again before moving off to start life on their own.

Modern spiders are predators that capture their prey in some of the most ingenious ways. Webs, snares, sticky glues, attractive **pheromones**, mimicry, ambush, stealth and sheer speed are just some of the methods used by these incredible hunters.

The diet of modern spiders is also varied. Some will feed upon any small animal they can snare or overpower, and others are specialists, focusing on a particular species as their food of choice. Insects are by far the most common food source, but for some spiders other **invertebrates** (including other spiders) and even small vertebrates make up their diet.

Spiders cannot eat solid food; it must be sucked through their filter-type mouthparts in liquid form. Spider **venom** plays an important role in this feeding process. As well as killing the prey, chemicals in venom help to break down many parts of the animal into an edible juice. Some spiders simply suck out the liquid through a hole they pierce in their prey's **exoskeleton**. Others salivate continuously onto their prey as they mash and squeeze it using their **chelicerae**, before sucking up the liquid. Any hard parts of the prey that cannot be eaten are discarded.

Most of the spiders in this group are regarded as harmless and are not aggressive This is because their fangs are too small to bite us, or their venom is too weak. Although nearly all have venom, only the Redback has venom that is life threatening. The risk of a bite while keeping any spider can be reduced simply by avoiding direct hand contact. The safest way of doing this is by using a jar to transport your spider. You can do this by ushering it into the jar with a soft implement such as a paintbrush, or by placing the jar over the spider and slipping a piece of paper under the spider to contain it.

Most spiders are cannibalistic and cannot be housed together. In most cases they also cannot be housed with other invertebrate groups because of their predatory nature; however, some exceptions are possible. Invertebrates such as snails and slugs can be kept with many spiders as they are not considered prey.

Spiders are delicate animals and need to be treated gently. Damage to their exoskeleton often will not heal, and any wound to the main body parts (cephalothorax or abdomen) will usually cause the spider to bleed to death. A spider can deal with a leg wound by the process of **autotomy**. The injured leg can come off at the point where it meets the body, with the release point closing up rapidly to stop the blood loss. Spiders may also lose legs in this way to free themselves from the grip of a predator, so never restrain your spider by its limbs! Spiders will regrow lost limbs between moults. The new leg appears at the next moult – an amazing process.

Modern spiders are becoming more commonly kept, but are not often sold by pet shops or dealers. Some species are kept by enthusiasts and, due to their common occurrence, spiders from this group are often collected by children for the home or classroom.

(Note: Redback spiders should not be collected by children as they are highly venomous.)

Modern spiders make great displays, as long as the display takes the habits of the species into consideration. For example, creating overhangs, nooks and crannies against the front window will encourage spiders to shelter where you can actually see them, rather than hiding at the back in a corner.

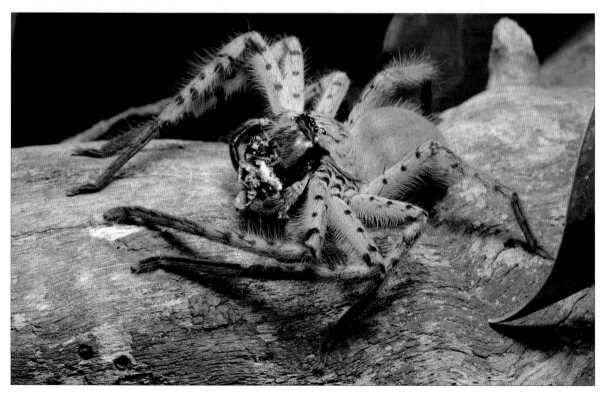

The Tiger Huntsman (*Typostola* sp.) is one of Australia's most spectacular modern spiders, and thrives in captivity. Only recently discovered by the authors, this species is yet to be described scientifically.

Badge Huntsman *Neosparassus diana*

Level of difficulty

beginner   advanced

Badge Huntsman spiders get their name from the bright badge-like pattern that has two fake eyes on the underside of their abdomen. When they are threatened, they will raise up their body with four legs in the air, exposing the badge to scare away predators. These spiders are nocturnal, and hunt on the foliage of plants for insects and smaller spiders to feed on. Females bind clusters of leaves together with silk to make retreats to live in, and to protect their egg sacs.

Housing

 Enclosure: Terrarium or jar; minimum size 15 cm H × 10 cm W × 10 cm D

Substrate: Absorptive layer only (coco-peat, sand or leaf litter)

Enclosure fit-out: Sticks, leaves and branches

 Individual

 18–26°C

 Humidity 40–60%

 None required, dislikes bright light

Food and water
- Live insects such as crickets, cockroaches, flies
- Mist spray

Routine care
Daily: Mist spray to allow spider to drink from enclosure surfaces

Twice weekly: Introduce a small live insect into enclosure, and remove wastes and any dead or uneaten insects

Sexing
Male: Small body up to 16 mm, and long, thin legs, with noticeably enlarged bulbs on the pedipalps

Female: Larger, up to 20 mm in body length

Breeding
Introduce the male into the female's enclosure. It is best to do this in a large enclosure so that the male has space to enter without bumping straight into the female. Courtship will begin with the male using a number of tapping and vibrating movements to signal his intentions to the female. If the male doesn't do this it is best to remove him and try again a week later. Mating involves the male reaching under the female with one pedipalp at a time. Remove the male after they have separated. The female's abdomen will expand in size until she produces an egg sac within her silk retreat. At this stage it is important to ensure that your enclosure will be secure enough to contain the tiny spiderlings. The eggs will usually hatch 30–60 days later and the spiderlings will swarm around the mother for a week or so before leaving the retreat. The little spiderlings are difficult to feed, and they need to be kept individually or they will eat each other. Tiny insects such as vinegar flies may be used as food at this early stage.

Lifespan
1–2 years

Captive behaviour
Badge Huntsmen spend most of the day sitting motionless and will roam around the enclosure at night in search of live prey. They will detect prey by vibrations the insects make while they walk or fly. You can use a dim red light to view your spiders, as it will not disturb them while they are hunting.

Special considerations
Badge Huntsmen can climb smooth enclosure walls easily and are fast runners. They will often shelter on the underside of the enclosure lid, so take care when opening it. Although not regarded as dangerous, bites from these spiders have been known to cause pain, headaches and nausea.

Compatibility with other species
Not recommended

Species with similar care requirements
Other badge huntsmen (*Neosparassus* species)

Banded Huntsman *Holconia immanis*

Level of difficulty

| 1 | 2 | 3 | 4 | 5 |

beginner   advanced

This very impressive spider is one of the largest of the Australian huntsmen, and can reach a body size of 45 mm and a leg span of up to 160 mm. It is found over much of eastern Australia, and is a common but often unwelcome guest in many houses, due to its size and rapid scuttling movement. Like other huntsman spiders, this species has the ability to run sideways, and its flattened body is perfectly suited for hiding under loose sheets of bark. It is a nocturnal wandering hunter that feeds mainly on insects and smaller spiders, which are overpowered and captured without the use of silk.

Food and water
- Live insects such as crickets, flies, cockroaches
- Mist spray

Routine care
Daily: Mist spray to allow spider to drink from enclosure surfaces

Twice weekly: Introduce a live insect into the enclosure or feed it to your spider using forceps. Remove wastes and any dead or uneaten insects.

Sexing
Male: Obvious bulbs on the ends of the pedipalps, small abdomens and long legs

Female: Abdomen larger than cephalothorax, more robust; body length to 45 mm

Breeding
Introduce both spiders into a large enclosure when pairing them. This allows the male spider room to escape from the female if she is not interested in mating. Feed the female several times prior to breeding until her abdomen is quite large, as she will be less interested in eating the male. Ensure that when the male is introduced he is allowed to move at his own pace, which may be very slow and cautious. If the female is interested, he will make shuddering movements with his body and use his pedipalps to follow the female's scent. Remove the male if the female is aggressive towards him. Mating involves the male reaching under the female with one pedipalp at a time and this may take hours. It is best to remove your male after mating. Eggs may be produced as soon as a week after mating. The spiderlings will emerge around 4 weeks later and cluster around the mother and the egg sac.

Once they begin to leave the mother they will begin to feed on each other and need to be separated. Spiderlings can be housed in small jars and will require a fine mesh cover to prevent them escaping.

Lifespan
2–3 years

Captive behaviour
These spiders will spend most of their time sitting still on a vertical surface. They will hide if given the opportunity, but will often sit in full view if not disturbed. They are most active at night, when they move around searching for prey.

Housing

Enclosure: Terrarium or custom; minimum size 20 cm H × 30 cm W × 20 cm D

Substrate: Absorptive layer only (coco-peat, sand, or leaf litter)

Enclosure fit-out: Large pieces of flat bark leaning against enclosure wall

 Individual

 18–26°C

 Humidity 40–50%

 None required, dislikes bright light

Special considerations
Banded Huntsmen are very fast spiders, and are able to climb smooth surfaces easily. Secure lids are required, as these spiders have the ability to squeeze through very small gaps. Spiderlings will require fine mesh or fly screen to prevent their escape. They will often be at the top of their enclosure, so be careful when opening and closing the lid.

Compatibility with other species
Not recommended

Species with similar care requirements
Other huntsmen including *Holconia* species, *Heteropoda* species *Isopedella* species and *Typostola* species

Note: tropical species require higher humidity

Garden Wolf Spider *Lycosa godeffroyi*

Level of difficulty

1	2	**3**	4	5

beginner   advanced

These spiders are easily spotted at night, as their large eyes reflect brightly in torchlight. They have eight eyes: four large and four small. Two of the large eyes point forward like headlights, the other large set face to the rear. Garden Wolf Spiders grow to 27 mm in body length. They are burrowers and hunt by running down insects and overpowering them with an incredible burst of speed. They are found in bushland and suburban gardens around southern Australia, and are often seen carrying their round egg sacs around with them.

Food and water
- Live insects such as crickets, cockroaches, flies
- Mist spray

Routine care
Daily: Lightly mist spray to allow spider to drink from enclosure surfaces

Twice weekly: Introduce a live insect into enclosure or feed it to your spider using forceps. Remove waste and any dead or uneaten insects.

Sexing
Male: Obvious bulbs on the ends of their pedipalps, small abdomen and long legs

Female: Abdomen larger than cephalothorax, more robust

Breeding
This is best achieved in a large terrarium that allows the spiders space to move around. Ensure the female has been well fed prior to the introduction of the male. The male will court her by approaching with a series of rapid leg drumming and vibrations, in combination with raising and lowering his forelegs. If the female is ready to mate she will remain still and allow him to approach. Remove him immediately if she shows any aggression towards him. If she is willing he will make contact with her and tap her with his legs as he gets into a mating position. This involves reaching under her with his outstretched pedipalps. Once the spiders have separated after mating they should be housed independently. The female's abdomen will expand before she produces an egg sac that she carries around with her, attached to her spinnerets. Hatching can take place 30–40 days later, after which the tiny spiderlings ride upon their mother's back for several weeks. Once they begin

to disperse from the mother, they will become cannibalistic and will need to be separated into small jars or a toolbox set-up (p.158). Feed the juveniles live insects such as tiny crickets.

Lifespan
2–3 years

Captive behaviour
Garden Wolf Spiders will spend most of their time sitting still. When prey is introduced they will rapidly chase it, often flipping over with tremendous impact as they catch it. When they are not hungry they will often run away from their prey. Remove the insect if this happens.

Housing

 Enclosure: Terrarium; minimum size 15 cm H × 20 cm W × 12 cm D

Substrate: Sand, coco-peat or mix, minimum depth 3 cm; dry throughout

Enclosure fit-out: Flat bark as shelter or burrow

 Individual

 18–26°C

 Humidity 40–50%

 No specialised lighting required

Special considerations
Wolf spiders are fast movers, and can occasionally become aggressive.

Compatibility with other species
Herbivorous invertebrates much larger than the spider

Species with similar care requirements
Other wolf spiders (Lycosidae)

Golden Orb-weaver *Nephila edulis*

Level of difficulty

| 1 | 2 | 3 | 4 | 5 |

beginner   advanced

These spiders build spectacular large webs in which some of the silk lines are yellow-gold in colour, giving the spider its name. This species is common in arid areas and, like other orb-weavers, builds the classic orb-web in which they sit both day and night. The silk of this species is incredibly strong and can trap large insects. Large numbers of these spiders can often be found close to one another; the mass of individual webs making the flight of any insect a dangerous one. When an insect becomes trapped, the spider will quickly move to it, biting it first and then wrapping it in silk before taking it back to the centre of the web to be eaten.

Food and water
- Live or dead insects such as crickets, cockroaches, flies
- Mist spray

Routine care
Daily: Mist spray web for spider to drink

Twice weekly: Feed by placing a live insect into the web, or offering freshly dead insects directly to the spider using forceps

Sexing
Male: Very small, 6 mm in body length, with distinctive bulbs on the pedipalps

Female: Large, up to 30 mm in body length

Note: Due to the small size of adult males, juveniles exceeding 6 mm in body length can be assumed to be females

Breeding
Release the male on the outermost fringes (support lines) of the female's web. This will allow him to make his way into the web in his own time. There is always a chance that he will be eaten when he does this, but by plucking at the web he is able to send signals to the female to alert her of his intentions. He will mate by moving to her underside so he can reach her genital opening with his pedipalps. Near the web, the female will produce a fluffy yellow egg sac that can contain more than 300 eggs. The spiderlings that emerge 30–60 days later are very small and need to be fed tiny insects, such as vinegar flies, once they build their own webs. The spiderlings can be housed together in an enclosure with lots of sticks on which to build their webs.

Lifespan
Up to 2 years

Captive behaviour
Females will spend their entire lives within the web, only leaving it if disturbed or to lay eggs. Mature males will leave their webs to search for females. These spiders do not replace their webs each night; they will repair their web and completely replace it only when it gets damaged. They will also keep the remains of their meals strung up above them in the web, to make it harder for predators to see them among all the bits and pieces.

Housing

 Enclosure: Orb frame, span 50 cm (p.157).

Substrate: None

Enclosure fit-out: None

 Individual

 22–28°C

 Humidity 50–70%

 No specialised lighting required

Special considerations
These spiders may wander if exposed to drafts (by releasing silk drift lines), and spiders may end up with webs in positions that are completely unexpected!

Compatibility with other species
Not recommended

Species with similar care requirements
Other golden orb-weavers including *Nephila plumipes*, *N. maculata* (Note *N. maculata* requires temperature 26–28°C and humidity 70–90%).

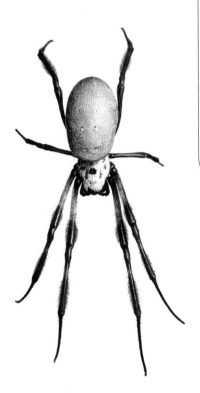

Green Jumping Spider *Mopsus mormon*

Level of difficulty

1	2	3	4	5

beginner   advanced

These intriguing spiders can capture insects many times larger than themselves. They are found in the tropical north of Australia and are Australia's largest jumping spiders, growing to a length of 16 mm. They have extraordinary eyesight for such a small animal. Two of their eight eyes are much larger than the rest, which allows them to judge distances accurately when leaping. They can move forwards, backwards and sideways very quickly, and are excellent climbers.

Housing

 Enclosure: Jar or glass tank; minimum size 15 cm H × 10 cm W × 10 cm D

Substrate: Absorptive layer only (coco-peat, sand or leaf litter)

Enclosure fit-out: Sticks, branches and green leaves

 Individual

 24–30°C, hotspot to 40°C optional

 Humidity 60–80%

No specialised lighting required, dichroic lamp optional

Food and water

- Live insects such as crickets, flies

- Mist spray

Routine care

Daily: Lightly mist spray enclosure surfaces for the spider to drink

Twice weekly: Introduce a live insect into enclosure, and remove waste and any dead or uneaten insects

Sexing

Male: Black face with long white 'sideburns', obvious enlarged bulbs on the pedipalps, 12 mm body length

Female: Green with white hair around the eyes, 16 mm body length

Breeding

Introduce the male into the female's enclosure. It is best to do this in a large enclosure so that the male has space to visually locate the female from a safe distance. Courtship will begin with the male using waving and flagging movements with his legs and pedipalps to signal his intentions to the female. If the courtship is successful the male will make physical contact with the female and then lean under her with one pedipalp at a time. Remove the male after mating has finished and the spiders have separated. The female will produce an egg sac within a silk retreat on a flat surface, such as on a leaf, and remain nearby until the eggs hatch. The spiderlings are tiny and very difficult to feed. Tiny insects such as vinegar flies may be used as food for spiderlings, which need to be housed individually in vials or small jars.

Lifespan
1–2 years

Captive behaviour

Green Jumping Spiders are very active animals and they will spend quite a bit of time moving around the upper parts of the enclosure within the foliage, and on the walls. They are fascinating to watch, as they are constantly swivelling their bodies to look at where they intend to leap, or at the insect they are stalking. They will also spend time within their flat silken retreat, which they enter via a silk tunnel.

Special considerations
Green Jumping Spiders have been known to give a painful bite, but are not aggressive

Compatibility with other species
Not recommended

Species with similar care requirements
Other jumping spiders (Salticidae)

Redback *Latrodectus hasselti*

Level of difficulty

| 1 | 2 | 3 | 4 | **5** |

beginner   advanced

Redbacks are Australia's most well-known and recognisable spiders, growing to 12 mm in body length. They are found Australia-wide, but are much more commonly found living around us than in natural environments. They will live under almost any solid object that gives them protection and allows them to construct a web. Rocks, logs or rubbish, including old drums, upturned pots and cardboard boxes, are used by Redbacks. At first glance the web of a Redback appears to be a random array of threads; however, it is a well-engineered trap. The upper level provides support for the spider to move around on, and links to vertical trip-lines that run to the ground. These lines have sticky droplets of liquid silk just above ground level that snare any small animal that bumps into them. The silk is so strong that small mice, lizards and snakes have been found snared in these webs. Redbacks are feared due to their highly toxic venom; however, since the development of antivenom in 1956, no human fatalities have occurred.

Food and water
- Live insects such as crickets or cockroaches
- Mist spray

Routine care
Twice weekly: Lightly mist spray the web around the spider

Weekly: Introduce live insects into the web, and remove leftover food (without destroying the web)

Sexing
Male: Small, abdomen coloured white, cream and brown with flecks of red or orange; obvious bulbs on the pedipalps

Female: Round pea-sized abdomen, brown to black with red stripe

Breeding
The female Redback should be settled and have her web and retreat set up before you introduce a male. The male will seek out the female if she is ready to mate, and does so by plucking her web and tapping her with his legs. He will climb under her to mate. Most male Redbacks are eaten by the female after mating. A female Redback only requires a single mating to produce a large number of eggs over a long period of time. If the female is well fed, she can produce more than 10 egg sacs, each around a month apart. The tiny young spiderlings that emerge can escape through fly mesh, so a fine mesh is required. The juveniles will need to be separated and fed individually after a week or so. They can be housed in small jars and fed tiny insects.

Lifespan
1–3 years

Captive behaviour
A female Redback will construct a web, and then spend most of its time hanging upside down at the top of it in a sheltered position. When it detects prey, the spider will move swiftly towards it and throw a mass of sticky threads over the prey to secure it before biting it. The prey will then be hoisted up to a feeding position high in the web. When Redback males mature they will leave their web and wander in the search of a mate.

Housing

 Enclosure: Jar or terrarium; minimum size 15 cm H × 10 cm W × 10 cm D

Substrate: Gravel, leaf litter or newspaper

Enclosure fit-out: Any secure object that provides an overhang with space beneath it.

 Individual or group

 18–28°C

 Humidity 40–50%

 None required, sensitive to bright light

Special considerations
These spiders are not suitable for children or classrooms. As they are highly venomous, care should be taken when keeping Redbacks. If you are bitten, seek medical attention immediately. Juvenile Redbacks are extremely small, and although not dangerous they can escape through fly mesh. If housing Redbacks in groups ensure you have enough space and retreats for all spiders, or they will eat each other.

Compatibility with other species
Not recommended

Species with similar care requirements
Brown Widow (*Latrodectus geometricus*), brown house spiders (*Steatoda* species)

Social Huntsman Spider *Delena cancerides*

Level of difficulty

These large flat spiders get their name from their tendency to live in groups, a habit that is very rare among spiders. Spiderlings of most species will move away from where they emerged from their egg sac, but Social Huntsman spiderlings will often remain and grow up around their mother and other older siblings. They will often share prey too, which is also unusual among spiders. Social Huntsman Spiders are found in south-eastern Australia, and are particularly common under loose bark of Blackwood trees (*Acacia melanoxylon*). They are a timid, harmless species and do very well in captivity. They make an impressive display in large numbers.

Housing

 Enclosure: Terrarium or custom; minimum size 20 cm H × 30 cm W × 20 cm D

Substrate: Absorptive layer only (coco-peat, sand or leaf litter)

Enclosure fit-out: Large, flat bark pieces arranged to allow the spiders to squeeze between

 Individual or group

 18–24°C

 Humidity 40–60%

None required, dislikes bright light

Food and water
- Live insects such as crickets, flies, cockroaches
- Mist spray

Routine care
Daily: Lightly mist bark with water

Twice weekly: Introduce live insects, one per spider. Remove waste and dead or uneaten insects.

Sexing
Male: Obvious shiny black bulbs on the end of the pedipalps, small body up to 20 mm

Female: Abdomen large, usually exceeding the size of the cephalothorax, large body up to 30 mm

Breeding
Although they tolerate each other more than other species of spiders, the introduction of a new male to a female can still lead to cannibalism. To begin a colony, it is best to pair up a male and female in a large terrarium to allow the male to seek out the female carefully. It is also wise to feed the female very well prior to this to reduce the chance of her eating him. Like many hunting spiders the male will signal his intentions to her by tapping with his legs and vibrating his body. If the female is aggressive towards the male, you should remove him and try again a week later. Mating involves the male leaning under the female with one pedipalp at a time. If mating is successful, the female will produce a round white egg sac the size of a 10– or 20–cent piece. This is usually placed under a piece of bark or on a protected flat surface. Spiderlings will emerge 30–60 days later, and can be left in the parents' enclosure, providing that you have fine mesh covering the ventilation holes. Feeding a growing colony requires a different approach, and a range of prey types and sizes need to be offered regularly.

Lifespan
1–2 years

Captive behaviour
Social Huntsman Spiders are nocturnal and will usually spend the day hidden, or sitting still on flat surfaces. When active, they will wander for short distances and then stop and wait. If housed as a group, one moving will often stimulate another to do so, and so on. These spiders, particularly the young spiders, will often share their food, and will cluster around the prey insect from all angles.

Special considerations
These spiders are very fast, extremely flat and expert at escaping through the smallest of gaps. Servicing a group can be quite tricky, and as soon as you open the lid you are dealing with a multitude of fast-running spiders. Advanced keepers displaying these spiders can use carbon dioxide to sedate the spiders before servicing; the spiders recover fully several minutes later. An alternative to this is to have a custom-made enclosure with a small well-designed access door.

Compatibility with other species
Not recommended

Species with similar care requirements
None

St Andrew's Cross Spider *Argiope keyserlingi*

Level of difficulty

| 1 | 2 | 3 | 4 | 5 |

beginner   advanced

These colourfully banded spiders are well known for the white silk cross they make in the centre of their round 'orb' webs. This cross is called a stabilimentum and is believed to have two functions. The first is to attract insects to the web by reflecting ultraviolet light, and the second to scare off predators such as birds. These spiders sit on their webs with their legs in pairs, each pair aligned with the four arms of the cross. They are found over much of eastern Australia, including suburban backyards.

Food and water
- Small live insects such as crickets, flies, cockroaches
- Mist spray

Routine care
Daily: Mist spray web for spider to drink

Twice weekly: Feed by placing a live insect into the web, or offering freshly dead insects directly to the spider using forceps

Sexing
Male: Very small, grow to about 5 mm in body length, with distinctive bulbs on the pedipalps

Female: Large, up to 16 mm in body length

Note: Because of the small size of adult males, juveniles exceeding 5 mm in body length can be assumed to be females

Breeding
Release the male on the outermost fringes (support lines) of the female's web. This will allow him to make his way into the web in his own time. There is always a chance that he will be eaten when he does this, but by plucking at the web in a set way, he is able to send signals to the female to alert her of his intentions. He will mate by moving to her underside so he can reach her genital opening with his pedipalps. The female will produce a pear-shaped egg sac near the web. The sac is made of greenish-coloured silk and can contain more than 300 eggs. Spiderlings will emerge 30–60 days later. The spiderlings are tiny and very difficult to feed as their webs are extremely delicate – tiny insects such as vinegar flies or smaller may be used to feed them. They can be housed together in an enclosure with lots of sticks on which to build their webs.

Lifespan
1–2 years

Captive behaviour
Female St Andrew's Cross Spiders will spend their entire lives within the web, leaving it only if disturbed or to lay eggs. They are very sensitive and if disturbed will drop quickly from the web on a safety line. They will return later when they feel secure. They will also 'trampoline' on their web if they are disturbed. Although they do not actually leave the web they will bounce the web back and forth rapidly until the disturbance has gone. Mature males will leave the web in search of females. These spiders do not replace their webs each night. They will repair the web and completely rebuild it only when it is badly damaged.

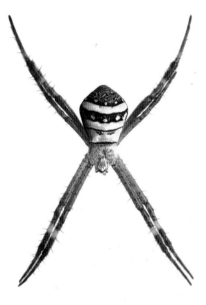

Housing

 Enclosure: Orb frame, span 40 cm (p.157).

Substrate: Not required

Enclosure fit-out: Not required

 Individual

 20–28°C

 Humidity 60–80%

No specialised lighting required

Special considerations
These spiders may wander if exposed to drafts (by releasing silk drift lines), and may end up with webs in completely unexpected positions! They are energetic feeders and will often begin to wrap up your forceps along with their insect food when offered to them. To avoid this, grip the food insect by the tip of its abdomen so that it can be released easily.

Compatibility with other species
Not recommended

Species with similar care requirements
Enamelled Spider (*Araneus bradleyi*) and other orb-weavers in the genus *Argiope*

Water spiders *Dolomedes* species

Level of difficulty

| 1 | 2 | 3 | 4 | 5 |

beginner   advanced

These agile spiders have specialised tufts of hair on their feet, which allow them to walk on the surface of water without falling in. They are found throughout Australia, and live close to permanent or semi-permanent water. They are relatively large spiders, growing up to 25 mm in body length, and hunt by overpowering their prey without using silk. When hunting, they will usually sit at the edge of the water with the tips of their front four legs touching the surface of the water to feel for the small vibrations caused by insects and tiny animals in or on the water. When they detect prey, they will rush onto (or sometimes into) the water to catch it.

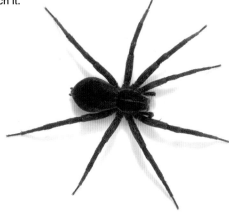

Food and water
- Small live insects
- Free water or moisture in substrate

Routine care
Daily: Lightly mist spray if using sphagnum moss instead of water

Twice weekly: Introduce one live insect into enclosure, and remove wastes and any dead or uneaten insects

Weekly: Change water

Sexing
Male: Small (15–20 mm) with thin legs, bulbs on the pedipalps and white stripes along the side of the cephalothorax

Female: Large (20–30 mm) with thicker legs and yellow-brown stripes along the side of the cephalothorax

Breeding
Ensure there is plenty of shelter, such as rocks and plants, for each spider. The male will approach the female using his legs to tap vibrations to make her aware that he is not prey. Occasionally the female will consume the male before or after mating. Mating involves the male reaching under the female with one pedipalp at a time to fertilise her. The female will produce a round egg sac containing hundreds of eggs. She will usually stay in one place but can carry it around using her fangs. The eggs will hatch 30–60 days later and the young will mass around the open sac on their fine silk threads before they disperse. They are very small and difficult to raise without a supply of tiny insects. The young can be housed together for a few weeks, and then separated into small vials or easy-feeders (p.158).

Lifespan
1–2 years

Captive behaviour
Water spiders will spend long periods of time sitting very still. When hunting they sit with their legs splayed out wide, usually in contact with the water if you have set up an aquatic enclosure. It is fascinating to watch them feeding, as they will run across the surface of the water to collect their prey.

Housing

Enclosure: Terrarium or glass tank; minimum size 20 cm H × 30 cm W × 20 cm D

Substrate: Aquarium gravel, rocks (with water) or moist sphagnum moss (without water)

Enclosure fit-out: Rocks can be placed in shallow water (3–5 cm deep) for the spider to sit on, or aquarium gravel can be built up at one end to form a 'beach'

 Individual or as pair

 18–25°C

 Humidity 60–90%

 No specialised lighting required

Special considerations
These spiders will often hide underwater if disturbed (e.g. when the enclosure lid is opened). Don't be alarmed if they do this, as they can survive underwater for long periods of time by breathing air that is trapped on hairs around their abdomen.

Compatibility with other species
Slugs and snails

Species with similar care requirements
Giant Water Spider (*Megadolomedes australianus*) and aquatic wolf spiders (Lycosidae)

White-tailed Spider *Lampona cylindrata*

Level of difficulty

1 2 3 **4** 5
beginner   advanced

These well-known spiders have a bad reputation because of the mistaken belief that their bite causes ulcers that do not heal. In reality, most confirmed bites from this species cause only minor symptoms. White-tailed Spiders are wandering nocturnal hunters that spend the daylight hours hidden beneath the bark of trees, or within dark crevices in our homes. They differ from most modern spiders in that they have a very specialised diet consisting only of other spiders. They stalk and capture their victims without the use of silk, often taking the prey out of its own web.

Food and water
- Small live spiders such as Black House Spiders (*Badumna insignis*) or Daddy Long-legs (*Pholcus phalangioides*)
- Mist spray

Routine care
Daily: Mist spray to allow the spider to drink from the enclosure surfaces

Weekly: Introduce a small live spider into enclosure or feed it to your spider using forceps. Remove waste and any dead or uneaten spiders.

Sexing
Male: Small body up to 15 mm, very thin with distinctive bulbs on the pedipalps

Female: Large robust body, up to 20 mm in length

Breeding
Feed the female until her abdomen is quite large before breeding. Introduce the male while she is occupied with her prey as this also reduces the chance of cannibalism. The male will slowly approach the female and court her using stroking actions with his legs. He will then reach under her with his pedipalps to fertilise her. Remove the male after they have separated. The female will produce an egg sac a number of weeks after mating. The spiderlings will emerge around 4 weeks later and cluster around their mother. Once they begin to move away from her they will become cannibalistic, and require independent care if they are to be kept. They can be set up in vials and fed tiny spiders, smaller than themselves.

Lifespan
1–2 years

Captive behaviour
They will spend most of their time sitting still, hidden or on the wall of their enclosure. They are most active at night and will move around slowly searching for prey. When feeding, they will approach other spiders with a great deal of caution, before springing at them and biting them on the cephalothorax.

Housing
 Enclosure: Jar; minimum size 15 cm H × 10 cm W × 10 cm D

Substrate: Absorptive layer only (coco-peat, sand or newspaper)

Enclosure fit-out: Bark strips as shelters

 Individual

 18–26°C

 Humidity 40–50%

 None required, sensitive to bright light

Special considerations
Do not allow 'prey' spiders, particularly Daddy Long-legs, to settle and build webs in your White-tailed Spider's enclosure, as this can lead to the White-tailed Spider itself becoming the prey! Never free handle these spiders; always use a jar as these spiders can become aggressive at times.

Compatibility with other species
May be housed with herbivorous insects

Species with similar care requirements
White-tailed Spider (*Lampona murina*)

Scorpions use sensory hairs on their bodies to detect vibrations in the air.

Scorpions Order: Scorpiones

Estimated number of species in Australia: 150

Scorpions are living relics and are much the same today as they were more than 400 million years ago. They are very well known animals, but are rarely encountered as they are nocturnal and spend the day hidden in a burrow or sheltering beneath rocks or tree bark. Although Australian species are not considered dangerous, they are feared by many people, probably because of their sinister appearances in movies and on television.

Scorpions occur throughout Australia and live in a wide variety of habitats. We have species that dig deep burrows in sandy deserts, species that are rock and bark dwellers in the eucalypt forests, and various species in our tropical rainforests. Species vary in appearance to suit their specific habitats, but they all have the same basic features outlined below.

Scorpions have many unique features. The **pedipalps** have specialised ends called **chelae** (pincers) that are used for gripping prey, mating and digging. The sting, which protrudes from the **venom** bulb, or 'telson', is used to kill prey and for defence. On their underside, scorpions have comb-like organs called **pectines**. It is believed that the pectines help the scorpion to sense chemicals (by smell), vibrations, temperature and humidity. They have tiny eyes – two central (median) eyes and 2–5 pairs at the front corners of the head, but their vision is relatively poor.

Sexing most Australian scorpions can be quite tricky. Generally, females are more powerfully built, the males tending to be slender in comparison. Other features used to sex scorpions are quite small and some are on the underside of the body. To see these, place

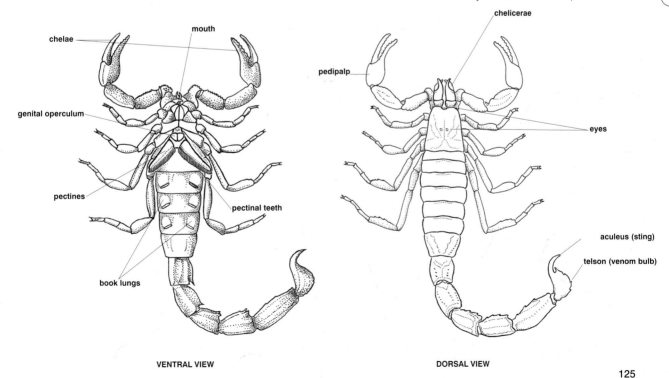

VENTRAL VIEW

DORSAL VIEW

your scorpion in a small petri dish with a lid, and use a magnifying glass to examine them. One of these features is the genital **operculum**, which in some species is divided in males and fused (one piece) in females. The comb-like pectines can also assist you to sex your scorpion, as males often have pectines with longer and more numerous 'teeth'. The fifth tail segment is often longer in male scorpions than in females, but you'll require both sexes together for comparison. The easiest species to sex is the Rainforest Scorpion (*Liocheles waigiensis*), as males have an obvious 'tooth' on the bottom claw of each pedipalp, which fits into a notch in the upper claw.

Scorpion reproduction is fascinating. The male clasps the female by the chelae (claws) and attaches a tiny **spermatophore** to the substrate. He then proceeds to 'dance' with her in what is called the *promenade a deux*, as he attempts to position her genital operculum directly over the spermatophore. The two shuffle back and forth, often for quite some time, until her position is perfect. When the female's genital operculum is in contact with the spermatophore, he catapults the sperm into her. While the two are locked together it is not uncommon for the male to sting the female. This doesn't seem to harm her but may sedate her to make his job easier.

Scorpions have remarkably long gestation periods; for some species it is well over a year. They give birth to fully formed live young that are born soft and pale. Immediately after birth baby scorpions climb onto their mother's back and will remain there for the first few weeks of life. They usually leave their mother soon after **moulting**. Scorpions will moult 7–10 times to reach maturity, the number of moults depending on the species.

All scorpions are predators, and feed mostly upon insects, spiders and other scorpions. They capture their prey with a combination of crushing, using the pedipalps, and the injection of venom using the sting. Some species rely more on venom and others on their powerful **chelae**. Not surprisingly, those with large stings and small chelae are usually more venomous. Scorpions do not rely on vision to locate their food, instead they detect prey by their remarkable sensitivity to vibration. The tiny sensory hairs located on their pedipalps can detect the slightest airborne vibrations caused by animals moving nearby. They also sense vibrations on the ground with their pectines.

Scorpions cannot eat solid food, and must crush it and suck it up as a liquid. They actually semi-digest the food before eating it by mixing digestive fluids with it as they crush it with their **chelicerae**. Tiny hairs around the scorpion's mouth filter out any remaining solid pieces before it is swallowed.

Although all Australian scorpions are venomous, none are regarded as life threatening. Most species are only capable of giving a painful sting if handled incorrectly or irresponsibly.

Handling scorpions is relatively easy if the right tools and methods are used. The easiest way to move a scorpion is to usher it into a small plastic container by gentle prompting with a padded implement. If it is necessary, a scorpion can be picked up safely with a pair of padded forceps, gripping the scorpion gently by the end of its tail. A good way to do this is to attach some self-adhesive foam to the tips of your forceps. Being gentle is very important, as any rupture in the scorpion's **exoskeleton** can kill it.

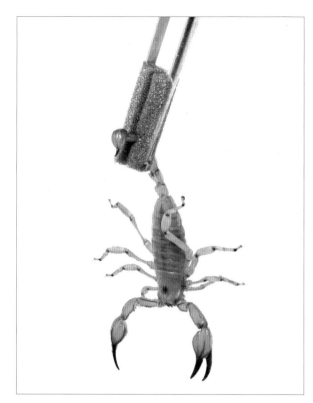

You can pick up your scorpion safely with padded forceps.

Scorpions will fluoresce when exposed to ultraviolet light.

One amazing quirk of scorpions is that they fluoresce when exposed to ultraviolet light. This is fascinating to see as they glow a similar green to many of the glow-in-the-dark novelty toys. You can see this by shining an ultraviolet light on your scorpion in a dark room. It still is not known exactly why they fluoresce, but some researchers believe that scorpions may attract insects at night by glowing under the tiny amount of ultraviolet light that is around.

Several species of Australian scorpions are becoming widely available in captivity, and no doubt more will follow in the future. They are a popular display species, and most are very hardy animals if set-up correctly. They will display well, provided that the design of the exhibit is well thought out. Cutaway burrows and the use of ultraviolet light make for creative displays that still enable the scorpion to feel at home and act naturally.

Obtaining your scorpions requires responsibility. If you plan to collect your own, it is very important that you do not take large numbers, and that you cause a minimal amount of disturbance to their habitat. Some scorpions can be affected by over-collecting, as they may occur in localised areas and breed quite slowly. As **invertebrate** enthusiasts, it would be a disaster to contribute to the demise of wild populations of the very animals we are so passionate about. If you are interested in collecting your own scorpions, check with your state's or territory's environmental authority before doing so.

Black Rock Scorpion *Urodacus manicatus*

Level of difficulty

1	2	3	4	5

beginner   advanced

Black Rock Scorpions are one of the most common scorpions being sold commercially. They are found in forests in south-eastern Australia, and grow to about 40–50 mm from head to tip of tail – a reasonable size by Australian standards. Their favoured habitat is the granite rock outcrops in which they make their homes. They are nocturnal, spending the day sheltered from light and heat in a shallow burrow they create by scraping out soil and debris from under the rocks. They feed mostly on insects and spiders, but will also eat other scorpions. Unfortunately, large numbers of these scorpions are being taken directly from the wild for commercial sale, which seems to be causing populations to dwindle and localised habitat destruction in some areas.

Food and water
- Live crickets and cockroaches
- Water sponge

Routine care
Daily: Mist one end of the enclosure's substrate with water to keep it damp. Ensure water sponge is moist.

Weekly: Introduce one live insect into enclosure, and remove wastes and any dead or uneaten insects. This species may not eat every time food is offered.

Sexing
Male: Slender body in comparison with females, a longer fifth tail segment and divided genital operculum

Female: Larger bodied, with a fused genital operculum

Breeding
The male should be introduced to the female in an enclosure large enough to allow him to be released well away from her. If she is interested in mating the male will start to make jerky movements and seek out the female. Like all scorpions they will mate by clasping claws. The male should be removed once they have separated to ensure his safety. This species has a very long gestation period. The female's body will gradually become rounder, and she will give birth 16 months after mating. Feed your scorpion dead insects when the birth is nearing, to prevent live insects causing interference. Black Rock Scorpions will give birth to 10–20 babies, which ride on their mother's back for the first few weeks of life.

Once they leave their mother they should be removed and housed individually. The toolbox method (p. 158) is ideal. These scorpions will take a little over 2 years to mature.

Note: If this species is being kept as a group, the scorpions may mate without you actually noticing

Lifespan
6–10 years

Captive behaviour
These scorpions are most active at night and will emerge from under their rocks and forage around the enclosure looking for food. They can be viewed under dim red light and will still behave normally. They cannot climb glass or plastic, so enclosures do not necessarily need a lid.

Housing

Enclosure: Terrarium or glass tank; minimum size 20 cm H × 30 cm W × 20 cm D

Substrate: Granite sand, sand, or coco-peat, minimum depth 3 cm; maintain a damp and a dry end

Enclosure fit-out: An assortment of small flat rocks, bedded into the substrate so they are stable

 Individual or group

 18–24°C

 Humidity 40–60%

 None required, dislikes bright light

Special considerations
If you have a female with young it is critical not to disturb her or she may eat her offspring. It is important to observe her, but do so carefully.

Compatibility with other species
Not recommended

Species with similar care requirements
Wood Scorpion (*Cercophonius squama*)

BUGS ALIVE!

Inland Robust Scorpion *Urodacus yaschenkoi*

Level of difficulty

(1 | 2 | **3** | 4 | 5)

beginner   advanced

These impressive scorpions are one of Australia's largest species, growing to about 70 mm from head to tail. They are found in the inland sandy deserts, often on the slopes of sand dunes. They live in deep spiral burrows that go down to depths of up to a metre, in which they shelter from extremes of temperature and their many predators. These scorpions hunt at night by ambushing small animals that pass their burrow. They are very sensitive to vibrations and will either sit with their chelae sticking out of the burrow or venture just outside it. These scorpions have powerful pedipalps and a large sting that they use to catch their prey and to defend themselves, and can be quite aggressive if provoked.

Food and water
- Live insects
- Water sponge

Routine care
Daily: Mist one end of the enclosure's substrate with water to keep it damp, and ensure that the water sponge is moist

Weekly: Introduce one live insect into enclosure, and remove any dead or uneaten insects. This species may not eat every time food is offered.

Sexing
Male: Slender body in comparison to female, with a longer fifth tail segment and divided genital operculum

Female: Larger bodied, with a fused genital operculum

Breeding
The male should be introduced to the female in an enclosure large enough to allow him to be released well away from her. A male interested in mating will seek out the female and begin making jerky movements. This species will perform the classic scorpion mating dance, and once mating is completed the male should be separated again to ensure his safety. Inland Robust Scorpions have a very long gestation period. The body of the female will gradually become rounder and she will give birth 18 months after mating. At this point, remove any live food immediately if she doesn't feed, to prevent interference during the birth. They will give birth to about 20 babies, which ride on their mother's back for the first few weeks of life. Once they leave their mother they should be removed and housed individually, the toolbox method of housing is ideal (p. 158). They will take about 4 years to mature.

Lifespan
10–15 years

Captive behaviour
These scorpions are most active at night and will come to the entrance of their burrow and wait to ambush insects moving by. They will sometimes come completely out of the burrow and hunt around the enclosure. When they capture an insect they sometimes take many hours to eat it, and will sit quite still while they feed. It is common to see them digging as they expand their burrow.

Housing

 Enclosure: Terrarium or glass tank; minimum size 30 cm H × 35 cm W × 20 cm D

Substrate: Sand, minimum depth 8 cm; maintain a damp and a dry end

Enclosure fit-out: Burrow, bark or flat rocks as shelters

 Individual

 18–24°C

 Humidity 40–60%

 None required, dislikes bright light

Special considerations
If you notice sand clumping on the feet of your scorpion it may be that the substrate is too wet. The scorpion's feet can be cleaned by placing it in a small container on paper towel and gently washing off the sand with a spray bottle in the 'stream' setting. Minimise disturbance if you have a mother with young on her back, as she may consume her offspring if distressed.

Compatibility with other species
Not recommended

Species with similar care requirements
Flinders Ranges Scorpions (*Urodacus elongatus*), and other desert scorpions (*U. armatus, U. novaehollandiae*)

Rainforest Scorpion *Liocheles waigiensis*

Level of difficulty

| 1 | 2 | 3 | 4 | 5 |

beginner   advanced

These flat-bodied scorpions are found in the rainforests of northern Australia. They live in cracks and gaps in rocks, where they lie in wait to ambush passing insects. They grow up to about 60 mm long, but have a different build from most other Australian species. Rainforest Scorpions have extremely large pedipalps for their size but a very small sting. It is likely that most of their prey is simply overpowered and killed by crushing rather than by using venom. They are quite docile scorpions, and have become popular with invertebrate keepers. They are one of the most common species being sold commercially in Australia.

Food and water
- Live crickets or cockroaches
- Water sponge

Routine care
Daily: Mist the substrate with water to keep it damp. Ensure water sponge is moist.

Weekly: Introduce one live insect per scorpion into enclosure, and remove waste and any dead or uneaten insects. This species may not eat every time food is offered.

Sexing
Male: Slender body with much longer tail, larger and longer pedipalps; obvious tooth and notch in chelae

Female: Robust body, and relatively short tail

Breeding
A male interested in breeding will make jerky movements as he approaches the female, but if your scorpions are housed as a pair it is sometimes hard to know if courtship has occurred. If mating is observed the male should be removed to prevent him interfering with the birth. The gestation period of these scorpions is at least 9 months and up to 20 babies are born. They ride on their mother's back for several weeks and may stay close to her for up to 2 months after birth. They should be separated into their own enclosures once they leave her and are noticed moving around the enclosure on their own. They can be housed using the toolbox method (p.158, and require very small insects as food.

Lifespan
5–10 years

Captive behaviour
These scorpions are inactive during the day but at night (or in subdued light) they will emerge from their shelter, often with just their claws visible to wait for food. Sometimes they will actively forage around the enclosure, feeling around and under objects as they go. If your scorpion is out in bright daylight conditions it may indicate that it has a health problem.

Housing
 Enclosure: Terrarium or custom; minimum size 20 cm H × 30 cm W × 20 cm D

Substrate: Coco-peat or sphagnum moss, minimum depth 3 cm; moist throughout

Enclosure fit-out: Flat rocks or bark as shelters

 Individual or pair

 24–28°C

 Humidity 60–90%

 None required, dislikes bright light

Special considerations
Although these scorpions are reluctant to sting, they have a reasonably powerful 'pinch'. They are good climbers, and will cling onto rough objects but cannot climb up smooth surfaces such as glass.

Compatibility with other species
Not recommended

Species with similar care requirements
None

Spider Hunting Scorpion *Isometroides vescus*

Level of difficulty | 1 | 2 | 3 | **4** | 5 |
beginner   advanced

These slender scorpions are expert spider hunters. They specialise in capturing burrowing species, such as trapdoor and wolf spiders, but will also feed on a variety of insects. They are found in the arid areas of southern and central Australia and grow to about 45 mm from head to tail. Spider Hunting Scorpions are quite distinctive, with slender delicate pedipalps and a large tail and sting. With this body form they rely more on venom than on sheer crushing power to kill their prey. They grip and hold their prey at arm's length then sting it. Spider Hunting Scorpions are nocturnal, sheltering beneath objects such as rocks during the day and wandering in search of prey at night.

Housing

Enclosure: Terrarium or custom; minimum size 15 cm H × 20 cm W × 12 cm D

Substrate: Sand or gravel, minimum depth 2 cm; dry throughout

Enclosure fit-out: Small flat rocks or bark as shelters

 Individual

 18–24°C

 Humidity 40–60%

 None required, dislikes bright light

SCORPIONS

Food and water
- Small live insects
- Water sponge

Routine care
Daily: Lightly mist spray the shelters and substrate with water, ensure water sponge is moist

Weekly: Introduce one live insect into enclosure, and remove waste and any dead or uneaten insects. This species may not eat every time food is offered.

Sexing
Male: Slender body, with a longer fifth tail segment; longer more numerous pectinal teeth

Female: Robust body, pectinal teeth relatively small

Breeding
Feed the female well before introducing the male into her enclosure. Watch your scorpions closely during this phase. The male should investigate the enclosure, and his initial reactions to her and vice versa are very important. If neither scorpion is interested in mating, one may be killed and eaten by the other. Indications of interest include the male approaching the female, remaining near her, or making jerky, vibrating motions. It may take a long time for anything to happen, and it may happen overnight when you are not watching, so sometimes it may be hard to know if successful courtship has actually occurred. If mating does occur, the male should be removed from the enclosure. The female will gradually become rounder in the body, until she gives birth several months later. The live-born babies will ride on their mother's back for several weeks. Once they leave their mother the young should be removed and housed individually, the toolbox method (p.158) of housing is ideal.

Lifespan
3–10 years

Captive behaviour
These scorpions are inactive during the day, but at night (or in subdued light) they will actively forage around their enclosure. They will use their pedipalps to feel under objects, checking around for hidden insects. If they do detect food they will often freeze and open their pedipalps wide before they attack.

Special considerations
The venom of this species is most likely stronger than that of most other Australian scorpions and may cause painful effects, so care should be taken when keeping them. Females with young on their backs may eat their own babies if stressed or disturbed frequently during this time.

Compatibility with other species
Not recommended

Species with similar care requirements
Marbled scorpions (*Lychas* species)

Centipedes are venomous predators and have specialised
legs under their head called 'venom claws'.

Centipedes Class: Chilopoda

Estimated number of species in Australia: 150

Centipedes are fast becoming popular with **invertebrate** keepers. With their many legs, elongated body and rapid movements, they are very different from other invertebrate groups and very exciting to watch. Centipedes are found throughout Australia in a wide range of habitats that include deserts, tropical rainforests and even suburban backyards. They are **nocturnal** hunters, preying mainly on invertebrates, but in the wild the biggest species can capture frogs and small reptiles. Australian centipedes are **venomous**, and although the venom is not considered life-threatening to people centipedes are capable of giving a very painful bite. The largest centipedes should be treated with particular care, as their bite may cause more severe effects.

The name centipede suggests that they have exactly 100 legs, but this is not the case as most have fewer than 50, while a few species have more than 300! Centipedes have one pair of legs attached to each body segment, which makes them easy to tell apart from millipedes, which have two. There are a number of groups of centipedes in Australia, many of which are tiny. This chapter will focus on the two groups that are regularly kept: the largest centipedes (Scolopendrids) and the house centipedes (Scutigerids).

The most popular centipedes in captivity, the Scolopendrids, have a total of 21–23 pairs of legs. They have a single claw at the end of each leg. House centipedes have a cluster of tiny hairs instead, which helps them to grip smooth surfaces. All centipedes also have two pairs of specialised legs. One pair, the anal legs, are at the rear of their body. These anal legs protrude and are used for sensing and defence. The other pair of specialised legs are under the head. These are known as **venom claws** and are used as fangs. Centipedes only have tiny eyes, so they mainly use their antennae to sense their way around. They breathe through **spiracles**, which can be seen down either side of their body.

Sexing centipedes visually is extremely difficult, and without having both sexes to compare it is almost impossible. Males tend to have thinner bodies and the anal legs are longer than those of females.

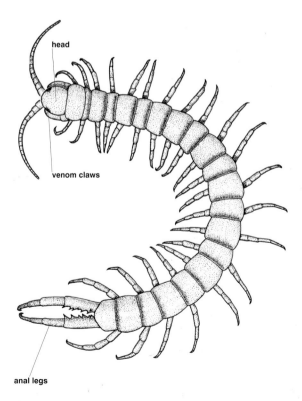

head

venom claws

anal legs

The courtship of centipedes begins with a pair gently tapping each other with their antennae. The male then either spins a web mat on which to place his **spermatophore** for the female to pick up, or he deposits it directly onto her genital opening. The method varies with different species. Female centipedes lay eggs, and usually do this in moist, dark places such as under a rock or log. Some species lay their eggs singly and bury them before leaving, while others will actually curl around their eggs to protect them, staying with the eggs until they hatch. Young centipedes look like miniatures of their parents when they hatch, although some species do not initially have as many pairs of legs, and gain them as they grow. They **moult** their **exoskeletons** to grow, and do so about 10 times, depending on the species, before reaching maturity. Centipedes usually eat their exoskeleton after they moult, so it is rare to find the old exoskeletons lying around.

Centipedes are predators that seek out their prey using chemical receptors in their antennae. They hunt systematically, working their way across the ground and sensing as they go. Some are particularly fond of burrowing spiders. Many centipedes will raise the front half of their body off the ground as they hunt, with their antennae high in the air sensing for prey. Food is caught by using a combination of speed, strength and venom, and the prey is gripped tightly by many legs as it is bitten. Sometimes centipedes can catch many small animals at once; feeding on one while holding the others tightly to its body with its legs. Centipedes feed using the cutting and grinding action of their special mouthparts, and can consume most parts of their prey.

Handling centipedes can be difficult due to their speed, body shape and number of legs. They tend to cling to objects very well, and they may be damaged if you attempt to prise them off. Never do this with your hands; the best way to pick up the larger centipedes is with padded forceps or kitchen tongs. Smaller delicate species such as house centipedes should be ushered into a jar with a soft tool such as a small paintbrush.

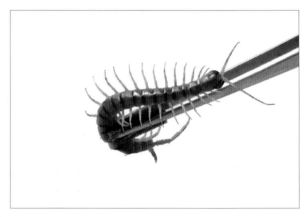

A centipede is held using padded forceps.

Several species of centipedes are commonly kept in Australia, and sold commercially. They require secure housing, and if kept properly are relatively long-living invertebrates.

Banded Desert Centipede *Scolopendra morsitans*

Level of difficulty

| 1 | 2 | **3** | 4 | 5 |

beginner   advanced

Banded Desert Centipedes are found throughout the arid parts of Australia, and are one the largest species in the country, growing to 175 mm. They shelter from the dry heat in narrow underground tunnels that they dig with their venom claws and legs. The air in the tunnels is cool and moist, and provides the environment to which they are best suited. These centipedes emerge after dark – particularly on warm wet nights – to hunt for food. Their diet consists mainly of other invertebrates, particularly burrowing spiders. They are very fast centipedes that cruise effortlessly over the ground, stopping to check cracks and burrows in which prey may be hiding.

Food and water
- Live crickets and cockroaches
- Water sponge

Routine care
Daily: Mist spray the substrate at one end of the enclosure to keep it damp and top-up the water sponge

Twice weekly: Feed by introducing a live insect into enclosure. Remove any dead or uneaten insects.

Sexing
Male: No obvious characteristics; often have longer anal legs than females

Female: No obvious characteristics; often have larger and wider bodies than males

Breeding
There is little information available on the breeding of these centipedes. As they are difficult to sex, there is always the risk of putting two of the same sex together. Be prepared to separate them quickly to prevent cannibalism. Feed your female well before pairing her up with a male, and use an enclosure that gives both sexes plenty of space and a number of shelters to choose from. Watch them closely after introducing the male. If they show any aggression, it is best to separate them immediately. Gentle interaction such as antennae touching is an indication of courtship. If mating occurs, the male will transfer a spermatophore to the female. Once they separate they should be housed individually again. If mating was successful, the female will lay eggs and guard them until well after they have hatched. It is very important not to disturb a female with eggs or young as she may eat them. Separate the juveniles as soon

as they leave their mother. They can be housed on their own in jars and fed tiny insects such as hatchling crickets.

Lifespan
2–5 years

Captive behaviour
These centipedes are most active at night, but may come out during the day if live food is introduced. They may get used to light and remain in a visible position if they feel safe, which they often do when they have their body pressed up against a solid object. This can be used to your advantage and their shelter can be set up against a glass wall so that they can be seen easily. When they are hungry, these centipedes will actively hunt around their enclosure, and this is the perfect time to feed them.

Housing

 Enclosure: Terrarium or glass tank; minimum size 20 cm H × 30 cm W × 20 cm D

Substrate: Sand, or coco-peat and sand mix, minimum depth 5 cm; maintain a damp and a dry end

Enclosure fit-out: Flat rocks or bark as shelters

 Individual

 18–24°C

 Humidity 60–70%

 None required, dislikes bright light

Special considerations
Banded Desert Centipedes are very fast and venomous, so be careful when interacting with them. They are experts at squeezing through small gaps, and although they cannot climb smooth surfaces, they can reach up enclosure walls to almost their full body length.

Compatibility with other species
Not recommended

Species with similar care requirements
Other centipedes from arid areas

Giant Rainforest Centipede *Ethmostigmus rubripes*

Level of difficulty 1 2 3 **4** 5
beginner   advanced

This spectacular species is Australia's largest centipede, and some individuals grow up to 140 mm in length. They live in the wet forests of northern Australia, where they shelter by day under logs, rocks and leaf litter. At night they venture out to feed and capture animals smaller than themselves, including insects, spiders, scorpions, other centipedes and even small reptiles and frogs. They are very fast and are excellent climbers, having no trouble foraging through the maze of roots, leaves and branches on the rainforest floor. They are becoming popular as pets and are being sold commercially.

Food and water
- Live crickets and cockroaches, dead 'pinky' mice
- Water sponge

Routine care
Daily: Mist spray one end of the enclosure's substrate with water to keep it damp.

Twice weekly: Feed by introducing a live insect into enclosure. A dead 'pinky' mouse can be offered occasionally using forceps. Remove any food waste.

Sexing
Male: No obvious characteristics; often have longer anal legs than females

Female: No obvious characteristics; often have larger and wider bodies than males

Breeding
Very little is known about breeding Giant Rainforest Centipedes. Because of the difficulty in sexing them, there is always the risk of putting two of the same sex together. This may end in cannibalism if you are not quick to separate them. Feed your pair well before putting them together, and use an enclosure that gives both plenty of space and a number of shelters to choose from. Watch them closely after introducing them. If there is any aggression separate them immediately. Delicate interaction such as antennae touching is a good sign. This touching is part of courtship and should lead to the male transferring a spermatophore to the female. Separate your centipedes after they have moved apart and seem disinterested in each other. The female will lay eggs and guard them until well after they have hatched. It is very important not to disturb a female with eggs or young as she may eat them. Separate the young as soon as they leave their mother, and house them individually in jars. They should be fed tiny insects such as hatchling crickets.

Lifespan
3–5 years

Captive behaviour
Giant Rainforest Centipedes are most active at night in captivity and in the wild, but may come out during the day if live food is introduced. Some individuals may get used to light and remain in a visible position if they feel safe, which they often do when they have their body pressed up against a solid object. This can be used to your advantage and their 'shelter' can be set up against a glass wall so that they can be seen easily. When they are hungry they will actively forage around the enclosure, and this is the perfect time to introduce their live food.

Housing
 Enclosure: Terrarium or custom; minimum size 30 cm H × 35 cm W × 20 cm D

Substrate: Coco-peat or sphagnum moss, minimum 2 cm; damp throughout

Enclosure fit-out: A substrate depth of 5 cm, or a shallow substrate with a flat rock or piece of bark for the centipede to shelter under

 Individual

 24–26°C

 Humidity 60–90%

 None required, dislikes bright light

Special considerations
Giant Rainforest Centipedes are very fast, nervous and venomous, so be careful when interacting with them. Bites from this species have caused severe pain that lasts several days. They are experts at squeezing through small gaps, and although they cannot climb smooth surfaces they can reach up walls of enclosures to almost their full body length.

Compatibility with other species
Not recommended

Species with similar care requirements
Other centipedes from rainforest areas

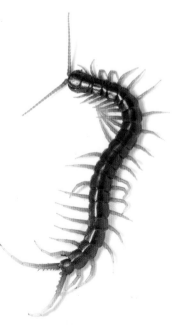

House Centipede *Allothereua maculata*

Level of difficulty

(1 | **2** | 3 | 4 | 5)

beginner   advanced

House Centipedes are amazing invertebrates. They have 15 pairs of fine, long legs and seem to float along like a hairy hovercraft. They are found throughout southern Australia and are commonly found in backyards, often sheltering under garden objects such as logs, rocks and pot plants. The name 'house centipede' comes from some of their overseas relatives, which are often found in houses. This species occasionally comes indoors, but is much happier outside. House Centipedes are predators and will chase down other small invertebrates for food. They are the only centipedes that have **compound eyes**, and rely on their very long antennae to sense their way around. They are venomous, but are not regarded as dangerous to humans.

Food and water
- Live crickets and cockroaches
- Water sponge

Routine care
Daily: Mist spray one end of the enclosure's substrate with water to keep it damp

Twice weekly: Feed by introducing small live insects into the enclosure and remove any dead or uneaten insects

Sexing
Male: No obvious characteristics; often have longer anal legs than females

Female: No obvious characteristics; often have larger and wider bodies than males

Breeding
House Centipedes are very difficult to sex, so keeping a number together in a group is probably the easiest way to breed them. Ensure that there are enough shelters in the enclosure for all individuals. Any delicate interaction between two centipedes such as antennae touching is a sign that mating may take place. If the female is receptive the male will leave his spermatophore on the ground for her to pick up. If you do see any breeding behaviour like this, or a female laying her eggs, it would be wise to remove the others. House Centipedes lay eggs individually into the substrate, and once the female has finished laying her eggs she can be removed to prevent her eating the young when they hatch. Incubation times are not known, so watching for hatchlings is important. The hatchlings are very small and can be housed together

and fed tiny insects such as hatchling crickets. Young House Centipedes do not have all 15 pairs of legs when they hatch, and so they look a little different from the adults.

Lifespan
1–3 years

Captive behaviour
House Centipedes are most active at night, but may come out during the day if live food is introduced. They may get used to light and remain in a visible position if they feel safe, which they often do when they are able to cling underneath a solid object. This can be used to your advantage and their shelter can be set up against a glass wall so that they can be seen.

Housing:

 Enclosure: Terrarium; minimum size 20 cm H × 30 cm W × 20 cm D

Substrate: Sand or coco-peat and sand mix, minimum depth 2 cm; maintain a damp and a dry end

Enclosure fit-out: Pieces of bark for shelter

 Individual or group

 18–24°C

 Humidity 50–60%

 None required, dislikes bright light

Special considerations
House Centipedes are very fast and can climb relatively smooth surfaces, but usually not plastic or glass.

Compatibility with other species
Larger herbivorous invertebrates, such as grasshoppers, phasmids and snails

Species with similar care requirements
Other species of house centipedes

Rainforest millipedes are the largest in Australia and play
an important role as recyclers in the rainforest.

Millipedes   Class: Diplopoda

Estimated number of species in Australia: 2000

Have you ever felt a millipede walk across your hand? It is a special experience to feel the many legs working in unison to move. Millipedes are often confused with centipedes but they are in a class of their own. Millipedes can be distinguished by having two pairs of legs on most body segments; centipedes have only one pair. Millipedes have a segmented body and short antennae. The name 'millipede' actually refers to 'thousand' in terms of the many legs, but they do not really have 1000 legs, the number of legs is always less. They are found in temperate and rainforest areas of Australia.

Many species of millipedes are a glossy black colour but some can be brown or red. The biggest Australian millipede can reach a length of 200 mm. When disturbed millipedes will secrete a yellow-brown liquid from along the sides of their body. This liquid is a defensive response to predators, it is foul tasting and many predators will not eat millipedes. If this liquid comes in contact with your skin it may stain it a brown colour for a couple of days. It has never been known to cause serious harm to people, although washing your hands and keeping them away from your mouth and eyes is recommended.

In this chapter we describe two broad groups of millipedes: the short, stout pill millipedes (Sphaerotheriida) that can curl up into a tight ball, and the longer, more slender millipedes. Both groups are fairly similar in their captive care, but breeding and sexing the two groups is different. There are a number of other distinct groups that are less suitable for keeping and so are not described here.

Millipedes are scavengers and **detritovores**; they eat soft vegetation such as decaying leaf litter, mosses and pollen. They often occur in undisturbed, deep leaf litter or other places that have composting plant material. Because of this fairly specific habitat requirement, this group of animals needs high humidity and minimal disturbance in their captive care. With the right care millipedes can live for long periods of time, and Australian rainforest millipedes (Rhinocricidae) can live for more than 10 years.

Identifying and sexing millipedes can be very difficult; often it is only achievable after the death of the animal. This is because the body parts that need to be looked at are under the body and extremely hard to see. You need to count body segments, number of legs per body segment or small reproductive organs. Looking at the underside of the millipede and making it uncurl can be distressing for the animal and cause premature death.

One way to minimise disturbance to your millipede is to place it on a piece of glass and look at it from below. A petri dish is perfect because it reduces the risk of the millipede walking off the glass and falling. If you can see and count body segments, longer millipedes can be sexed by looking at the seventh body segment. On this segment males have modified legs called **gonopods**, but females have functional walking legs. Males use their gonopods to transfer a **spermatophore** to the female during mating. Pill millipedes are a little different from other millipedes, and in males the last pair of legs are modified to clasp the female during mating and insert the spermatophore into her.

It is best to have a male and a female side by side when you start to identify sexes of this group.

There are certain times of the year when millipedes actively seek out mates and reproduce. This is the time they will be out wandering and you may see them in the wild. Females will lay clusters of eggs underground. The tiny white millipedes that emerge will have fewer legs than their parents; most will hatch with three or four pairs. They grow by undergoing a series of **moults**, and as they moult they develop more legs and segments. You rarely see a millipede moulting, as they tend to do it underground. Like the adults, juvenile millipedes will feed on decomposing material. There is evidence that millipedes will also feed on the waste of other millipedes. For this reason, if you have juveniles do not clean out the enclosure completely. Always leave at least half of the substrate to ensure the waste is left as food.

Millipedes, especially the rainforest varieties, are becoming a popular animal to keep. They require very little care and can be housed in groups. Their behaviour is wonderful to watch. Millipedes are **nocturnal** and displaying them successfully can be a challenge. Reversing the day and night cycle, providing red light or developing artificial burrows are three ways to overcome this problem. If you want to handle millipedes, pick them up gently out of the enclosure and place them on the hand. Wear disposable gloves if you want to avoid staining your hand. They will walk around the hand, but ensure they do not fall to the ground as this could damage your animal.

A millipede can be sexed easily in a petri dish.

Australian rainforest millipedes Rhinocricidae

Level of difficulty

| 1 | 2 | 3 | 4 | 5 |

beginner   advanced

Australian rainforest millipedes are the largest millipedes in Australia and can grow to a length of 200 mm. They are tropical and can be found in backyards of houses in northern Australia. It is also becoming quite common to see them for sale commercially. This family of millipedes is one that is commonly found in far north Queensland and in pet stores, but other millipedes can also look very similar. Their size and the fact they need minimal care makes them the perfect introductory animal to keep at home. They are a great educational tool as they are easy to handle and they have distinct body parts.

Housing

 Enclosure: Terrarium or custom; minimum size 20 cm H × 25 cm W × 15 cm D

Substrate: Coco-peat and pulpy wood, minimum depth 15 cm; damp throughout

Enclosure fit-out: Leaf litter

 Group

 20–28°C

 Humidity 70–90%

 None required, dislikes bright light

Food and water
- Fruit or vegetables, pulpy wood, millipede food
- Moisture in substrate

Routine care
Daily: Mist spray substrate to maintain humidity

Weekly: Replace fruit and vegetables and add a half teaspoon of millipede food

Yearly: Change 50% of substrate

Sexing
Male: The two pairs of legs on their seventh segment modified into gonopods

Female: Legs all the same

Note: The gonopods of young males will still be developing. The gonopods will not be as distinct as in larger males but will become larger with each moult.

Breeding
A male will wrap himself around the body of the female and deposit a spermatophore into her genital opening. The mated female will then lay clumps of eggs below the surface of the substrate. The juvenile millipedes that hatch from the eggs are white and have three pairs of legs. More legs and body segments will develop each time they moult. It takes at least 2 years for these millipedes to reach maturity. Do not separate millipedes into individual enclosures, as they feed on the scraps and wastes of others in the enclosure.

Lifespan
More than 10 years

Captive behaviour
Adults will bury themselves deep into the peat during the day and only leave tunnels as an indication of where they have been. Juveniles will be closer to the surface during the day, generally in the top 3 cm of substrate. During the night and in subdued lighting your millipedes will come up to the surface and feed.

Special considerations
Calcium provided in the diet appears to be an important factor in raising young millipedes. Feeding the millipede food described on p.173, cuttlebone or even chalk will help to maintain this important nutrient. Millipedes also need a relatively undisturbed and moist environment, so wherever possible reduce any digging through the substrate. When changing the food or substrate ensure you do not dispose of small juveniles with the waste material.

Compatibility with other species
Other rainforest herbivores

Species with similar care requirements
Other rainforest millipedes

MILLIPEDES

Pill millipedes Sphaerotheriida

Level of difficulty

| 1 | 2 | 3 | 4 | 5 |

beginner   advanced

Pill millipedes have the amazing ability to curl up into a tight ball if disturbed, so that they only expose the hard upper surface of the body and keep the head and legs safe. They can often be mistaken for slaters, because of their short body length. They have 11–13 body segments and 21 pairs of legs. They are less than 40 mm in length but have thicker-set bodies than other Australian millipedes. They are found throughout Australia in places where moist leaf litter is present. They are nocturnal but occasionally wander about on a warm overcast day.

Housing

Enclosure: Terrarium or custom; minimum size 20 cm H × 25 cm L × 15 cm W

Substrate: Coco-peat and pulpy wood, minimum depth 5 cm; damp throughout

Enclosure fit-out: Leaf litter

 Group

 22–26°C

 Humidity 60–80%

None required, dislikes bright light

Food and water
- Fruit or vegetables, pulpy wood, millipede food
- Moisture in substrate

Routine care
Daily: Mist spray substrate to maintain humidity

Weekly: Replace fruit and vegetables, and add a half teaspoon of millipede food

Yearly: Change 50% of substrate

Sexing
Male: Last two pairs of legs modified into claspers

Female: All legs the same

Breeding
A male will use his claspers to grasp the female. He will then deposit a spermatophore into her genital opening. After mating the female will lay single eggs coated in faecal material just beneath the substrate surface. The juveniles that hatch will be tiny and have only three pairs of legs. They develop more legs and body segments with each successive moult. Keep the young millipedes together in the main enclosure, so that they can feed on the scraps and waste of others.

Lifespan
Unknown, greater than 2 years

Captive behaviour
Adults will bury themselves into the substrate during the day and only leave tunnels to indicate they have been active at night, when they come up to the surface and feed. Juveniles will always be close to the surface, generally in the top 2 cm of substrate.

Special considerations
Calcium in the diet appears to be an important factor in raising millipedes. Using the millipede food described on p.173, cuttlebone or even chalk will provide this important nutrient. Millipedes also need a moist and relatively undisturbed environment, so minimise the amount of digging through the substrate. When changing the food ensure that you do not dispose of juveniles with the waste.

Compatibility with other species
Other herbivorous invertebrates

Species with similar care requirements
None

Portuguese Millipedes *Ommatoiulus moreleti*

Level of difficulty

1 | 2 | 3 | 4 | 5
beginner — advanced

Portuguese Millipedes were introduced to South Australia from Portugal and Spain in the 1950s. Since then they have spread to Western Australia, the Australian Capital Territory, Victoria and Tasmania. They can occur in plague numbers and have even been known to stop trains! In 2002, trains west of Melbourne had to be stopped because the numbers of squashed millipedes on the tracks resulted in the trains not getting any traction. These millipedes grow to 45 mm and are often found in gardens around southern cities. Their numbers can explode during autumn and spring and they will invade houses. They can be distinguished from native millipedes by the characteristic way in which they curl flat. Native millipedes from this region form looser coils and are rougher skinned.

Food and water
- Fruit or vegetables, pulpy wood, millipede food
- Moisture in substrate

Routine care
Daily: Mist spray substrate to maintain humidity

Weekly: Replace fruit and vegetables and add a half teaspoon millipede food

Yearly: Change 50% of substrate

Sexing
Male: Legs on seventh segment modified into gonopods

Female: Legs all the same

Note: The gonopods of young males will still be developing. The gonopods will not be as distinct as in older males, but will become larger with each moult.

Breeding
A male will wrap himself around the body of the female and deposit a spermatophore into her genital opening. The mated female will then lay clumps of eggs just below the surface of the substrate. The juvenile millipedes that hatch have three pairs of legs. They will develop more legs and body segments with each successive moult. It takes 2 years for these millipedes to reach maturity. Keep the millipedes in the main enclosure, so that they can feed on the scraps and waste of others.

Lifespan
2–3 years

Captive behaviour
Adults will bury themselves deep in the substrate or hide under the shelter during the day. Juveniles will be close to the substrate surface during the day, generally in the top 2 cm of substrate. At night they come up to the surface and feed.

Housing

 Enclosure: Terrarium or custom; minimum size 15 cm H × 20 cm W × 10 cm D

Substrate: Coco-peat and pulpy wood, minimum depth 5 cm; damp throughout

Enclosure fit-out: Leaf litter, bark shelter

 Group

 18–26°C

 Humidity 60–80%

 None required, dislikes bright light

Special considerations
Maintaining calcium in the diet appears to be an important factor in raising young millipedes. Using the millipede food described on p.173, cuttlebone or even chalk will provide this important nutrient. Millipedes also need a moist and relatively undisturbed environment, so wherever possible minimise the amount of digging through the enclosure. When changing the food or substrate ensure that you do not dispose of small juveniles with the waste.

Compatibility with other species
Other temperate zone herbivores

Species with similar care requirements
Other temperate zone millipede species

Snails and slugs have eyes on the tips of their longest pair of tentacles.

Snails and slugs Subclass: Pulmonata

Estimated number of species in Australia: approximately 1081

Gliding along on a bed of slime at speeds of up to 0.05 km an hour does not make snails and slugs sound like very exciting animals to keep. Snails and slugs are often seen in our backyards, but we do not appreciate just how incredible they are, or how different from most other animals.

Snails and slugs belong to a group of animals called **gastropods**, which means 'stomach foot' and refers to their soft body, called a foot, on which they move and which contains all their organs. Snails and slugs are very similar in body structure, but vary in the size of their shells. Snails have a large shell into which their entire body can retreat. Slugs generally have either no shell, or the shell is reduced to a hard plate buried within the mantle. Most people are familiar with these, but there are others – the semi-slugs, which share the characteristics of both snails and slugs. Semi-slugs have shells that are too small to house their entire bodies.

Most snails, slugs and semi-slugs have two pairs of tentacles on their head – the large pair contains the eyes, the smaller pair are feelers. Some species only have one pair of tentacles.

Most of the major organs of these animals are located just behind the head. This is where you will find their respiratory (pneumostome), reproductive (genital pore) and digestive openings. (Yes, the anus of a snail or slug is just behind its head!) You will often see brightly coloured poo being excreted from this area after it has had a meal of carrots and cucumber!

Snails and slugs have intriguing modes of reproduction, as they are **hermaphrodites** – each individual has both male and female reproductive organs. Hermaphroditic snails and slugs are not able to fertilise themselves – they still need to find a mate to breed. When they mate, they exchange sperm either by shooting a small dart into each other or via a penis. Both individuals are capable of laying eggs after mating. Snails and slugs have extensive mating rituals. These involve circling around each other, touching with their tentacles and even biting, before they twist their bodies together. This ritual can last for about an hour, and mating itself can last up to 8 hours.

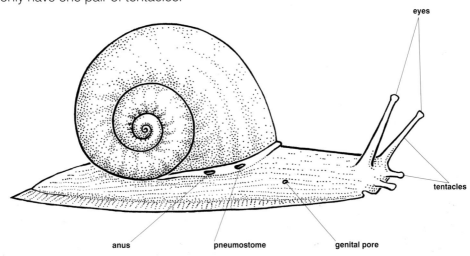

eyes

tentacles

anus   pneumostome   genital pore

Eggs are laid somewhere moist, either in a shallow burrow in the soil or under rocks and logs. They are creamy white and can be laid singly or in clusters. Tiny miniatures of the adults will emerge from the eggs and continue to grow until they reach maturity. Some species do not lay eggs but give birth to live young. The juveniles can take between 4 months to 4 years to mature, depending on the species. Some snails have been known to live for 12 years.

Many snails and slugs are **herbivorous** and will feed on plant matter or fungi, other species are **carnivorous** and will prey upon other **invertebrates**. They feed using a **radula** – a tongue-like structure covered by rows of rasping teeth. You can see these teeth in action when your animal is moving across a clear surface.

Snails have been bred in captivity for a long time for commercial uses. The Common Garden Snail (*Cantareus aspersa*) is bred for the hospitality industry and sold as escargot. Most children have collected a snail or slug from the backyard to keep as a pet, but until fairly recently snails and slugs have not been kept in captivity for display. They can make an interesting and unusual display if their enclosure is kept moist enough to keep them active and visible. A snail that has retreated into its shell is not very exciting, and a slug that has sheltered under a log is not a great display, but if the enclosure is kept wet and there is food to forage on, your gastropods will display well. Snails and slugs are able to be housed with most other invertebrates, except carnivorous snails that prey on other snails.

It is much easier to handle a snail or slug if you have a wet hand, and they will happily cruise around on your skin. Both snails and slugs will retract their tentacles and heads into their bodies if they are startled, so handle them with slow gentle movements.

Black Carnivorous Snail *Victaphanta atramentaria*

Level of difficulty

| 1 | 2 | 3 | **4** | 5 |

beginner   advanced

Imagine a snail chasing down and eating another animal. It seems laughable, but that's exactly how the Black Carnivorous Snail hunts. This is the largest carnivorous snail in Victoria, growing to 35 mm in shell diameter. It is a specialist predator that feeds on other soft-bodied invertebrates such as worms and other molluscs. It has a large glossy black shell that gradually becomes lighter to a yellowish white at its centre. The body is black with an orange-red frill around the foot. The Black Carnivorous Snail is found in temperate rainforests of eastern Victoria, south of the Great Dividing Range, where it shelters in deep leaf litter.

Food and water
- Earthworms and/or juvenile Common Garden Snails
- Moisture in substrate

Routine care
Daily: Mist spray enclosure and substrate to keep substrate moist

Twice weekly: Feed your snail live earthworms or juvenile snails by releasing them near your snail

As required: Substrate should be replaced at least every 6 months, or when it becomes very sodden and smelly

Sexing
These snails are hermaphrodites

Breeding
Adults need to be introduced to each other after they have both fed, as they may attempt to eat each other. Not much is known about their breeding, but like other snails they will pair up and exchange sperm so that both are capable of laying eggs. If mating has been observed, it is wise to separate individuals to prevent cannibalism. Eggs will possibly be laid beneath deep leaf litter in cool

substrate. Hatching times of eggs will vary, depending on substrate temperature and humidity. Juveniles can be difficult to raise. Offer them chopped earthworms on a flat dish. If you do see eggs or young in the enclosure, move the adult to a separate enclosure.

Lifespan
2–4 years

Captive behaviour
By day Black Carnivorous Snails will shelter in leaf litter or under any shelter you provide. They are most active at night, when they feed and move around the enclosure. They tend to stay on the ground and they do not usually climb vertical surfaces.

Housing

 Enclosure: Terrarium, custom or glass tank; minimum size 15 cm H × 20 cm W × 12 cm D

Substrate: Coco-peat or sphagnum moss, minimum depth 3 cm; damp to wet throughout

Enclosure fit-out: Deep leaf litter or plastic containers to shelter under

 Individual

 12–20°C

 Humidity 60–80%

 None required, dislikes bright light

Special considerations
These snails are sensitive to constant warm temperatures. Ensure your enclosure does not overheat.

Compatibility with other species
Not recommended

Species with similar care requirements
Otway Black Snail (*Victaphanta compacta*) which is a protected, endangered species

Common Garden Snail *Cantareus aspersa*

Level of difficulty

1	2	3	4	5

beginner   advanced

If you've ever had escargot in Australia, chances are you've eaten a Common Garden Snail. This species is farmed commercially for the hospitality industry. It was introduced to Australia from Europe in the early 1800s. Frequently found in gardens around Australia, these snails love feeding on vegetable gardens and newly planted seedlings. As a result, they are considered pests. They are a medium sized snail, growing to a shell diameter of 35 mm. Common Garden Snails are most active in wet weather, when it is easy for them to move around without the risk of drying out. When the weather is hot and dry, the snails will retreat into their shells and create a mucus cover – an **epiphragm** – over their shell opening to prevent them from drying out. In dry weather snails can often be found sheltering in any crevice they can find.

Food and water
- Fruit and vegetables (especially cucumber), mollusc mix and cuttlebone
- Moisture in substrate

Routine care
Daily: Replace fruit and vegetables, remove uneaten food and waste products, and mist spray the substrate

Weekly: Offer mollusc mix as an alternative to fruit and vegetables

As required: Substrate should be replaced at least every 6 months, or when it becomes very sodden and smelly. Replace cuttlebone as it is eaten.

Sexing
These snails are hermaphrodites

Breeding
Adults will pair up and exchange sperm so that both snails are capable of laying eggs. These snails are fertilised by a small sperm-containing dart that is shot into their body by their mate. This usually happens at night in late spring and summer. Eggs will be laid in a shallow burrow 5–10 days after mating. The opaque white eggs are 3–4 mm in diameter and can range in number from 40–90 eggs. Hatching times of eggs vary, depending on substrate temperature and humidity, but will generally occur in about 18–21 days. The snail hatchlings have translucent shells and begin feeding immediately. They are mature when the shell develops a flare or lip at the opening. There is no further growth once this lip is formed, but it can take from 4 months to 2 years to develop.

Lifespan
Up to 12 years

Captive behaviour
Common Garden Snails are only active if their enclosures are very damp or wet. If your enclosure is too dry, the snails will cease activity and retreat into their shells. Your snails will also cease activity if the temperature in their enclosure gets too cool or too warm. They will feed both day and night, and will explore all surfaces of their enclosure.

Housing

 Enclosure: Terrarium, custom or glass tank; minimum size 15 cm H × 20 cm W × 12 cm D

Substrate: Coco-peat or sphagnum moss, minimum depth 5 cm; damp to wet throughout

Enclosure fit-out: Leaves or plastic containers to shelter under

 Group

 16–24°C

 Humidity 60–80%

 No specialised lighting required

Special considerations
If snails do not have access to a source of calcium such as found in mollusc mix or cuttlebone, their shells may become brittle and break easily.

Compatibility with other species
Temperate zone herbivorous invertebrates

Species with similar care requirements
Other garden snails

Giant Panda Snail *Hedleyella falconeri*

Level of difficulty

1	2	3	4	5

beginner — advanced

Giant Panda Snails, which can have a shell diameter of 100 mm, are Australia's largest snail. They are most active in wet weather, and are found in the leaf litter in the forests around the border of New South Wales and Queensland. These nocturnal, ground-dwelling snails shelter in damp places under logs and piles of leaves during the day. They are active after heavy rains and you would be lucky to see one in the wild. They have two pairs of dark tentacles.

Housing

 Enclosure: Terrarium, custom or glass tank; minimum size 30 cm H × 20 cm W × 20 cm D

Substrate: Coco-peat or sphagnum moss, minimum depth 10 cm; damp to wet throughout

Enclosure fit-out: Large leaves or plastic containers to shelter under

 Group

 18–24°C

 Humidity 60–80%

 No specialised lighting required

Food and water
- Fruit and vegetables (especially cucumber), mollusc mix and cuttlebone
- Moisture in substrate

Routine care
Daily: Replace fruit and vegetables, remove uneaten food and waste products, and mist spray the substrate

Weekly: Offer mollusc mix as an alternative to fruit and vegetables

As required: Substrate should be replaced at least every 6 months, or when it becomes very sodden and smelly. Replace cuttlebone as it is eaten.

Sexing
These snails are hermaphrodites

Breeding
Giant Panda Snails kept in a group will pair up if a willing mate is encountered. Mating will take place at night, with the two snails exchanging sperm. Both individuals are able to produce eggs. The creamy white eggs will be laid in clusters of 15–20 eggs. It takes 3–4 days to lay the eggs in a shallow burrow about 5 cm deep in the substrate, which is then covered in leaf litter. Eggs are 18 mm in diameter and take about 40 days to hatch. When young hatch from the eggs their shells are translucent. In the wild, mating and egg laying will occur in late summer, when it is warm and humid. In captivity it may occur at any time of the year if these conditions are replicated.

Lifespan
2–8 years

Captive behaviour
Giant Panda Snails are most active at night, and this is when they will feed. During the day they will retreat into their shells and shelter under leaf litter or anywhere that is dark and damp. These snails will sometimes feed during the day in low lighting conditions. They are generally ground dwelling. If your snail has burrowed, it may be an indication that it is laying eggs.

Special considerations
If snails do not have access to a source of calcium such as mollusc mix or cuttlebone their shells may become brittle and break easily. Giant Panda Snails cannot tolerate constant high temperatures, so if you have raised the temperature for breeding, make sure you lower it again.

Compatibility with other species
Subtropical zone herbivorous invertebrates

Species with similar care requirements
Mitchell's Rainforest Snail (*Thersites mitchellae*)

Leopard Slug *Limax maximus*

Level of difficulty

| 1 | 2 | 3 | 4 | 5 |

beginner   advanced

Leopard Slugs are spectacular slugs that grow to about 200 mm in length. They have been introduced to Australia from Europe. They have a mantle on their back that covers a hard plate that was once a shell, and an obvious respiratory opening that looks like a hole on the right-hand side of their foot. Leopard Slugs are found all over Australia, and are common in backyards after rain. They feed mainly on fungi, plants and dead animal matter, and occasionally they will prey on other slugs.

Food and water
- Fruit and vegetables (especially cucumber) and mollusc mix
- Moisture in substrate

Routine care
Daily: Replace fruit and vegetables, remove uneaten food and waste products, and mist spray the substrate

Weekly: Offer mollusc mix as an alternative to fruit and vegetables

As required: Substrate should be replaced at least every 6 months, or when it becomes very sodden and smelly

Sexing
These slugs are hermaphrodites

Breeding
Two slugs that are both ready to mate will become entwined as they hang from a structure on a thread of mucus that can be up to a metre long. Mating will take place at the end of this thread. Each slug will extend its reproductive organ, which is translucent blue/white and emerges from behind the head. The reproductive organs of both slugs also intertwine and flange out as the slugs exchange spermatophores. Once mating is finished, the slugs will climb back up the mucus thread, eating it as they go. Leopard Slug eggs are clear and are laid in the soil in groups of up to 100 eggs. The eggs take up to 20 days to hatch, and the young slugs that emerge look like miniature versions of their parents, without the obvious spotted markings.

Lifespan
2–4 years

Captive behaviour
Leopard Slugs will explore all surfaces of their enclosure. They are active both by day and night and will leave a slimy trail in their wake. They will find a moist secluded area to rest in.

Housing

 Enclosure: Terrarium, custom or glass tank; minimum size 15 cm H × 15 cm W × 15 cm D

Substrate: Coco-peat or sphagnum moss, minimum depth 5 cm; damp to wet throughout

Enclosure fit-out: Leaves or plastic containers to shelter under

 Group

 18–24°C

 Humidity 60–80%

 No specialised lighting required

Special considerations
If the conditions in your enclosure become too hot and/or dry, your slug will not be active, will not feed and could possibly die. Young slugs can often get thrown out with leftover food, so check all dishes you remove from the enclosure. Slug substrates can get dirty very quickly and may need regular changes.

Compatibility with other species
Other herbivorous invertebrates

Species with similar care requirements
Great Yellow Slug (*Limacus flava*)

Rainforest Snail *Hadra webbi*

Level of difficulty

1	2	3	4	5

beginner   advanced

The Rainforest Snail is one of the largest snails in Australia, growing to 70 mm in shell diameter. They are found in the tropical rainforests of northern Australia, and can be found in the leaf litter or on the trunks of trees. They will often emerge from their leafy shelter after heavy rains. They are **omnivorous** and feed on plant matter and fungi, and sometimes even dead animals.

Housing

 Enclosure: Terrarium, custom or glass tank; minimum size 20 cm H × 30 cm W × 20 cm D

Substrate: Coco-peat or sphagnum moss, minimum depth 5 cm; damp throughout

Enclosure fit-out: Large dried leaves or plastic containers as shelters

 Group

 20–26°C

 Humidity 60–90%

 No specialised lighting required

Food and water

- Fruit and vegetables (especially cucumber), mollusc mix and cuttlebone

- Moisture in substrate

Routine care
Daily: Replace fruit and vegetables, remove uneaten food and waste products, and mist spray the substrate

Weekly: Offer mollusc mix as an alternative to fruit and vegetables

As required: Substrate should be changed over at least every 6 months, or when it becomes very sodden and smelly. Replace cuttlebone as it is eaten.

Sexing
These snails are hermaphrodites

Breeding
Adults will pair up and exchange sperm so that both snails are capable of laying eggs. Mating usually occurs at night in late spring and summer and can be stimulated by heavily mist spraying your enclosure to mimic monsoonal rain. About 20–30 eggs will be laid in a shallow burrow the snail digs in the substrate. The opaque white eggs are about 6–8 mm in diameter. Hatching times vary depending on substrate temperature and humidity, but may take between 3 and 6 weeks. The cooler the substrate temperature, the longer the hatching time. Not all eggs will hatch at the same time. The young snails that hatch have shells that are translucent and fragile.

Lifespan
2–6 years

Captive behaviour
Rainforest Snails will explore all surfaces of your enclosure, and as they move they leave a slimy trail in their wake. They are most active in conditions of low light, which is when they will forage for food. You will notice that your snail's poo will be the same colour as the food it is eating! Your snail will retreat into its shell when it is resting, but if your snail hardly ever comes out of its shell, it may be due to unfavourable conditions.

Special considerations
If snails do not have access to a source of calcium, such as found in mollusc mix or in cuttlebone, their shells may become brittle and break easily. If your snail has retreated far into its shell, it could indicate that it is dehydrated or not feeding, and will need improved care. Snail substrates can get dirty very quickly and need regular changes.

Compatibility with other species
Other tropical zone herbivorous invertebrates

Species with similar care requirements
Rainforest snails (*Sphaerospira* species)

Red Triangle Slug *Triboniophorus graeffi*

Level of difficulty

beginner   advanced

The Red Triangle Slug is found in forests and woodlands of the east coast of Queensland and New South Wales and is the largest native slug in Australia, growing to a length of about 140 mm. It has a distinctive red triangle on its back and a body that may be green, red, yellow, pink or grey. It has one pair of tentacles and a respiratory pore that is located within the red triangle on its back. These slugs feed at night on the microscopic algae growing on the trunks of eucalypts. They have been observed on wet mornings descending to the forest floor, where they spend the day sheltering. Red Triangle Slugs are also common backyards, and have been known to come into houses and feed on bathroom algae!

Housing

 Enclosure: Terrarium, custom or glass tank; minimum size 20 cm H × 30 cm W × 20 cm D

Substrate: Coco-peat or sphagnum moss, minimum depth 5 cm; damp to wet throughout

Enclosure fit-out: Leaves or plastic containers to shelter under

 Group

 18–24°C

 Humidity 60–80%

 No specialised lighting required

Food and water
- Spirulina flakes, mollusc mix, fruit and vegetables such as cucumber
- Moisture in substrate

Routine care
Daily: Replace Spirulina flakes (offered in a dish and lightly mist sprayed to moisten) and replace fruit and vegetables. Remove uneaten food and waste products and mist spray the substrate.

Weekly: Offer mollusc mix as an alternative to fruit and vegetables

As required: Substrate should be replaced at least every 6 months, or when it becomes very sodden and smelly

Sexing
These slugs are hermaphrodites

Breeding
Two slugs that are ready to mate will pair up and curl their bodies around each other to exchange sperm. Both individuals are capable of laying eggs. Clusters of around 20 creamy white eggs will be laid in moist places. Young slugs will emerge from the eggs as miniature versions of the adults; however, their triangle is brown and its colour will intensify as the slugs grow.

Lifespan
About 2 years

Captive behaviour
Red Triangle Slugs will feed and be most active at night. You may be able to stimulate activity by providing low lighting conditions. They shelter during the day where it is cool and moist. They will explore all surfaces of their enclosure, and you may be able to observe their mouthparts in action when they forage over the glass or plastic of their enclosure.

Special considerations
If your Red Triangle Slug is not feeding or begins to look shrivelled, it is an indication that conditions in its enclosure are either too dry or too hot.

Compatibility with other species
Other herbivorous invertebrates

Species with similar care requirements
None

Snug *Fastosarion brazieri*

Level of difficulty

| 1 | 2 | 3 | 4 | 5 |

beginner   advanced

Snugs are a type of semi-slug, growing to 30 mm. They are peculiar in that they are neither a snail nor a slug but show characteristics of both. They have small, thin shells that are too small for their bodies to retreat into, but enable them to utilise narrower spaces than snails. Like slugs they rely on their moist environment to prevent them drying out, and they cover their tiny shells with a protective layer of mantle when they are at rest. They have two pairs of tentacles on their heads and an unusual ridge on their tail. They are found among leaf litter in the wet tropics of northern Queensland.

Housing

Enclosure: Terrarium, custom or glass tank; minimum size 15 cm H × 20 cm W × 12 cm D

Substrate: Coco-peat or sphagnum moss, minimum depth 5 cm; damp to wet throughout

Enclosure fit-out: Leaves or plastic containers to shelter under

Group

20–26°C

Humidity 60–80%

None required, dislikes bright light

Food and water
- Fruit and vegetables (especially cucumber), mollusc mix and cuttlebone
- Moisture in substrate

Routine care
Daily: Replace fruit and vegetables, remove uneaten food and waste products, and mist spray the substrate

Weekly: Offer mollusc mix as an alternative to fruit and vegetables

As required: Substrate should be replaced at least every 6 months, or when it becomes very sodden and smelly. Replace cuttlebone as it is eaten.

Sexing
Snugs are hermaphrodites

Breeding
Mating may take place without you seeing it. Two snugs that are ready to mate will pair up and curl their bodies around each other to exchange sperm. Both individuals will be able to lay eggs after this encounter. The translucent white eggs are laid in clusters in shallow burrows or under logs in moist places. Young Snugs will emerge from the eggs as miniature versions of the adult, although when they are small their shells are very tiny and they closely resemble slugs.

Lifespan
About 2 years

Captive behaviour
Snugs will explore all surfaces of their enclosure. They will actively feed both during the day in low lighting conditions, and at night. They will shelter under leaves or in other moist places when not feeding. Snugs will sometimes bury themselves under the substrate, although they tend to not go very deep.

Special considerations
Snugs do not have a shell they can retreat into when conditions are too dry, so their enclosure will need to be kept cool and damp to wet at all times, to prevent them drying out. Be careful not to throw out any young Snugs when changing substrate, as they can be mistaken for adult Snug poo.

Compatibility with other species
Other herbivorous invertebrates

Species with similar care requirements
Other tropical zone semi-slugs

Setting up the right kind of housing for your bug will help it thrive in captivity.

Housing

Housing is a very important element for keeping healthy invertebrates. The choice of appropriate housing will determine whether your bugs are going to thrive in captivity. For example, it is not appropriate to use a tall enclosure for a ground-dwelling invertebrate that needs a lot of floor space. In most cases, it is best to try to imitate the environment your invertebrate would experience in the wild. This will allow your invertebrate to behave as it would in the wild, and to go through normal processes, such as breeding, with little intervention.

The term 'housing' means more than just the kind of enclosure in which you keep your bug. It also covers elements such as substrate types, lighting, heating, humidity, enclosure fit-out and escape prevention. All of these elements together will help your invertebrate feel at home. If any of these elements are deficient, your invertebrate could become distressed. The following sections look more closely at the different kinds of housing that are available.

Enclosures

There are many kinds of enclosures that could be suitable for the type of invertebrate you want to keep. The enclosures listed in the care guides are the minimum sizes we recommend for your adult animal.

Terrariums

Terrariums are readily available from pet stores or aquariums. They are a great enclosure for beginners to use and come in a variety of sizes and brands. They are very easy to set up and maintain, and can be used both horizontally and vertically. The lids click on to the rim of the terrarium and have a smaller access door within them. The lid allows for plenty of ventilation, but it may have to be modified if you are housing very small animals, to prevent them from escaping through the ventilation slits. The lid can be modified by attaching aluminium fly wire to the inside. The fly wire can be fused to the lid by using a soldering iron to melt the plastic around the wire.

Terrariums can be used vertically for tree-dwelling species.

A terrarium like this makes an excellent enclosure for many invertebrates.

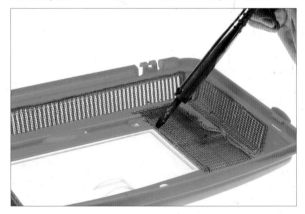
A terrarium lid being fitted with aluminium fly wire inserts.

Glass tanks

A standard glass tank is ideal for many different invertebrates. These tanks are easily purchased from pet stores and aquariums. There are some standard sizes that can be purchased – 1, 2, 3, 4 or 6-foot tanks are all useful. These tanks provide plenty of horizontal space for ground-dwelling species, and can be used for burrowing species if a deep substrate is provided. Glass tanks often do not come with suitable lids so you may have to make one yourself. This can be done using a timber frame with fly wire stapled to it.

Glass tanks can also be modified to suit tree-dwelling invertebrates. The glass tank can be turned onto its end. A front-opening door can be constructed from either timber or aluminium with mesh ventilation.

Glass tanks can be modified to suit your invertebrate.

Custom

If you require a specialised enclosure for your invertebrate, there are a number of glaziers, pet stores and aquariums that will make up a glass enclosure to exact specifications. This is especially relevant if you are setting up a display enclosure within your home or within an educational facility. There is no limit to the size and shape of the enclosure you may want built; your only constraint may be the price. Another option is to build an acrylic enclosure. Acrylic enclosures are not as durable as glass enclosures as they tend to get scratched easily, but they are lightweight and easily modified.

Custom-built enclosures can be a little more expensive, but they look great.

Mesh

Specialised mesh enclosures are made for housing reptiles and are easily sourced over the Internet or from specialist pet stores. These enclosures are ideal for many invertebrates, especially stick insects. They are lightweight, provide excellent ventilation and perching areas, and can be folded away when not in use. Small portable mesh enclosures are also available and are great for when you are out collecting your own bugs. They can collapse for easy storage.

Mesh enclosures are very versatile.

Jars

Glass jars make great enclosures for smaller invertebrates. Coffee jars or pasta sauce jars – just about any jar – can be re-used for this purpose. Make sure that jars are thoroughly washed out and free of soapy detergents. The humidity level your animal requires will determine the type of lid you should have on the jar. Animals that need low humidity can be contained simply by using mesh and a rubber band. The best jars for this purpose have a lip so that the rubber band will not slip off. If your animal needs high humidity, drill some holes into the lid of the jar and this will help retain moisture.

You will need to help your spider construct the first silk line of its web.

Re-using jars to house your invertebrate is simple and effective.

Orb frames

Orb frames are essentially two branches fixed to a wooden base, between which an orb-weaving spider can construct a web. This is a great way to house orb-weaving spiders as the frame is portable and it allows for close-up observation of the spider without having to look through glass. You will need to help your spider construct the first silk line of its web between the two branches; in the wild the spider would do this by letting wind transport this silk line. To start the web, place the spider on one branch, allowing it to settle and attach its silk to the branch. Gently guide the spider across to the other branch, ensuring that the silk line remains intact. You can use a small stick or a pair of forceps to move your spider. Once this initial silk line is made, the spider can do the rest on its own.

Once the spider has a silk line spanning the frame it can build its web between the sticks.

The spider in its completed web.

Vials

Vials are perfect enclosures for juvenile invertebrates. They are small and don't take up much space. Use a small piece of paper towel or tissue in the bottom to soak up any moisture, so your bug does not drown. Make sure that any lid has ventilation, whether it is a foam stopper or a fine mesh (or even a bit of muslin or cotton that will allow air through) secured with a rubber band. Some vials have a lid that can be modified with a bit of mesh glued into it for ventilation. Once the juvenile has outgrown the vial, it should be moved to a larger enclosure such as a jar or a terrarium.

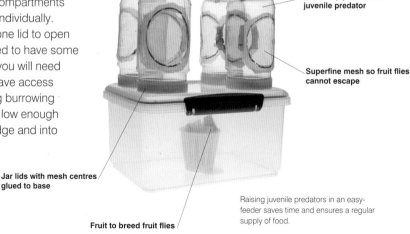

Toolboxes make easy and efficient enclosures in which to raise juvenile invertebrates.

A vial makes a good enclosure in which to raise juvenile invertebrates and takes up very little space. The lid can be modified to allow for ventilation.

Easy-feeders

These home-made enclosures are ideal for raising young predatory bugs that need to be fed on small prey such as vinegar flies. The set-up consists of small jars connected to the lid of a larger container, with some fly wire between them. Vinegar flies are bred in the large container and the small jars are used to house the juvenile predators. The vinegar flies can then move freely through the fly wire into the jars for the juvenile predators to feed on. The jars will need to be ventilated with extra fine mesh to prevent the vinegar flies from escaping. This type of set-up works extremely well with any species that can climb vertical surfaces. Once the predators are large enough to feed on small crickets or cockroaches, they can be upgraded to a larger enclosure such as a jar or terrarium.

Toolbox

Some toolboxes make great enclosures in which to house juvenile invertebrates that are not able to climb vertical surfaces. These toolboxes have compartments that can hold a number of small animals individually. They are very compact and there is only one lid to open to access all your animals. The lid will need to have some air holes drilled into it for ventilation, and you will need to make sure that all the compartments have access to some of these holes. If you are housing burrowing species, ensure that the substrate is kept low enough to prevent the animal crawling over the edge and into another compartment.

Screw top jar to house juvenile predator

Superfine mesh so fruit flies cannot escape

Jar lids with mesh centres glued to base

Fruit to breed fruit flies

Raising juvenile predators in an easy-feeder saves time and ensures a regular supply of food.

Escape prevention

With some invertebrates a lid is not enough to keep them in. You may need to escape-proof your enclosure to keep your bug inside.

Oil

Cooking or vegetable oil applied with a cloth or rag to a vertical surface provides a slippery coating that prevents climbing invertebrates escaping from their enclosures. The oil is readily obtainable from supermarkets. The oil coating may need to be re-applied if it becomes sticky and attracts dirt, as a dirty coating can provide grip for invertebrates to climb on.

Climbing invertebrates such as these cockroaches are prevented from escaping.

Apply a thin, even layer of oil to the rim of your enclosure.

Fluon

Fluon is Teflon paint, that once dry on a vertical surface, creates a smooth coating that provides no grip. This prevents climbing invertebrates from walking up it. It is a great escape-preventer to use with ants or cockroaches. The Fluon must be applied as a thin continuous coating and is best applied with a cloth, rag or paintbrush. If the coating is too thick, it may provide some grip for invertebrates to climb on. This coating is easily scratched, and may need to be thoroughly cleaned off and re-applied. It is available online and at specialist pet stores.

Silicone spray

Silicone spray comes in an aerosol can and is available from hardware and automotive stores. It is a spray-on lubricant that creates a smooth surface that prevents invertebrates from climbing vertical surfaces. The silicone can be sprayed onto the surface, or applied with a cloth or rag. It will need to be re-applied regularly to prevent escapes. Be aware that some silicone sprays contain other products designed for automotive use; these should be avoided.

Moats

Moats are a good method of escape prevention, although there are very few situations in which they would be required. They work especially well with ants, the Green Tree Ant (*Oecophylla smaragdina*) in particular, as this species can get past other barriers such as Fluon, oil and silicone. If a single ant finds a means of escape, be assured that the whole colony will be made aware of it and will attempt to cross before you can catch it!

If you a building a moat for Green Tree Ants, you need to consider the following things:

- The moat should be at least 5 cm wide and 5 cm deep.

- The water should be free of any objects that could be used as a bridge.

- No objects should over hang the moat – including the plant the ants are living on.

- The water in the moat should be level with the substrate the ants are living on, so if they fall in they can easily pull themselves out.

A moat for Green Tree Ants is a reasonably complicated construction, and requires the use of fibreglass or moulded plastics. An example of a moat is shown in the chapter 'Display Your Invertebrates' (p.185).

Temperature

Providing the correct temperature for your invertebrate will help with its health and growth. You must be careful not to over-heat your enclosure as this can be harmful. Different species have different temperature requirements; some species are able to tolerate a broad range of temperatures while others cannot. Be sure to follow the guides offered in this book. The simplest way to measure temperature is to place a thermometer in the enclosure. Some options for controlling temperature are listed below.

Note: All electrical wiring must be carried out by a certified electrician.

Heat mats

Heat mats are used to heat the bottom or side of larger enclosures. They can be purchased either readymade or as parts from specialist reptile pet stores. It is critical that you place the heat mat under no more than half of your enclosure so your invertebrate can escape to the cooler end of the enclosure if it gets too hot. The disadvantage of heating the bottom of your enclosure is that it is not a source of heat your animal would experience in the wild. Burrowing animals will often dig deeper to escape heat, but in this case would go closer to the source.

Heat mats provide ground heating for your invertebrate.

Heat lamps

Heat lamps provide both the heat and light essential for the survival of many invertebrates. The heat from the lamp can be localised to provide a hotspot for your invertebrate to bask in. This kind of heating should mimic the hottest part of the day. Heat lamps should be positioned at one end of the enclosure to provide a temperature gradient. Your invertebrate is then able to move to the cooler end of the enclosure if it gets too hot. Position your lamp so that the temperature at the basking site is approximately 40°C. This kind of heating is great for invertebrates that are active during the day as it mimics nature by providing heat from above. Some heat lamps are small and can be mounted either inside or outside the enclosure. However, they are extremely hot and care should be taken to position them where they will not present a fire risk. Heat lamps should never be used with plastic enclosures as they may melt the plastic. Suitable heat lamps include 12 V 50 W dichroic lamps, 60 W reflector lamps, and 120 W flood lamps for larger enclosures.

Dichroic lamps provide a hotspot for your invertebrate to bask in.

Household heaters

Household heaters are a simple way to increase the temperature of an entire room if you are holding a large number of invertebrates together. Using a timer with your heater can give you greater flexibility with temperature control.

Air conditioners

A simple way to cool an entire room if you are keeping many invertebrates together is to use an air conditioner. The main issue is that the humidity will drop considerably, as the air conditioner will dry out the air.

Wine cooling cabinets

Some bugs need to be kept at cool temperatures, and wine cooling cabinets are a good way of doing this. The temperature range they offer is ideal for many temperate and alpine zone invertebrates. They can also be valuable for cooling eggs to replicate winter conditions.

Humidity

Humidity plays an important role in the lives of invertebrates. Whether it is needed for daily survival or for when your invertebrate is undergoing its moulting process, it is vital to provide appropriate levels of humidity for your species. Burrowing species need a humid environment for essential bodily functions. For example, primitive spiders need a humid environment for breathing and invertebrates that lay eggs in soil need humidity in order for their eggs to survive in the substrate and for the young to emerge from the eggs. Most invertebrates that moult their exoskeleton will need a humid environment to prevent the new exoskeleton drying too quickly before they have fully expanded to their new size. Not providing correct levels of humidity could lead to serious deformities or even death. You can measure levels of humidity with a hygrometer, which can be purchased online.

Mist spraying

Using a spray bottle is a simple way of raising the humidity in small enclosures. Spray bottles can be purchased cheaply from some supermarkets or hardware stores. Mist spraying the substrate or vegetation within the enclosure will raise the humidity, and spraying often will help maintain the levels.

Spray bottles are inexpensive and easy to use to create a humid environment. Humidifiers produce a cool mist to keep an entire room humid.

Humidifiers

Humidifiers are perfect if you have a separate room set up especially for invertebrates that need a humid environment. They can be controlled by a hygrostat to keep humidity levels constant. They are commercially available but expensive.

Ventilation

The amount of ventilation in your enclosure will determine how well it will maintain its humidity. An enclosure with a large ventilation area will lose humidity very quickly. This can be overcome by using plastic sheeting to reduce the amount of ventilation. Make sure that there is still some ventilation available to your invertebrate. Alternatively, if the humidity is too high mould may grow in the enclosure, in which case you will need to increase the ventilation.

Lighting

Lighting is both for us to see and appreciate our bugs and for their health. Many invertebrates are nocturnal and do not like light, while others will actively seek out certain sources of light. Light will help your invertebrate distinguish between night and day, and can provide some heat and ultraviolet light needed for healthy growth. The amount of time an animal is exposed to light (photoperiod) will help it to determine the season. In the wild invertebrates will breed at particular times of the year, and by manipulating the photoperiod in captivity you can recreate their breeding season whenever you want. Timers can be set to turn lights on and off automatically each day.

The lighting requirements for each particular species are listed in the care guides, and they are explained in more detail here.

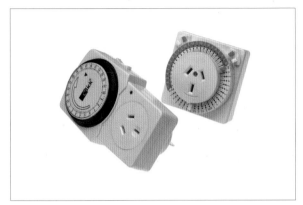

Using a timer can control the amount of light your invertebrate receives.

None required, dislikes bright light

Bugs in this category are often nocturnal or spend their lives underground and will try to get away from bright light. They do not need light to live healthy lives. To see these animals behaving normally you need to view them in dim light. A good alternative is to view them under red light, because many invertebrates cannot see red light, and so they still think it is dark. This can be as simple as looking at your invertebrates in a dark room using a torch with red cellophane over the front, but there are many other options. Red incandescent globes (sold as party lights) are ideal for this, and can be mounted above your enclosure. Reflector (heat) lamps also come in red, as do light emitting diodes (LEDs). One important consideration is to make sure that the red light does not overheat your invertebrate's enclosure. LEDs are particularly good because they give off very little heat. A lighting shop will be able to help you to find the type of red light that suits your needs best. If you are really enthusiastic and have many of these animals, you could use a red light to light the whole room!

No specialised lighting required

Invertebrates in this category do not try to get away from light, but don't need light to live healthy lives. This means that many types of lighting can be used for these animals as long as the other conditions inside the enclosure are kept as they should be. Many species in this category can be housed under standard room lighting, but if you wish to light them further you could place a fluorescent light in a hood and mount it above the enclosure.

Specialised lighting

Many invertebrates require particular types of lighting to survive and thrive in captivity. These lights provide a number of important things:

- ultraviolet light
- heat
- conditions for plant growth.

There are different types of lighting that provide these essential things.

Note: All electrical wiring must be carried out by a certified electrician.

Dichroic lamps

Dichroic lamps are low voltage and provide your invertebrate with both light and heat. They can be sourced from hardware or lighting stores. Open-faced dichroic lamps can emit ultraviolet light, which appears to be beneficial to some species. Position your lamp approximately 15 cm above the substrate. These lamps are small and can be mounted either inside or outside the enclosure. However, they are extremely hot and care should be taken to position them where they will not be a fire risk. Dichroic lamps should never be used with plastic enclosures as they can reach very high temperatures and may melt the plastic.

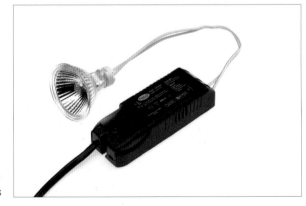

A dichroic lamp set-up is a simple way to provide both light and heat for your invertebrate.

Fluorescent lighting

Fluorescent tubes provide basic lighting for enclosures. They are easily sourced from supermarkets, hardware stores or pet stores. The tube is housed in a hood that can sit easily over the top of your enclosure. The hoods (and tubes) come in a range of standard sizes that match the sizes of standard glass tanks.

Ultraviolet lights

Ultraviolet (UV) lights are a specialised form of fluorescent lighting. They provide essential wavelengths of light for the health and growth of your invertebrates. These lights produce UVB, a particular wavelength of UV, and are used extensively by reptile keepers worldwide. It is important that you do not use the purple 'black light-blue' UV lights as these may be harmful to your animals. Without UV light, whether it is from the sun or from a globe, some invertebrates may not thrive in captive conditions. Many diurnal species thrive under UV light, but burrowing or nocturnal species are not so reliant on exposure to it. Some ultraviolet lights need hood housing, but compact forms are now appearing on the market. They can be sourced from pet stores and specialist lighting suppliers.

Metal halide lamps

Metal halide lamps are powerful lights and can be purchased from specialist lighting and hydroponics stores. Some lamps will also provide UV light to your bugs. These are best used for larger enclosures, particularly those on display. A range of different globes are available that have varying Kelvin values. The lower the Kelvin value, the more yellow the output of the light; the higher the Kelvin value, the more blue the light. Generally it is best to use a lamp that has a Kelvin value of 5400, which is the value that mimics daylight and provides a white light. These lamps will also promote the health and growth of any live plants you have in the enclosures. Metal halide lamps are powered by a ballast that will need a few minutes to power up once it is switched on. If the lamp is switched off, the ballast will need at least 10 minutes to power up before the light will come on again. These lamps also require hood housing. Do not touch the glass lamps with bare hands as the oils from your skin may cause the glass to shatter when it is powered up. Always handle the lamp with either rubber gloves or a cloth.

Mercury vapour lamps

Mercury vapour lamps emit both heat and light, and also produce some UV light. They are best used on large enclosures, and are great display lights. The lamps require a round aluminium housing and may be easily suspended above enclosures.

Light emitting diodes (LEDs)

LEDs are being used more regularly for animal displays. They do not emit much heat and are low voltage. They come in a variety of colours and some will emit UV light. They can be sourced from specialist lighting suppliers.

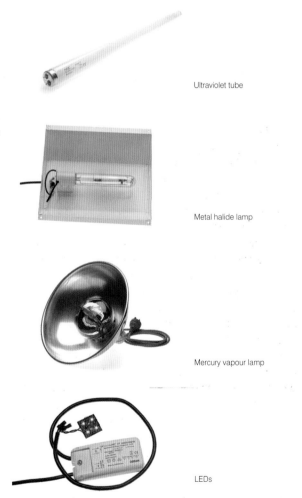

Ultraviolet tube

Metal halide lamp

Mercury vapour lamp

LEDs

Ultraviolet tubes can be purchased from pet stores and specialist lighting suppliers. Metal halide lamps provide bright light that promotes both animal and plant health. Mercury vapour lamps are available from specialist lighting suppliers and some pet stores. LEDs can help create an interesting display and are particularly useful when heat is not desired.

Substrates

There are a number of different substrate types that can be used for invertebrates, and which type and how much of it to use is largely determined by the species of invertebrate you wish to keep.

Substrate depths

Different depths of substrates can be provided for your invertebrate, and the depth required is specified in the care guides for individual species. For example, animals that rely on substrates for burrowing or laying eggs will need a deep substrate. Arboreal or surface-dwelling animals may only need a thin layer, or an absorptive layer – a thin layer of substrate that is used to soak up any excess moisture at the bottom of the enclosure, and is not essential for the animal to carry out normal behaviour.

Substrate moisture

Different species of invertebrates require different levels of moisture in their substrate. Moisture is used to keep humidity levels high in the enclosure for burrowing or egg-laying animals, or for animals that originate in humid environments.

There are different levels of substrate moisture.

- **Dry:** No moisture is required in the substrate and a mist spray is all that is required to keep humidity levels constant.

- **Damp throughout:** The substrate needs to have an even dampness from the surface right down to the bottom of the enclosure. An easy way to determine dampness is to scratch the surface of the substrate. If the substrate holds together in a clump, it is damp enough. If the substrate is crumbling, it needs more water. There should be no pools of water at the bottom of the enclosure.

- **A dry and a damp end:** The substrate needs to have a moisture gradient and be damp at one end of the enclosure and dry at the other. This is to allow your invertebrate to choose its preferred environment.

- **Wet:** This indicates that the substrate should be fully saturated with water.

Newspaper

Newspaper is the simplest substrate and provides an absorbent material to soak up excess water. It can be changed easily and also enables easy collection of eggs from species such as stick insects.

Sand

Sand can be used with a multitude of invertebrates and at varying depths, depending on the animal's needs. It is easily sourced from garden suppliers and pet stores, or you can collect it. There are various types of sand, and some are better than others. Sand that retains moisture is preferable for species that burrow or lay eggs in the substrate and rely on high humidity levels. These sands will also easily hold their shape when tunnelled into. Beware of sands that become muddy and stick to your bug's feet.

Coco-peat

Coco-peat is cheap, easy to use and environmentally friendly. It can be bought from garden suppliers and comes in brick form. It expands to a large volume when water is added to it. It works well with tropical species, and it can sometimes be added to sand to give it a different texture. Damp coco-peat is easy to burrow into, but when dry it has a very crumbly texture and will collapse. Ensure your coco-peat does not have any added fertilisers.

Soil

Backyard soil is a good, easily accessible substrate for use with your invertebrates, and it's free! Different soils are good for different uses. Clay soils hold their shape and moisture and are ideal for burrowing species, and sandy soils provide good drainage. A downside to backyard soil is the potential to bring in other invertebrates that could harm your animal. One way to reduce this risk is to freeze your backyard soil before using it as a substrate. Beware of using potting mixes as substrates as they contain fertilisers that can be harmful to your invertebrate.

Leaf litter

This is a fantastic natural substrate, and can often be used as an additive to sand or coco-peat. Many types of leaves can be used, but try to use leaves from the natural habitat of your invertebrate. Larger leaves also create good sheltering spots for your invertebrates.

Sphagnum moss

Sphagnum moss is an excellent substrate for many tropical species, particularly those requiring high humidity and constantly damp substrates. It is relatively inexpensive and can be purchased from gardening supply stores, plant nurseries and some supermarkets.

Silty clay

This kind of substrate is able to hold moisture extremely well and, when dry, will crack to form hiding places for your invertebrate. This substrate is suitable for animals that need deep moisture for burrowing and dry surfaces to run around on. It is ideal, for example, for the Tiger Beetle (*Megacephala australis*) as it is very similar to its natural habitat around the edges of saltpans. You may be able to source this substrate from specialist garden suppliers.

Clockwise from top left: sand, coco-peat brick, leaf litter, sphagnum moss and moist coco-peat.

Enclosure fit-out

Enclosure fit-out is the placement of objects into your enclosure to provide the essential parts of your invertebrate's habitat. Basic things such as perching branches and shelters are examples of this. These materials are very important as they will allow your animal to perform vital activities such as moulting, breeding and resting. Having a selection of these items on hand is always good practice, as you may have to replace something unexpectedly.

Bark

Bark can help give your enclosure a naturalistic setting, as well as provide shelter for your animal. Curled pieces of bark are great for use with invertebrates such as beetles, which can crawl inside to shelter. Larger sheets of bark work well as shelters for large spiders, such as the Australian tarantula, when they are positioned over depressions in the substrate. Bark is lightweight and reduces the risk of crushing your animals. Collect bark that has already fallen from a tree – peeling bark off a tree may cause the tree some damage.

Rocks

Rocks provide a good cover for some invertebrates to burrow under. Multiple rocks stacked in an enclosure can create a number of sheltered areas. Rocks with a flat surface will provide a perfect basking area on which to direct the beam of a heat lamp for sun-loving species. Make sure that any rocks used in an enclosure are firmly placed so that they will not fall and harm your invertebrate. Rocks can be collected from your backyard or purchased from garden supply stores. Moving rocks should be done with care, as invertebrates can easily be squashed beneath them.

Branches

Sticks and branches make good natural perching areas for invertebrates such as praying mantids and katydids. For invertebrates that feed on vegetation, the food plant you place in your enclosure will do the same job. Branches give invertebrates a greater surface area and the option of staying on the ground or climbing. They also provide essential places for many invertebrates to moult. Household items such as wooden skewers and pipe cleaners can be used for this purpose also. It is important that all these items are placed in a stable position within the enclosure so that they cannot fall over.

Vegetation

Any type of vegetation can be used to create a great naturalistic enclosure set-up. Leaf litter, native grasses such as tussocks or spinifex, or groundcover plants can all provide lots of perching space or ample shelter for your invertebrate. Live plants can be planted, dried grasses can be propped up in the substrate and leaf litter can be scattered over the surface. Any vegetation is easily attainable from garden suppliers or your own backyard.

Burrows

If you are housing a burrowing species, sometimes it is helpful to compact the substrate you are using, and to assist your invertebrate to begin its burrow. This is especially useful for invertebrates that are opportunistic and require an existing hole to live in. You can help these species begin their burrow by using your finger or a pen to push into the substrate. This small indentation will encourage your invertebrate to continue to create the burrow. This can encourage invertebrates to burrow in areas where they will be visible. For more elaborate display burrows made out of artificial materials, see the chapter 'Display your invertebrate' (p.185).

This Giant Burrowing Cockroach was encouraged to make its burrow against the side of the enclosure.

Plastic or cardboard containers

Empty shoeboxes, tissue boxes, empty toilet rolls, egg cartons and ice-cream containers all provide excellent shelter for your invertebrate. Simply cut an entrance hole in the side of the container, place upside down and your invertebrate will be able to move in. Cardboard containers will start to break down and become soggy if used in humid environments, so be sure to keep an eye on them and replace them when necessary.

Hide box

This is a fully enclosed container with a small entrance hole for your invertebrate. The hide box should create a dark place that can be used as shelter. It needs to be made of a material that will not break down easily in humid environments, such as wood or plastic. A hide box works especially well for Lord Howe Island Stick Insects (*Dryococelus australis*). Small bird boxes are readymade hide boxes.

Egg-laying containers

Many invertebrates lay their eggs underground. In captivity one way to guarantee that you can easily find your invertebrate's eggs is to provide a container that encourages them to lay eggs within it. An open-topped container filled with several centimetres of damp substrate (such as coco-peat) will provide such an option. The depth of the substrate in the container will be determined by how your invertebrate lays its eggs. For example, some katydids have long ovipositors for laying eggs so they will need a deep substrate. Ensure that the substrate in the main enclosure is too shallow for laying eggs so that the bug uses the container instead.

Food and water

Providing food and water for your invertebrates sounds like a simple thing to do, but it requires a thorough understanding of your animals. For example, if you put a water bowl in the enclosure of a tropical spider that never leaves its web, the spider will die from dehydration, but if you spray the web (to mimic rain) the spider will get all the water it needs. If you consider the needs and behaviour of your bugs, you are much more likely to manage their diet successfully and your bugs will thirve.

Food

The foods that may be provided for invertebrates in captivity are hugely diverse, and each species has its own particular needs and preferences. Some invertebrates are herbivores, some carnivores (or insectivores) and others are omnivores and feed on both plant and animal material.

Feeding time is part of the fun of keeping invertebrates.

The foods for all invertebrates in captivity can be grouped into two categories: natural foods and artificial foods. Natural foods are the foods that your invertebrate would feed on in the wild, such as the leaves of particular plants or live insects. They include substitute food plants and animals that are not of the same species as its wild food but similar enough to be a suitable food source.

Artificial foods are very different in appearance to the foods the animals would normally encounter, but have all the ingredients that your animals need to survive and thrive.

Complete artificial diets have been developed specifically for only a few invertebrates, so in most cases it involves using foods (or a combination of ingredients) that are used for other animal groups that feed on similar things.

Whether you use natural or artificial foods depends on the species of invertebrate you are keeping, as some species are flexible in what they can and will eat, but others are not. It may also depend on the availability of the natural food, particularly if you are keeping an invertebrate that is not from your local area. In some cases a combination of natural and artificial foods may be required to ensure the health of your invertebrates.

Natural foods

Plants

Many of the herbivores included in this book feed on fresh plants and leaves. You can supply these either as living plants in pots, or as browse that you keep fresh in a vase for several days before replacing the eaten browse.

When using any plant material as food for invertebrates it is critical to check that it was not exposed to insecticides before you bought it from the nursery or clipped it from the garden. Insecticides can have disastrous effects on your invertebrates – and some chemicals will remain in the plant for many months after they have been applied. Also check the foliage carefully before putting it in your enclosure to make sure you are not accidentally introducing a wild predator or parasite. Spiders may often be found lurking under pots or in the foliage. When removing plants from your enclosure, be aware that there is a chance that eggs (or the invertebrates themselves) could hitchhike out. Apart from losing your precious animals, it is very important not to allow this to happen to avoid introducing species into areas of Australia where they are not found naturally.

Many different plant species are used to feed the invertebrates in this book, including both native and introduced plants. These plants are listed in the care guides for the relevant invertebrate. Those listed are the most commonly used plants for each species; however, there may be other suitable plants that you discover by further research or by experimenting.

Potted plants: Providing live plants is the most natural option; however, a number of plants need to be rotated in and out of the enclosure. Even if low numbers of herbivorous invertebrates are being kept, the plants will still need time to recover and to have exposure to natural light. Plants that are heavily chewed may need to be pruned back to encourage leaf growth. Using potted plants can be expensive and requires time and space to care for the plants. It is wise to get your plant supply organised before obtaining your invertebrates.

Fresh foliage: Using cut foliage to feed your invertebrates is a relatively simple process (providing you have suitable plants nearby), and is a less expensive option. Some plants will last for up to a week if kept in clean water. To maximise the time the plants remain fresh, ensure you get the stems into water as soon as possible after cutting. The choice of leaf material is very important too, as most plant-eating invertebrates prefer fresh healthy growth, free of disease. Many juvenile insects, such as phasmids and grasshoppers, prefer soft young leaves, and are unable to chew into old leaves. It is also important to ensure that the water container in which you keep the cut plants does not present a drowning risk for your animals. Some coffee jars are excellent for this purpose as the lids can be pierced for the plant stems to go through.

Fresh grass: Many species of invertebrates feed on grasses. Grass can be supplied to them by simply collecting it and giving to your animals daily in a shallow dish. Placing it in a dish allows you to remove the uneaten or dried grass easily. If grass is not readily available to be collected it can be grown in seedling trays. Grass seed or bird seed purchased at supermarkets will germinate within a few days and can be offered directly to your animals.

Fruit and vegetables

Fruit and vegetables are an excellent food source for many different groups of invertebrates. Some species, particularly those from rainforests where fruits are common, will prefer soft fruits and are able to cope with their high sugar levels. These fruits include mango, banana and cantaloupe. Invertebrates from drier climates often prefer harder fruits and vegetables such as carrots and apples. Although there is no hard and fast rule on this, beware of feeding your animals sugar-rich fruits if they would not have them in the wild. Offer fruit and vegetables in small quantities to reduce waste; cubes of 1 cm are ideal for many species. Presenting fruit and vegetables on a small dish makes it easier to remove the leftovers and reduces the risk of fungal and bacterial build-up within your enclosure.

Pulpy (decomposing) wood

Many beetles, katydids and millipedes require decomposing wood for feeding and breeding. Softwoods (including many introduced trees) are ideal when they are broken down to a crumbly, pulpy stage. Collecting a supply of partially decomposed wood and keeping it in a wet spot in the backyard (or partially submerged in a tub of water) is a good way of having this food on hand. The best way to provide this to your animals is to half bury it in damp substrate to prevent it drying out.

Pulpy wood is an important food for many invertebrates.

Live food

Live food is essential for many invertebrate predators, as many require some stimulation by live prey animals to trigger them to feed. The main source of live food for predatory invertebrates is insects. Although it is possible to use caught insects as food for your predator, this is often time consuming, and it can be difficult to ensure a regular supply. There are, however, several species of insects that are bred commercially for use as food. Crickets, cockroaches and mealworms can be purchased from many pet shops or directly from the breeders; some will even deliver the live insects to your door.

Approach slowly, with the food clearly protruding from the forceps.

Methods of feeding live food

Live food may be offered in several ways. The simplest way is to release the live food insect directly into your enclosure, and remove it later if it is has not been eaten. Live or freshly killed food can also be offered directly to your animal using forceps or tweezers. Freshly killed insects can also be left in a small bowl for scavengers such as carnivorous beetles. Dead insects dry out quickly and become less valuable as food, so they should be removed within 24 hours if not eaten. Live food insects can be killed humanely by putting the insects into your freezer for 30 minutes. The insects need to be thawed to room temperate before using.

Make delicate contact with the mouthparts of your predator.

Forceps feeding your predators: This is the simple technique of offering live or freshly killed insect prey to your predators using forceps or tweezers. Sometimes it is easier and more convenient to forceps feed your invertebrate than to release live food into your enclosure as you will know immediately if your animal has eaten. It also eliminates the risk of having live food insects, such as crickets and cockroaches, interfering with your animal during vulnerable periods such as moulting or egg-laying. Although many species of invertebrate predators will accept food in this way, some will not. Mantids, predatory katydids, spiders, beetles and scorpions are some that readily accept food from forceps, but all require a very delicate approach. The trick is to gently touch the food to the mouthparts of the animal without bumping your animal or giving it a fright. This requires a steady hand and sometimes it may take several attempts before the food is accepted. It may also help to mash the end of the dead food slightly to make it a little 'juicy'. Once your animal senses the food, it will grasp on to it. You will then need to release it carefully.

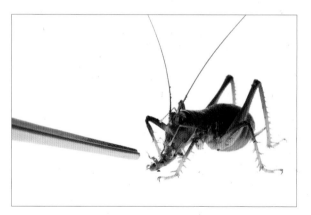
Release the food gently and move the forceps away slowly.

Crickets: Crickets are bred commercially worldwide for use as reptile, amphibian, bird and invertebrate food. The most common species bred is the Indian House Cricket (*Gryllodes sigillatus*). These grow to about 20 mm in length and are ideal food for spiders, mantids, carnivorous katydids, centipedes and scorpions. They are a nutritious food source, and will walk boldly around the enclosure, exposing themselves to your predatory invertebrate.

Cockroaches: The most common cockroach available commercially is the Speckled Cockroach (*Nauphoeta cinerea*), also sold as 'Woodies' or 'Feeder Roaches'. They are a good food source for a variety of invertebrate predators. However, these cockroaches are great at hiding and can remain uneaten within the enclosure for long periods of time without you knowing. In some circumstances they can also begin breeding, so remove any uneaten cockroaches to avoid this happening.

Mealworms: Mealworms are the larvae of the beetle *Tenebrio molitor*. They are bred worldwide as captive animal food, and are widely available from commercial suppliers in Australia. They have a shiny, hard exoskeleton that can be difficult for some invertebrates to penetrate, but for those that can feed on them they offer a good alternative food. Mealworms should not be relied upon as the sole diet as they are not overly nutritious. Be aware that Mealworm frass can cause allergic reactions in some people.

Blowflies: Although some breeders sell these as live food, they can be raised easily at home in batches to feed some predatory invertebrates. Simply place some meat outside when flies are active. Once eggs or maggots are on the meat place it into a bucket or container half filled with slightly moist sand. The maggots will leave the meat and bury themselves in the sand when they are ready to pupate. Simply sieve the sand several days later and collect the pupae. You can feed your predators the pupae, or the adult flies when they emerge. Some invertebrate keepers scatter fly pupae within animal enclosures such as those of web-building spiders, so that the flies emerge as ready meals. Just be aware that raising flies this way does smell a little!

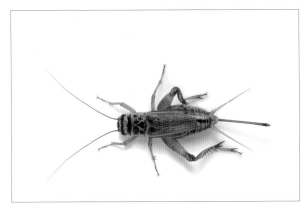

Indian House Crickets are sold commercially in Australia as animal food.

Speckled Cockroaches are a good live food option and can be purchased online and from pet shops.

Mealworms at all life stages are good alternative foods for some invertebrate predators.

Vinegar flies (*Drosophila*): These tiny flies are used worldwide for genetics experiments. They are also very common throughout Australia, and are often found in compost. They can be attracted to over-ripe fruit, and this can be placed in a jar with a fly mesh top to exclude other scavengers. Vinegar flies will lay eggs on the fruit you leave out, hatching into tiny maggots that feed and grow rapidly. Vinegar flies pupate above ground, and you will see their pupal cases attached to the remainder of the fruit, or on the side of the jar. The entire life cycle of vinegar flies only takes 9–20 days in normal household conditions, and they are excellent food for baby predators.

Other backyard invertebrates: There are a range of other invertebrates that can be used as food. These include moths, caterpillars, slaters, aphids, snails, slugs and earthworms. These can be collected from your own backyard, and will provide an adequate diet for many invertebrate predators. The most important thing is to ensure that these do not pose a risk to your animals by being poisonous or venomous, or affected by baits or pesticides.

Prey size

In the wild some invertebrate predators will tackle remarkably large prey, sometimes up to and larger than their own body size. This has its risks, however, and wild predators will often fall victim to the defences of their intended prey. In captivity there is no need to risk damage or death to your predators by offering them oversized live food. Crickets and cockroaches pose the greatest risk as they have powerful mandibles. In some situations in captivity, hungry crickets and cockroaches have been known to harass, kill and consume the predator for which they were intended to be food! It is far safer to give several small meals, rather than one large one.

The size of live prey that predatory invertebrates can cope with safely varies from species to species. The following table is a guide for the safe use of crickets and cockroaches as live food for predatory invertebrates.

Predator	Food size
Mantids	⅓ body size
True spiders (non web builders)	⅓ body size
True spiders (web builders)	½ body size
Primitive spiders	⅓ body size
Centipedes	¼ body size
Predatory katydids	¼ body size
Beetles	¼ body size
Scorpions	¼ body size
Assassin bugs	¼ body size

Artificial foods

Artificial diets can be very useful as supplements to natural foods, or as complete alternatives if natural foods are not available. The artificial diets listed in this chapter include products and ingredients that are easy to purchase and mix yourself.

Food placement and presentation

Putting these foods in a place that your invertebrate can access easily is very important. The basic rule is to offer the food in a position in which your animal would find it in the wild. If the species you are keeping forages above the ground in branches, then a dish on the ground is not ideal. In this case, mounting the food dish so that it can be accessed from the foliage is a better option.

It is also important that the dish in which you place food is accessed easily by your animals. For example, having a high-sided dish will make it hard for some ground-dwelling or small invertebrates to find their food, and they may have difficulty climbing in. The colour of the food dish can also play an important part. Insects that feed on nectar and pollen will often be attracted to bright colours, so having a bright yellow food dish for these animals may help them find their food.

Food on a pedestal feeder – a wooden skewer has been used to elevate the dish to a level where the katydids are active.

Orthopteran mix

This food is suitable for many different herbivorous and omnivorous invertebrates, including grasshoppers, crickets, cockroaches and some beetles. It is very useful for animals whose wild diet is relatively unknown, as it contains a variety of ingredients, allowing the animals to pick and choose the parts they want. This mix was adapted from a diet by Dr David Rentz.

Mix the following ingredients in a blender until a crumbly texture is obtained:

- 1 cup natural muesli
- 4 tablespoons fish flakes
- 2 tablespoons bird seed mix
- 1 tablespoon calcium carbonate powder
- 2 tablespoons bee pollen*
- ½ cup guinea pig pellets

* Be aware that bee pollen can cause allergic reactions in some people.

The authors have used the recipe above combined with several other ingredients (purchased through speciality reptile and bird food outlets) to include more options in the mix:

- 1 tablespoon Repcal Juvenile Bearded Dragon Pellets
- 1 tablespoon reptile multivitamin powder
- 1 tablespoon Wombaroo Reptile Supplement
- 2 tablespoons Wombaroo Finch Soft Food

This mix can be stored in an airtight container.

Mollusc mix

This is a food for snails and slugs that was originally developed to feed endangered Partula Snails being kept at London Zoo. It is ideal as a supplement to fresh vegetable material, but is relatively expensive.

Mix the following ingredients together and blend to a powder:

- 1 tablespoons calcium carbonate powder
- 1 tablespoons rolled oats
- 1 tablespoons dried grass powder (barley or wheat grass)
- ½ tablespoons trout pellets
- ¼ teaspoon multivitamin powder

Transfer powder into large bowl and add:

- 1 mL of vitamin E liquid

Add water while stirring until the mix reaches a paste-like consistency.

Divide the mix up into teaspoon-sized servings, and freeze in small dishes or ice-cube trays.

Millipede food

This is a simple but useful diet for millipedes, and contains only two ingredients:

- 1 tablespoon calcium carbonate powder
- 1 tablespoon crushed guinea pig pellets

Mix together to make a coarse powder. Add a small amount of water when serving to make a paste. Present in a small flat dish.

Spirulina flakes

This is an algae-based fish food that is used as a slug diet. A thin layer should be place on a small dish and mist sprayed to moisten.

Stag beetle diet (adult)

This is an excellent diet for adult stag beetles and contains three easy-to-obtain ingredients:

- 3 parts banana
- 1 part pure maple syrup
- 1 part natural yogurt

Mash the banana and mix with the other ingredients until evenly mixed. Serve on small dishes. This recipe should be freshly made and cannot be frozen.

Stag beetle diet (larvae)

For this enhanced diet for rearing stag beetles, combine:

- 1 part wheat germ
- 5 parts pulpy wood

Mulch the soft pulpy wood into a crumbly texture (using a blender or mortar and pestle), then add the wheat germ and mix thoroughly. This mix should be kept damp (as a substrate) and the larvae introduced into the enclosure.

Bottle tops make ideal food dishes for many invertebrates. The tops come in a variety of colours, shapes and sizes, and can be modified to suit your needs.

Butterfly diet

Butterflies require a diluted sugar diet. This recipe can be made in advance and frozen until required:

- 100 g liquefied fructose (or 65 g crystallised fructose)
- 65 g sucrose (household sugar)
- 45 g glucose or dextrose
- ¼ tsp honey

Dissolve the sugars in 250 mL boiling purified water, then add 250 mL purified water. Add honey (this is added later to reduce amino acid break down) and add extra purified water to make up to 1 litre.

This should be provided in such a way that the butterflies are drawn to it by bright colours (reds, yellows etc.); for example, a dish with nectar and bright beads in it. The beads should be a couple of millimetres above level of the nectar to allow the butterflies to perch while feeding. A butterfly will suck up the nectar with its proboscis. The serving dish could be placed in the enclosure on an elevated platform or simply placed on the base of the enclosure.

The colorful beads in this butterfly feeder attact the butteflies.

Sugar diets

Nectar-feeding invertebrates rely on simple sugars for much of their diet. There are a number of simple sugars, and some species have a preference for a particular form:

- sucrose (household sugar)
- fructose
- glucose
- honey

It is best to present the sugars as liquid or syrups, so granules or powders should be dissolved in water. Use saturated solutions; that is, dissolve the sugar in water until no more will dissolve. It is important to remember is that these solutions are sticky and only small volumes are required. This avoids your animals sticking and drowning, and messy enclosures caused by overflowing dishes.

Only use small quantities of sticky sugars such as honey.

Bee pollen

Bee pollen granules can be purchased from most health food outlets. Many herbivorous species discussed in this book will feed on bee pollen, and it can be offered in a small dish as granules or crushed to a powder. Be aware that bee pollen can cause allergic reactions in some people.

Bee pollen can be used as granules or in a crushed form.

BUGS ALIVE!

Water

Like all animals, invertebrates need water to survive. They get water in many different ways. Some get most of their water from their food, others need to drink quite a bit, and some absorb it from their environment. It is important that when water is provided it is done in a way that is safe for your invertebrates. Most species do not drink from bodies of water in the wild, so providing a water bowl as you would for a domestic animal is often unsuitable and can be a drowning risk. The following methods outline the ways in which water can be provided to invertebrates in a safe and usable manner.

A bottle cap with a sponge insert makes an excellent invertebrate water bowl.

Mist spray

In the wild many species will acquire water from dew or rain drops. Lightly spraying the animal and its surroundings is an excellent way of providing water for these animals. It is critical that the spray bottle used has never contained chemicals, and is dedicated to this purpose alone to avoid poisoning.

Water sponge

In the wild some species suck or chew water from the ground when it is wet. Using a small dish with a soaked sponge insert is an effective way of providing water for such invertebrates. The sponge prevents small individuals from drowning and prevents spillage. It is extremely important that the sponge is free of chemicals; always wash new sponges in water before use. The sponge can be cut up to fit your dish, and rinsed if it gets dirty. Cotton wool balls can be used as an alternative.

Moisture in substrates

Some species simply do not drink. They do however require their enclosure to be kept damp and will absorb water directly from it. Snails and slugs are good examples of invertebrates that get their water in this way.

Gravel-filled water dish

Butterflies require a water dish filled with gravel so that they can stand safely on it without drowning. The water level needs to be a few millimetres below the level of the gravel so that the surface is not under water. A butterfly will extend its proboscis down through the gravel to reach the water.

A simple dish filled with gravel and water will allow butterflies to drink water without the risk of drowning.

Health

Having healthy, good-looking and long-lived animals is every bug keeper's aim. Unfortunately, there are times when issues arise with the health of invertebrates. Many of these problems arise because the conditions in captivity do not meet the needs of the invertebrate. With any health concerns, the first step is a review of how the animals are being kept: temperature, humidity, shelter, food and the interaction with other animals in the enclosure.

The importance of observation

Recognising an unhealthy animal is all about getting to know what is normal for that species. You cannot expect to know the abnormal until you know what is normal! Spend time observing your invertebrates and make notes of behaviour patterns. You will note how behaviour changes over time, and depends on factors such as feeding, time of day and time of year. The postures that invertebrates adopt when they are resting is also a big indicator of health. Get to know their normal postures through regular observation. You will soon be able to tell if an animal is 'not quite right' by the way it is sitting, or how it is perched in its enclosure. Response to touch is another test of good health; most species will respond sharply or in a predictable way each time. If your invertebrate starts to respond sluggishly or in a different way, do not ignore it – something may be wrong.

If the animal is behaving in a manner that is different from usual there will be a reason, and investigating at this early stage is much better than waiting until things get worse. For example, if a scorpion is active suddenly in the middle of the day when it normally never leaves its burrow, it is a sign that something is not quite right. It could be that a heat mat under the enclosure is causing it to overheat, and the scorpion is trying to escape from the heat. Failure to act at this stage could result in the scorpion dying of dehydration or heat stress.

Record keeping

Record keeping is an extremely important part of animal care. As there is so little known about the care of invertebrates compared with other animal groups, any extra information that you can find out about the

A Sydney Funnelweb is very vulnerable during the moulting process.

invertebrates you keep can be extremely useful. The more details you record, the better prepared you will be to deal with any health issues should they arise. Basic records should include feeding, moulting, breeding, behavioural observations and enclosure conditions. Additional information such as weights and lengths can give you a greater understanding of the species you are keeping and what is normal.

It is easy to keep records on animals that are housed individually, but when they are housed in groups (such as stick insects or grasshoppers), it is hard to keep track of any one individual. You can, however, track the cycles of your group. Tracking the hatching of eggs, and estimating the numbers in the group on a regular basis, will give you a better idea of what is happening with your animals than keeping no records at all.

Why is my bug sick?

There is so little known about the health of these animals that it is often impossible to find out exactly what is wrong with 'sick' invertebrates. In most cases, taking your animal to the vet is not the best option, as few veterinarians have experience in treating invertebrates. (Contact the Australian Veterinary Association for a list of vets who deal with invertebrates.) If your invertebrate appears ill in some way and you believe it is not simply a case of old age, then the following checklist may help you to find the problem:

- **Enclosure** – Is the animal able to shelter, burrow or climb in the way that it would in the wild? Is it too confined or too exposed?

- **Temperature** – What is the temperature? Has it changed recently? Is there a range of temperatures (temperature gradient) within the enclosure so that the animal can choose its favoured zone?

- **Humidity** – Is it too dry? Is there too much ventilation? Is it too wet? Is there insufficient ventilation? Does it smell musty? Is there mould or fungal growth in the enclosure?

- **Lighting** – Is the animal able to get away from light? Does it need a light? Does it require ultraviolet (UV) light? Does it need a hotspot?

- **Water** – Is the animal drinking? Is the method of water provision suitable for the species?

- **Food** – When did it last eat? What did it eat? Is there another food option if it is not eating? Could the browse be affected by pesticides? Are there live food insects in the enclosure to harass it? Is the live food too big? (Many invertebrates will not eat if their housing conditions are not suitable.)

- **Handling** – How often is it being handled? How often are you disturbing it? Has it become lethargic? (Handling more than once a week can stress some species of invertebrates.)

- **Other animals** – Is it being harassed by other animals in the enclosure? Do you have too many in the group? Have pest species invaded the enclosure?

Reviewing these things is the first step to finding out what is wrong with an unhealthy invertebrate. Many of these questions relate to husbandry issues you should be recording. For instance, you should know when your invertebrate was last fed and what it was fed. Tweaking or experimenting with the conditions is also worthwhile, keeping in mind that the amount of information on keeping invertebrates is still relatively small. It is possible that you may uncover some valuable new techniques that solve your problems. Sometimes the problems may not be directly related to the care at all, and may be caused by a disease or parasite.

Quarantine

Quarantine is the process of keeping sick or newly acquired animals separate from others to help prevent the transmission of diseases or parasites. By keeping new animals separate, you are allowing a period of time to observe the invertebrate for signs of ill health. The last thing you want is your whole collection to die as a result of the introduction of a diseased newcomer. Periods of quarantine for vertebrates can vary from many weeks to several months, but such periods are not practical with most invertebrates because they have such short lifespans. Keeping a new invertebrate separate for a period of a few weeks is a good start. During this time regularly investigate it for any signs and symptoms of diseases and parasites. Quarantining new animals reduces the risks but it never eliminates them.

If you have identified a sick animal within a group that you are keeping, it is wise to separate it immediately. This form of quarantine is well worth the effort, and can reduce the impact of transmissible diseases or parasites in your group. Keep in mind that if you have separated an invertebrate for quarantine reasons, then everything within that animal's enclosure can potentially spread the disease back to healthy animals. This includes your hands and utensils. Do not reuse any logs, rocks or substrates from infected areas. Ideally, once the infected animal has been removed from a healthy population, the enclosure should be completely cleaned out and given new substrate and fit-out. It is worthwhile having separate cleaning utensils for your quarantine enclosures. If cleaning many enclosures at once, always clean the quarantine or suspect enclosures last, to help minimise the risk of disease transmission between enclosures.

Diseases

There are many diseases that can affect Australian invertebrates. Unfortunately, very little is known about most of them, or how to treat the affected animals. Many methods of treating sick invertebrates are experimental, as not much study has been done on these problems. A small number of common diseases and their symptoms are listed below.

Stick insect fungal disease

Monash University researchers have isolated a lethal fungal disease in Spiny Leaf Insects (*Extatosoma tiaratum*), that is transmissible. Insects affected have limp, floppy abdomens and their normally dry droppings are slimy in appearance. These insects usually die within a week. The disease is caused by a candida yeast infection, and seems to be contracted by stick insects feeding on eucalypt leaves infected with sooty mould (a black sooty growth on the leaves). Any insects displaying these symptoms should be quarantined immediately. Eucalypt leaves should be sourced from another location and checked carefully to avoid sooty mould. To date there is no treatment for this disease.

Caterpillar viruses

There are a number of viruses that affect caterpillars, the most common in captivity being nuclear polyhedral viruses (NPVs). These are particularly common in butterfly houses that rear large numbers of caterpillars, and they cause many deaths when present. NPVs can be contracted by bringing infected caterpillars into your collection, but they can also be brought in on plants and substrate. Affected caterpillars are inactive and have stringy, liquid droppings. The virus will destroy their internal organs and they will hang limply from the plants in their enclosure. There is no treatment for NPVs in caterpillars, but a good hygiene and cleaning routine is the best way to reduce the spread of the infection.

Mantis eye disease

There are two conditions that affect the eyes of praying mantids, particularly those bred in captivity. Both begin as a black spot on the eye (not to be confused with the pseudo-pupils), which gradually gets larger. The less severe of these conditions doesn't seem to affect the

mantid's ability to hunt or limit its lifespan noticeably. The mantis ends up with a large black spot (slightly irregularly shaped) on one or both eyes. The second eye condition is more severe and eats away at the eyes, so they seem to partially collapse, leading to blindness. There has been a reported case in which this condition was present in the mantids early stages, but then improved each time it moulted. The cause of these conditions is not known, and no treatments have been identified.

The early stage of a mantis eye disease eats away at the eye causing blindness.

As the mantis eye disease progresses, the mantis will become blind.

Spider blister disease

This is a disease that affects the abdomens of primitive spiders, and seems most common in funnelwebs. It begins as a small bump on the side or end of the spider's abdomen, and can make the abdomen look misshappen. As it gets worse it looks very much like a blister and can increase to more than a quarter of the size of the spider's abdomen. Spiders with this condition can live for quite a while, but ultimately die as a result. Research is being conducted on this problem, but at the moment neither cause nor treatment is known.

Parasites

Parasites are animals that survive by using the living bodies of other animals as hosts. There are many different types of parasites, many of which are invertebrates. The aim of the parasite is not to kill the host immediately but to live off it and reproduce. Some invertebrates can be parasites and some examples of these are listed below.

Parasitic mites

These are tiny mites that live upon the body of larger invertebrates and use their host as food (as fleas would a dog). These mites most often affect ground-dwelling invertebrates, including spiders, beetles and cockroaches. They are light brown to cream in colour, with a round body about the size of a pin head. They often cluster around the joints and softer parts of the invertebrate's body where they can feed easily. In small numbers they do not have an impact, but they can multiply to large numbers that severely affect the health of the animal, and in some cases even kill it. Not all mites are harmful, and seeing a few moving around the enclosure and occasionally over your invertebrates is not necessarily a problem. There are some, for example, that will actually 'clean' the exoskeletons of larger invertebrates, and some millipede keepers, in particular, believe that these are beneficial. However, large numbers of mites in the substrate can indicate that they are not parasitic mites but are feeding on food scraps.

Parasitic mites on invertebrates cannot be treated with insecticides, as these will kill both the mites and your animal. Physical removal of mites is often the only alternative. Low numbers can be brushed off with a fine paint brush or moist cotton bud, and this should be combined with a full substrate change to remove mite eggs. Heavy infestations need repeated treatments. One method that has proven to be successful is to remove your animal from its enclosure and place it on a moist paper towel in a sealed jar. Place the jar in a dark place for several hours, and then brush off as many mites as you can. Immediately transfer your animal onto a moist paper towel in another clean jar. By repeating this process multiple times the mites are progressively left behind.

Mites in these numbers on this Sydney Funnelweb can affect the health of the spider.

Parasitic flies

Parasitic flies lay their eggs on, in or near their helpless invertebrate host, and the parasitic maggots will begin to feed on it. Invertebrates caught in the wild are most likely to be affected by these parasites, but it is sometimes impossible to tell. Many will only be noticed if a fat maggot crawls out of the body. Some parasitic fly maggots are visible, as part of their body protrudes through a hole in the host's exoskeleton. With care and very fine forceps, these can be occasionally removed, but severe internal damage may already have been done. If you suspect you have had an animal die due to a parasitic fly attack, the most important thing is to remove the substrate and thoroughly clean the enclosure. This prevents any parasites that may be pupating in the substrate from starting the process again and attacking more of your invertebrate collection.

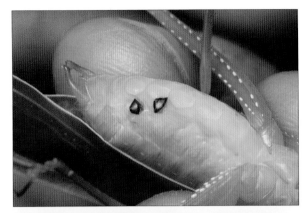

A parasitic fly larva is removed from the abdomen of a live katydid.

invertebrates, including spiders, cockroaches, crickets, mantids and even flies. They are usually undetectable except for the bloated appearance of the host, which can often be mistaken for the animal being gravid (pregnant). They will emerge from a dead or dying host to search for water, which is where they complete their life cycle, a fact that usually reduces the chance of them reinfecting in captivity.

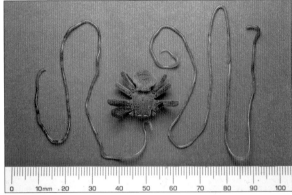

Two Gordian worms and the spider from which they emerged

Parasitic wasps

There are many species of parasitic wasps in Australia. Some have larvae that will stay on the surface of their host and can be removed easily, while others will be undetectable deep inside the host. Caterpillars are regular targets of these wasps, as are other insect larvae. Some parasitic wasps will attack the eggs of other invertebrates. The eggs of praying mantids, in particular, succumb to attack. The tell-tale signs are small round holes that appear over the oothecae from which the tiny wasps have emerged after eating the developing mantids. Unfortunately there is often not much that can be done for affected individuals, but removal of the substrate and cleaning the enclosure is the best response to suspected parasitic wasp attack.

Gordian worms

These bizarre parasites are long thin worms that have a hard outer skin. They are not soft and slimy like earthworms. These parasites infect many groups of

Mantispids

Mantispids are members of the lacewing group and are fascinating invertebrates in their own right. Some mantispids parasitise the eggs of spiders by laying an egg on a gravid female spider. This egg hatches into a sneaky larva that climbs into the egg sac as the spider builds it and is sealed inside along with the juicy spider eggs. The authors had one such experience, finding that a huge mantispid instead of spiderlings had emerged from the egg sac of a rainforest huntsman. Detecting this form of parasitism is very difficult, but shows that thorough inspection of any animals caught in the wild is worthwhile.

Mantispid

Moulting problems

This is one of the most common problems invertebrates face in captivity. Moulting is a critical time for those that grow in this way. They must get themselves into an appropriate position, split their old exoskeleton and 'pump' themselves out of it with their legs, antennae and other fine features intact. Invertebrates are extremely vulnerable during this period, and if things go slightly wrong it can lead to disaster.

Moulting problems usually arise for one of the following reasons:

- The enclosure humidity is too low, and the animal dries out too quickly and gets stuck while only partially out of the old exoskeleton. This is most common with tropical species.

- Overcrowding – too many animals housed together in too little space – can result in animals interrupting each other during moulting (e.g. stick insects).

- A lack of suitable perching space can be a problem for many species that need to hang freely from a branch or twig to moult without bumping the ground or another object (e.g. praying mantids and katydids).

- Live food insects such as crickets and cockroaches that are still in your animal's enclosure while it is moulting can chew on and damage the newly emerging animal or interrupt the moulting process (e.g. primitive spiders lying on their back in burrows).

Invertebrates that have problems during moulting will often die, as they become stuck in their old exoskeleton. Sometimes they will manage to get out but may be severely deformed, which usually results in death. Minor deformities that allow the animal to function in a semi-normal manner can be corrected by a successful subsequent moult. On occasions where a leg is stuck in the moult, the animal will often shed the leg to get free. This is known as autotomy. Stick insects and spiders can regenerate lost legs; spider legs appear miraculously as they emerge from their next moult! If your animal is stuck in the old exoskeleton by only a leg you can attempt to extract it, but do so with caution. The body is very delicate during this phase, and damage to it may result in death. If a leg is severely caught it can be detached where it joins the body (at the natural weak point) and the wound will quickly close over. To do this, grasp the leg firmly, apply steady upward pressure and it will come

away freely. Your invertebrate will not be able to stop the bleeding if the leg is detached at any other point.

When is my animal having difficulty moulting?

Although the postures that the various groups adopt while they moult varies a great deal, once they begin to moult they should all make steady progress. If more than 10 minutes has passed and nothing seems to be happening, chances are that your invertebrate is experiencing problems. Some species will only take 10 minutes to complete a moult, others up to an hour.

The moulting positions and approximate times taken to complete the moulting process are listed in the following table. The time specified is that taken from the time the old exoskeleton breaks open to when the animals are completely free, and covers species that most commonly encounter moulting problems in captivity.

Group	Moulting position	Approximate moulting duration
Praying mantids, stick insects, crickets and katydids	Hanging beneath a perch, or from the side of the enclosure	10–30 mins
Primitive spiders	Lying on their back	30 mins to 1 hour
Grasshoppers	Lying on their side	10 mins
Modern spiders (arboreal species)	Suspended from silk	10–30 mins
Modern spiders (ground dwellers)	Lying on the ground	10–30 mins
Butterflies and moths (emergence)	Suspended below chrysalis	10–40 mins

Physical injuries

The effects of physical injuries to invertebrates are very different from injuries to vertebrates. Many species cannot heal an injury to the body, and damaged legs are often discarded. Treating invertebrates is very difficult as most are small and unwilling patients. As already mentioned, legs can be removed if damaged (see 'Moulting problems'), but the invertebrate will usually do this itself. Injuries to the body are much more serious and must be treated if blood loss is occurring or death will result. Invertebrate blood is not red; in most cases it is blue-green and called haemolymph.

Many methods to stop the bleeding from the body of an invertebrate have been tried. Some work better than others and most are successful on small wounds (pin-prick size). A tiny piece of paper towel can be used as a Band-aid over these small injuries, and will help the wound to clot. Large tears or crush injuries are usually untreatable. The reason that body wounds are so serious is that the animal cannot close the wound by itself. This is because their body cavities are pressurised with blood (it is not contained in veins and arteries like ours). Blood will continue to pump out of the rupture in the exoskeleton until the animal dies. If you attempt to close the wound, you must stop the blood flow, prevent infection and prevent any material used to close the wound from getting inside. Many methods have been developed overseas for the treatment of tarantulas. The bodies of such large spiders will rupture easily if the spider is dropped while being handled. Products such as petroleum jelly and 'super glue' (cyanoacrylates) have been used to successfully treat small wounds. The authors have had some success using a medical version of super glue obtained from a veterinarian.

Damage to the cephalothorax of a Sydney Funnelweb is being repaired by the authors using medical 'superglue'. (Note the use of a petri dish to restrain the spider so that both 'patient' and 'surgeon' are safe during the procedure.)

Stress

Some invertebrates can suffer from a form of stress in captivity if overhandled or disturbed too often. This seems to be more common in burrowing invertebrates, animals that would normally spend long periods of time inactive in a dark burrow, with brief periods of activity when they feed. Scorpions, primitive spiders and burrowing cockroaches, in particular, seem to be most affected, with animals becoming more and more lethargic as the condition worsens. Inexperienced keepers can often mistake this as the animal calming down or getting used to very regular handling – until it dies! If you have an animal that falls into this category and it is exhibiting signs of stress, immediately stop any interaction. Allow your animal to keep to itself in its burrow or shelter, and observe it with minimal disturbance. If recognised early, many of these animals will bounce back as vigorous as ever after a few weeks. It is very important when handling or interacting with any individual invertebrate that you do not overdo it. In the case of educational animals that you may wish to use daily for giving talks or presentations, it is very wise to have a number of animals to use on a rotational basis.

Deficiencies in captivity

What are deficiencies?

Deficiencies are things that are missing from the diet or environment of animals in captivity and are important for their survival. It is likely that invertebrates, like many other animal groups, will suffer from various deficiencies from time to time. Not much is known about this in regard to invertebrates, as only a few species have been studied in such detail.

What are the signs of deficiencies in invertebrates?

There are many ways in which invertebrates with deficiencies could display signs of this problem. These include:

- stunted growth
- moulting problems and deformities
- chewing on enclosure mates (even if they are herbivores)
- egg-laying problems
- general ill health
- premature death.

It is most likely that invertebrates being fed one particular food (rather than a range of foods), or eating things that are very different from those they would eat in the wild, would be at higher risk of suffering from deficiencies. Calcium and protein are examples of nutrients that are required by invertebrates, but may not be available in the quantities they require. Some crickets have been known to start eating each other if they are protein deficient.

The best approach for most invertebrates is to provide your animals with a range of food options, as they know what they need better than we do. Some invertebrate predators will stop eating a particular kind of prey, giving the impression they are not hungry, yet when presented another kind of prey animal they will eat ravenously. Diets such as Orthopteran mix (p.172) are good because they contain a large range of ingredients that invertebrates can pick and choose from, depending on what they need. If your animals have health problems that you think could be due to a deficiency of some sort, try offering some alternative foods, keeping in mind what they would be eating in the wild.

Are all deficiencies related to food?

Deficiencies can sometimes be environmental. Some invertebrates seem to require UV light to thrive in

captivity. Species that do best when provided with UV light are those that are active during the day in the wild, and would bask in full sunlight as part of their normal behaviour. Diurnal cockroaches, grasshoppers, mantids and some katydids are examples of the animals to which this applies. There are no specific symptoms of UV deficiency; the animal may simply die before maturity when all other housing conditions appear fine. If your animal has health problems that could fall into this category, try exposing it to some UV light (p.163) and see if things improve.

Emergency food

On some occasions, otherwise healthy invertebrates get into situations where they require 'a hit' of high-energy food to get them back on track. An example of this is an escaped animal that has not had food or water for some time, and is still alive but too weak to feed normally. In these circumstances a simple mix of glucose and water offered directly to the mouthparts of the animal will sometimes give them enough energy to resume normal feeding. Try a mix of 1:4 glucose to water offered via an eye dropper or 1 mL syringe. If the animal drinks quite a bit of the solution, switch to offering water only. Some invertebrates respond very rapidly to this. If the animal regains strength and resumes a normal posture, offer its regular food and water immediately.

A Rainforest Scorpion receives a glucose solution from a syringe.

Effects of aging

Many invertebrates live somewhat fast and furious lives, while others take it a little easier. It is likely that in captivity most invertebrates reach ages beyond their normal wild lifespan, as they have food and water readily available, and do not have to survive the constant threat of predators.

While they are young and still growing, the moulting process ensures that their exoskeletons are repaired and replaced, but once they mature and have moulted for the final time this rejuvenation no longer occurs. Over time many mature invertebrates begin to look 'shabby'. Wear and tear is obvious on their exoskeletons, and with some old animals the tips of their legs begin to die off. It is not uncommon for older individuals of groups to lose the tips of their legs and parts of their antennae.

These parts often darken before simply falling off. This sounds horrible, but we must remember that their bodies are constructed very differently from our own. There is nothing that can be done about these things; it's simply a case of your invertebrates getting old. Some keepers may choose to euthanase animals at the point where they begin to lose function.

Euthanasia

In some cases you may find that there is no option other than to euthanase an invertebrate with a severe health problem. The recommended method for invertebrates is to first refrigerate them for 15 minutes (which sedates them by slowing down all their body processes), and then place them directly into the freezer for an hour.

The old katydid (left) has obvious signs of aging on the legs and antennae; the younger one (right) is in perfect condition.

Display your invertebrates

Whether you want to have an attractive animal enclosure in your lounge room, or to display your animal to the public at a zoo, the most important thing to think about is how to keep your animal alive and happy, and allow people to observe it at the same time. For some animals it is easy. Mantids, for example, can be displayed by strategically placing a branch across the enclosure to provide the perfect perching position for the mantid and for the visitor to view. Other animals are not so easy. Many burrowing spiders, for example, rarely get displayed well because of their nature to dig underground tunnels or sit in the darkest corner of the enclosure. These animals should not be ignored because of this behaviour. Instead, see it as a challenge to explore what you can do to ensure the animal's comfort while also creating a great display. Use your animal's behaviour to your advantage, observe the animal and see where it prefers to forage and sit. The best displays are designed with this in mind.

Thoughtful display of invertebrates can enhance the appearance of your animals as well as educate people. For example, rather than looking at a drab enclosure and imagining the ants working deep underground, people should be able to learn about the complex life cycles of a colony and the structure of an ant nest; a visible artificial burrow system will make this possible. Explanation or interpretation of the animal's behaviour and appearance in an educational context such as a zoo or school can be achieved in a variety of ways, including signage, video or audio recordings. Whether for professional display or home, the basis of any interpretation method is the well-designed animal enclosure.

The size of an invertebrate display can be very different from that of other animal groups. Invertebrates often do not need as much room as you may imagine. A single White-tailed Spider can be displayed in a 15 cm square enclosure with everything it requires. People often display invertebrates in large enclosures that have been built for frogs or lizards. If so, your invertebrate will often find a secluded spot right at the back of such an enclosure and never be seen by the viewers. You will find a small enclosure will draw your viewers in to look at these animals in greater detail, something that often cannot be done with larger animals.

Before you set up any display you should consider the following questions:

- Why are you making this display?

- What are you trying to show?

- What kind of environment does your invertebrate come from?

- How will the invertebrate's behaviour affect your design?

If you approach your display with these factors in mind, it will help you to achieve the best display possible for your animal.

This centipede is displayed in *Bugs Alive!* at Melbourne Museum. This enclosure was designed with the behaviour of centipedes in mind. Knowing that centipedes shelter in crevices in the wild, the enclosure was designed with a crevice at the front against the glass.

Tips for creating good displays

Getting creative and building displays for invertebrates is a lot of fun and a rewarding experience, even if it is only for your own viewing pleasure. Here are a few tips for creating a great display:

- Plan what you want to create, taking the behaviour of your invertebrate into account.

- Use materials and objects that will highlight the behaviour of your animal.

- Partially buried rocks look more natural and are more stable. Using several rocks of the same type will also present a more natural look.

- Making the substrate deeper at the back of the display will angle the display towards the viewer, making the animals more visible.

- Don't always limit yourself to natural materials; a variety of artificial materials can also be used to create displays.

Fibreglass

Fibreglass is waterproof, lightweight and strong. It can be painted or have substrate materials embedded in it (while it is still wet) to give it a natural look. The only disadvantage of fibreglass fit-outs is the time it takes to produce them and the safety considerations you need to bear in mind while building them. Fibreglass can be used for backdrops, burrows and moats, and for any large areas that need static landscaping.

Fun displays

Not all enclosures need to mimic natural habitats. Sometimes the best messages can be passed on with an obvious fun design. An enclosure with a model train and lots of Portuguese Millipedes (*Ommatoiulus moreletii*) would be a clear way to communicate a message that these millipedes stopped trains in Victoria in 2002. Such displays are often great support material for current issues in the media.

Natural displays

These displays can use any number of natural materials to create an attractive environment for your animal to live in. Rocks, logs, soil, moss, leaf litter and large live plants can all be combined to achieve the effect you are after.

Advantages:

- low cost

- suitable for many species

- materials are easy to get

- simple to construct

- holds humidity well

- easy to replace.

Disadvantages:

- burrowing species may hide

- could introduce pests and diseases

- may need regular replacement if it gets dirty.

Moats can assist you to display animals that cannot easily be displayed otherwise. Green Tree Ants are true escape artists and a fibreglass moat is ideal for keeping them in.

Case study – natural displays

Many animals have amazing camouflage. For example, Common Toadhoppers (*Buforania crassa*) are great at camouflaging into the red sands of central Australia. You will sometimes see them in the wild on black bitumen roads very easily as they sit there warming up in the sun. As soon as they are disturbed they will quickly move back onto the red sand and rocks and 'disappear'. Using natural materials is a perfect way to construct your enclosure and demonstrate this concept.

To develop the Common Toadhopper enclosure we used materials that reflected its natural habitat. We put down a bed of red sand that was about 2 cm deep at the front and 5 cm at the back. This slope helps viewers to look in at the display. By strategically placing the rocks in clusters rather than uniformly, we tried to mimic nature and to give interest to the landscape. Sand was sprinkled over the rocks to make them look as if they had been there for years. A heat lamp was added above, and we hid some water pots in the substrate in which to place fresh foliage for the animals to feed on. Rocks were positioned just below the heat lamp to create a hotspot in which the animals could bask.

This display succeeded because it highlighted the animals' natural behaviour. Because they like to bask, providing an obvious hotspot meant that we had a very high chance that at least one individual would be sitting under the light at any time. This display provides all the essential requirements for the animals, as well as an interpretive message for the viewer. This is the basis for a good camouflage display for this species.

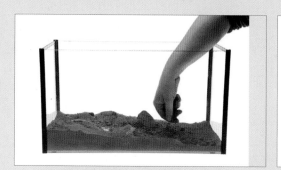

(1) Embed the rocks into the substrate so that at least 25% of the rock is underground. Sprinkle with sand.

(3) A heat lamp is added to create a hotspot on the rocks.

(2) Arid vegetation is added to enhance the display and as food.

(4) Common Toadhoppers basking under a hotspot – this display highlights the grasshoppers natural behaviour as well as providing the essential elements for the animals' survival.

Gypsum cement

Gypsum cement is a hard material that is ideal for the construction of the parts of your display that you do not want animals to alter. Hydro Stone is one of the best products for this purpose, and it can be used to create artificial burrows, landscapes and backdrops. It comes in powdered form and is mixed with water, just like plaster, and will harden in a short period of time. It can be poured easily into moulds to take on any shape you wish.

For animals that are strong diggers like the Giant Burrowing Cockroach (*Macropanesthia rhinoceros*) a display burrow made of Hydro Stone will ensure it remains on display in the burrow you have designed, rather than digging its own home.

Advantages:

- allows burrowing species to be displayed
- very hard, invertebrates cannot dig into it
- holds moisture to maintain humidity
- long lasting.

Disadvantages:

- very heavy
- difficult to clean
- animals cannot alter it to suit their needs
- cannot be easily modified
- time consuming to prepare.

Case study – gypsum cement

Bull ants are great to display, as they are one of the largest ant species in the world and it is easy for people to view all the stages in their life cycle. With the right enclosure design you are able to observe the different castes and their social interactions, as well as their feeding, egg laying, larvae and pupae.

A great way to display a burrowing species such as this is to create an artificial nest against glass. A system like this gives the animals the security of being underground and the viewer the opportunity to see the animals in action.

To start the display, we planned the tunnel system based on our knowledge of real ant nests, and drew it on paper. These bull ant nests have multiple chambers; many tunnels and a few openings at the surface.

A timber and clay mould was created so that the Hydro Stone ant nest would fit neatly inside the face of the display enclosure. Clay was used to make a negative relief of the tunnels, (anywhere we did not want Hydro Stone). We were careful to make sure that the burrows were going to be large enough for the ants to move in and out of freely. The entire Hydro Stone block was designed to cover just the bottom half of the display enclosure's front window, allowing for the surface (ground level) to be displayed also. Once we were happy with the final mould, the clay was lubricated with potter's soap to ensure the Hydro Stone would come away easily from the clay and timber.

Rather than having a pure white nest, we mixed through some cement dye to give the stone a more natural colour. Before pouring the mixture onto the mould, we lightly scattered the mould with sand to give the tunnels texture. When we poured the mixture into the mould, it was fluid enough to settle across the mould. We filled the mould to approximately 1 cm above the clay to give the nest extra stability when set. The nest was left in the mould for a couple of days in regulated humidity and temperature so that the cement set evenly, and to minimise the risk of warping or cracking.

When we were ready to separate the Hydro Stone, we gently worked the mould and the cast away from each other. We used gravity to help pull the Hydro Stone away from the clay and wood. (If the Hydro Stone does not come away easily, soak it in water to help loosen the clay and to lubricate between the wood and the Hydro Stone.) The residual clay was cleaned away from the nest.

We used a thin sheet of marine ply to create a false surface and covered it in a thin layer of natural materials. This ensured that the ants utilised the nest we had created for them and remained on display.

Ant nests need to be humid, so small volumes of water were regularly added to the absorbent Hydro Stone block to ensure this.

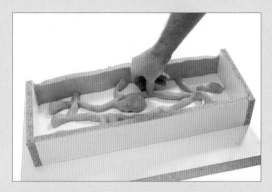

(1) A timber and clay mould was designed so that the Hydro Stone ant nest would fit neatly inside the face of the display enclosure.

(2) Sand was sprinkled onto the mould and the Hydro Stone is poured to cover the clay

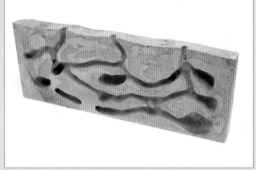

(3) The nest was carefully pulled out of the mould and excess clay cleaned off.

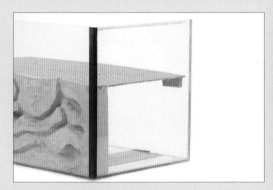

(4) The nest was placed into the display tank and a false surface added, made from marine ply, glue and sand.

(5) Ants utilise the nest chambers to successfully raise their brood.

Polystyrene and epoxy resin

Polystyrene is easy to obtain and, when combined with an epoxy resin, is an effective way of creating an artificial fit-out for display enclosures. Mocking up backdrops, burrows and tunnels is fairly simple and gives you a great deal of flexibility as to contours and rough natural texture. Coating the polystyrene with epoxy resin gives it a strong waterproof layer. A large variety of substrate types can be combined with the resin to give it a natural look. Araldite is an epoxy resin, but buying it in this form can be very expensive. It is more cost effective to purchase it in bulk.

We specifically recommend epoxy resin as some other types of resin may melt the polystyrene when they are applied. Ensure that you are careful when applying this resin and follow the product's safety directions.

Advantages:

- allows burrowing species to be displayed
- hard, many invertebrates cannot dig into it
- simple to make
- lightweight.

Disadvantages:

- strong burrowers can break through the epoxy resin coating
- may need repairing
- animals cannot alter it to suit their needs
- does not hold moisture well.

Case study – polystyrene and epoxy resin

Australian tarantulas are popular animals to keep and many people love to look at them up close. The spiders feel most comfortable in their burrows, so to develop an Australian tarantula display we needed to consider the type of burrow in which they are found in their natural habitats. Australian tarantulas dig straight tunnels that can vary in depth and end in a chamber. Our particular display was within a simple glass tank. A block of polystyrene was cut with a knife to occupy two-thirds of the front face of the tank. (Polystyrene blocks can be purchased from art supply shops or some hardware stores. If you cannot get blocks that are big enough you can glue sheets of polystyrene together.) We made sure the polystyrene did not fit too snugly into the space, about 3 mm is needed on the sides to allow for layers of epoxy resin and substrate.

The burrow needed to be wide enough for the spider to move through freely, and have a chamber at the end that was a little wider with a flat resting place for the spider. An outline of this burrow was drawn onto the polystyrene so it could be carved out. We continually placed the polystyrene back into the tank as we carved to see how it looked. We also created contours in the surface of the substrate (top of the polystyrene) to give it a natural look. (To cut into the polystyrene you can use a wide array of implements including knives, chisels, screwdrivers, sandpaper and hacksaw blades. All these objects will give a different effect.)

Coco-peat was chosen as a substrate and we used epoxy resin to glue a layer of it to the polystyrene, as it is similar in colour and texture to the soil in the spider's natural habitat. In the resin, the coco-peat dried darker than in its loose state, which is common for many substrates.

We only mixed 50 mL of resin at a time, as it comes in two components that when mixed will set relatively quickly, and we did not want to waste it. The resin was applied with a paintbrush to cover all polystyrene surfaces that would be seen by the viewers. Dry coco-peat was sprinkled over the wet resin until no white patches were visible, and was then allowed to set. (Coco-peat must be dry and crumbly to use for this purpose). The process of applying resin and adding coco-peat was repeated three times, with the excess coco-peat dusted off in between. The more layers you apply the stronger the finished product will be.

(1) The burrow can be created by carving into the polystyrene using a variety of instruments.

(2 and 3) A paintbrush is used to apply resin to all surfaces that can be seen by the viewer. Substrate is then sprinkled onto the resin and any excess shaken off.

(4) Resin and substrate were added until there was no visible polystyrene.

(5) The spider utilised the burrow as it was a good size and shape. If the burrow is too big or too small the spider may not use it.

Acknowledgements

The authors would like to thank the following people for their help and support during the writing of this book. Patrick Honan and staff at Melbourne Zoo Invertebrate Department, Melanie Raymond, Patti Brown, Marija Bacic, Rodney Start, Ken Walker, Mark Newton, Mark Kellet, Boris Lomov, Chris Rowley and Antonio Polak. We would particularly like to thank Luke Simpkin and all the staff from the Live Exhibits Unit at Melbourne Museum for their support and assistance during this project. We would also like to thank our families – Paul Whitney, and Caitlin, Annie and Tayen Henderson for their understanding and patience!

Illustrations

The illustrations were drawn by Kate Nolan, with the exception of the hemimetabolistic and holometabolistic drawings on p.9, which were drawn by Sharyn Madder, and the image of the centipede on p.133, which was drawn by Graham A. Milledge.

Photographs

All images in 'Amazing bugs' and the care guide chapters were taken by Alan Henderson, with the exception of the Botany Bay Weevil, on p.23, which was taken by Deanna Henderson.

Images in 'Housing' were taken by Rodney Start, with the exception of the vial on p.158 and the dichroic lamp on p.160, which were taken by Alan Henderson. 'Food and water': snails feeding on p.167, Indian house crickets on p.169, images on p.170 and the image of honey on p.174 by Alan Henderson. All other images in 'Food and water' were taken by Rodney Start. 'Health': all images taken by Alan Henderson with the exception of the Sydney Funnelweb in the petri dish on p.182, which was photographed by Deanna Henderson. 'Display your invertebrates': images taken by Rodney Start, with the exception of the centipede display on p.185, the Toadhoppers basking under the hotspot on p.187, the spider on p.191 and the moat on p.186, which were all taken by Alan Henderson.

The recipe for orthopteran mix on p.172 was reproduced from:
Grasshopper Country: The Abundant Orthopteroid Insects of Australia
By David Rentz
with the permission of the University of New South Wales Press

Authors

Alan Henderson

Alan has been coordinator of Melbourne Museum's Live Exhibits Department for the last eight years. From a young age he has had a fascination with invertebrates and animal husbandry. He developed and managed the Australian Nature Education Centre, earning him the Young Australian of the Year regional development award in 1998. Since then he has undertaken a central role in the development and running of the *Bugs Alive!* exhibition at Melbourne Museum.

Deanna Henderson

Deanna is a senior animal keeper at Melbourne Museum and has worked in the Live Exhibits Department since 1999. Her interest in all things small developed during her project work with butterflies at Melbourne Zoo. She played a key role in the development of *Bugs Alive!* at Melbourne Museum and has become internationally recognised for her work on keeping cockroaches.

Jessie Sinclair

Jessie is a senior animal keeper at Melbourne Museum's Live Exhibits Department. Her formal invertebrate work started with ant conservation in plantation timbers but has developed into interpretive education and husbandry. Her invertebrate interests are broad – ranging from aquatic through to terrestrial animals. She currently works supporting the *Bugs Alive!* exhibition.

Glossary

abdomen	the rear division of the body
autotomy	voluntary release of an appendage or leg
book lungs	paired respiratory organs in many arachnids, consisting of many thin folds of membrane resembling the pages of a book; located on the underside of the abdomen
browse	fresh plant foliage used for feeding animals
camouflage	colouration, shape or patterns that help an animal to blend in with its surroundings
carnivore	an animal that feeds on other animals
castes	the different body forms among social insects such as ants; includes queen, workers, soldiers, reproductive males
cephalothorax	the front body section of arachnids; the combined head and thorax
cerci	a pair of jointed appendages on the tip of the abdomen of insects and other invertebrates
chelae	the pincer-like claws on the end of a scorpions pedipalps
chelicerae	the foremost set of appendages that are the feeding structures of the arachnids; used for grasping and piercing
cocoon	a protective case of silk or other fibrous material for insects to **pupate** within
compound eyes	eyes which consists of many light-sensitive lenses, each forming a portion of an image
cryptic	an animal that uses colouration or patterning to help it **camouflage** and protect itself from predators
detritovore	an animal that feeds on decomposing material
diapause	a state of suspended development or growth
diurnal	an animal that is active during the day
egg sac	a structure made by spiders from their silk to house eggs while they incubate
elytra	the hardened forewings of beetles
epiphragm	a dried film of mucus used to seal the aperture of the shells of some land snails to prevent dehydration
exoskeleton	the hard outer layer of an invertebrate's body
frass	pellet-like invertebrate poo
gastropod	the group of molluscs that have a large muscular foot used for locomotion; some have a single coiled shell and others a shell significantly reduced or missing
gonopod	specialised leg used for the transfer of sperm in millipedes
gonopore	the external opening of the reproductive organs
gravid	pregnant
haemolymph	invertebrate blood; in most cases it is blue-green

hemimetabolistic	development of young in which they begin life looking like miniature versions of their parents; they **moult** a number of times getting bigger with each moult, these stages in between moults are called **instars**.
herbivore	an animal that feeds on plants
hermaphrodite	an animal that has both male and female reproductive organs
holometabolistic	development of young in which they begin life looking very different from their parents, development including egg, **larva**, **pupa** and adult phases; the larvae **moult** to grow and will go through a number of **instars** before pupating to change form completely and emerge as an adult
host	the organism in or on which a parasite lives
humidity	the percentage of moisture in the air
instar	the growth stage between successive moults
invertebrate	an animal without a backbone
larva(ae)	the immature state, between egg and **pupae**, of a **holometabolistic** insect, differs radically from the adult.
mandible	the hardened lower jaws of many invertebrates
morphological	relating to the body form and structure of an animal
moult	the periodic process of shedding the **exoskeleton**
nocturnal	an animal that is most active during the night
nymph	the immature stage of certain species of insects, in which the young resemble their parents but are smaller and lack wings
omnivore	an animal that feeds on both animal and vegetable matter
ootheca	the egg casing produced by some insects to protect their eggs
operculum	a flap or covering that protects an opening
ovipositor	a specialised organ extending from the tip of the **abdomen** used for depositing eggs
parthenogenesis	the ability to reproduce without fertilisation
pectine	the comb-like structure on the underside of a scorpion
pedipalp	the second pair of appendages after the **chelicerae** in arachnids, located either side of the mouth
pheromone	chemical substance released by animals as a form of communication
proboscis	the lengthened mouthparts in some insects that are modified to form a tube for piercing and sucking
pronotum	the upper surface of the first segment of the thorax of an insect, which may be enlarged to form a shield over the **thorax** and head.
pupa(ae)	the stage between **larval** and adult as insects undergo metamorphosis
radula	the tongue-like structure covered by rows of rasping teeth, used by snails and slugs to feed
rostrum	the elongated piercing and sucking mouthparts of true bugs; also applies to the snout of weevils
scavenger	an animal that feeds on dead or decaying material

sperm web	a web of few or many threads on which a male spider deposits sperm and then takes it into his **pedipalps**
spermatophore	packet or capsule containing sperm produced by the male to be transferred to the female for fertilisation
spinnerets	tubular structures found on the end of the abdomen of spiders and some insect **larvae**, which they use to produce silk for egg sacs, webs and cocoons
spiracles	specialised openings in an invertebrate's body, through which air passes for oxygen exchange (breathing)
stridulation	production of sound by rubbing two structures or surfaces together
substrate	the material that covers the floor of the enclosure
thorax	the middle section of the three major body divisions in insects, located between the head and the **abdomen**; wings and legs are appendages of the **thorax**
tibial spurs	spur-like appendages present on the tibia of the front legs of many male spiders, helping to hold the female up during mating
venom	a toxic liquid injected by one animal into another
venom claw	the specialised front legs of centipedes that act as fangs

Index

Note: Bold page numbers refer to species with a care guide.

A

abdomen 13, 21, 35, 75, 81, 97, 101, 111
Abelia grandiflora 68, 69, 70
Acacia
    melanoxylon 120
    species 23, 85, 89
Achillea millefolium 59
Acrida conica **71**
Acripeza reticulata **59**
Acrophylla
    titan 81, 85
    wuelfingi **85**
acrylic enclosures 156
ageing 184
air conditioners 161
Allothereua maculata **137**
Alpine Daisy Bush 59
Alpine Heath 59
Alpine Katydid 59
Alternathera denticulata 37
Ametrus tibialis **62**
Aname species **109**
ants 13–19
    as social insects 14
    bites and stings 13, 14
    Black House **15**
    Blue **98**
    body structure 13
    bull **16**, 189
    colony structure 14
    escape prevention 14, 159–60, 186
    feeding 14
    Green Tree 13, **17**, 159–60, 186
    Meat 14, **18**
    Spider 19
    sugar 12, **19**
    velvet 96, **99**
apricot trees 38
Araneomorphae 111–23
Araneus bradleyi 121
Araujia sericifer 41
Archimantis latistyla **78**
Arecaceae 60
Argiope
    keyserlingi **121**
    species 121
artificial burrows 188–9, 190–1
artificial foods 167, 172–4
    bee pollen 174
    butterfly diet 174
    millipede food 173
    mollusc mix 173
    orthopteran mix 172
    placement and presentation 172
    Spirulina flakes 173
    stag beetle diet
    (adults and larvae) 173
    sugar diets 174
Asclepias species 41
Assassin Bug 91, **92**
    Bee Killer 92
    Red 92
Atractomorpha australis 71
Atrax robustus **107**
Austracris guttulosa 70
Australian Grass Pyrgomorph 71
Australian Native Bleeding Heart 39
Australian rainforest millipedes 138, **141**
Australian tarantulas 102, **105**, 165, 191
Australostoma species 63
autotomy 83, 103, 113, 181

B

Badge Huntsman **114**
Badumna insignis 123
Banded Desert Centipede **135**
Banded Huntsman **115**
Banksia species 69
bark 165
bark cockroaches 43, 46
bark mantids 79
bark mimicking grasshoppers 72
Bee Killer Assassin Bug 92
bee pollen 174
beetles 21–33, 168
    bites 22
    black carabid 28
    body structure 21
    Chalcopterus **24**
    darkling 24
    Fiddler **26**
    Golden Stag 27
    Goldengreen Stag **27**
    Green Carabid **28**
    orthopteran mix 172
    Passalid **29**
    Pie Dish **30**
    Rainbow Stag **31**
    Rhinoceros 22, **32**
    sexing 22
    stag 22
    Tiger 20, **33**, 165
Betula species 38
black carabid beetles 28
black cockroaches 46
Black Carnivorous Snail **147**
Black Field Cricket **53**
Black House Ant **15**
Black House Spider 123
Black Rock Scorpion **128**
Blackberry 89
Blackwood trees 120
Blattodea 43–9
blister disease of primitive spiders 179
Blistered Pyrgomorph 64, 65, **68**
blowflies, as food 170
Blue Ant **98**
book lungs 101, 111
Botany Bay Cockroach **45**
Botany Bay Weevil **23**
bottlebrushes 55, 60, 86
Bracteantha species 69
branches 165
Buchan Cave Cricket **54**
Buforania crassa **69**, 187
bug keeping
    in Australia 5
    responsibility in 11
bugs
    reason for keeping 5
    sources of 6
    what are they? 7
    with exoskeletons 9
    with soft bodies 9
bull ants **16**
    displaying 189
burrowing cockroaches 43, 47, 166
    Giant 43, 44, **47**
burrows 166
    artificial 188–9, 190–1
butterflies 35–41
    Common Eggfly 34, 36, **37**
    compatibility with other species 36
    diet **174**
    food preferences 35, 36

gravel-filled water dish 175
    handling 36
    hatching problems 35
    keeping 36
    Lesser Wanderer 41
    moulting times 181
    Orchard 40
    sexing 35
    Wanderer **41**
buying bugs from commercial suppliers 6

C

Caedicia
    marginata 55
    simplex **55**
    species 55
Caelifera 65–73
calcium deficiency 183
Callistemon species 55, 60, 86
camouflage 55, 65, 81, 187
Camponotus species **19**
Cantareus aspersa 146, **148**
Carabidae 28
cardboard containers 166
Cardiodactylus novaeguinaea **58**
carnivores 52, 146
caterpillar viruses 178
caterpillars 35, 36
cave crickets 54
Cavernotettix buchanensis **54**
centipedes 132, 133–7
    Banded Desert **135**
    body structure 133
    displaying 185
    Giant Rainforest **136**
    handling 134
    House **137**
    hunting 134
    moulting 134
    reproduction 134
    sexing 133
    venom 133
cephalothorax 101
Cercophonius squama 128
Chalcopteroides species **24**
Chalcopterus beetles **24**
Chamaecytisus palmensis 86
Cheese Tree 38
chelae 125, 126
chelicerae 102, 112, 126
Children's Stick Insect 82, **84**
Chilopoda 133–7
Chlorobalius leucoviridis **61**
Chrysolopus spectabilis **23**
Cicindelidae 33
Citrus
    limon 40
    sinensis 40
    species 70
Ciulfina species 79
Coastal Rosemary 68, 73
Coccinellidae 25
cocoons 26
cockroaches 43–9
    as food 170
    Bark 43, 46
    black 46
    body structure 43
    Botany Bay **45**
    breeding 43, 44
    burrowing 43, 47, 166
    Common Shining 44, **46**
    compatibility with other species 44

Coulon 46
    displaying 44
    diurnal species 44
    Giant Burrowing 43, 44, **47**
    Giant Sand 45
    Glorious 49
    Green Metallic 45
    handling 44
    Knobbly 48
    Metallic 488
    Mitchell's 43, **48**
    orthopteran mix 172
    Pandanus 49
    sexing 43
    Speckled 170
    Spinifex 49
    Striped Desert 49
coco-peat 164
Coenomantis kraussiana 78
Coleoptera 21–33
collecting your own invertebrates 6
Common Eggfly Butterfly 34, 36, **37**
Common Garden Katydid **55**
Common Garden Snail 146, **148**
Common Green Mantid **76**
Common Shining Cockroach 44, **46**
Common Spotted Ladybird **25**
Common Toadhopper 69
    natural displays 187
cooking oil, for escape prevention 159
cooling 161
Coprosma species 70
Coryphistes species 72
Coscinocera hercules **39**
Cosmozosteria
    gloriosa 49
    zonata **49**
Cotton 93
Cotton Harlequin Bug 91, **93**
Coulon Cockroach 46
crickets 51–63, 65
    as food 170
    Black Field **53**
    Buchan Cave **54**
    feeding habits 52
    handling 52
    Indian House 53, 170
    Litter **58**
    moulting times 181
    orthopteran mix 172
    reproduction 51
    sexing 51
    Spider **58**
    Thick-legged Raspy **62**
    White-kneed King **63**
Crusader Bug 90, **94**
Ctenomorpha marginipennis 82, **87**
Ctenomorphodes tessulata 87
custom-built enclosures 156

D

Daddy Long-legs 123
Danaus
    chrysippus 41
    plexippus **41**
darkling beetles 24
decomposing wood 168
deficiencies
    dietary 182–3
    environmental 183
    signs of 182–3
    what are they? 182
Delena cancerides **120**

desert scorpions 129
Desmozosteria cincta 49
detritivores 139
Diamma bicolor **98**
diapause 22, 51, 65
dichroic lamps 160, 162
Didymuria violescens 84
Dindymus versicolor **95**
Diplopoda 139–43
diseases 178–9
displaying your invertebrates 185–91
    fibreglass 186
    fun displays 186
    gypsum cement 188, 189
    natural displays 186, 187
    polystyrene and epoxy resin 190, 191
    size of enclosure 185
    tips for creating good displays 186
    see also under specific types,
    eg. cockroaches
Dolomedes species **122**
Drosophila, as food 171
Drymaplaneta communis 44, **46**
Dryococelus australis 82, **86**, 166

E
easy-feeders 158
egg-laying containers 166
elytra 21
emergency food 183
Emperor Gum Moth **38**
emu bush 69
Enamelled Spider 121
enclosure fit-out 165–6
enclosures 155–8
    and health 177
Endacusta species 58
Ensifera 51–63
Epacris species 59
Eremophila species 68, 69
escape prevention 159–60
    ants 14, 159, 186
Ethmostigmus rubripes **136**
Eucalyptus species 38, 55, 84, 85, 87, 89
    sooty mould on 178
Eupoecila australasiae **26**
Eurycnema
    goliath 82, **85**
    osiris 85
euthanasia 169, 184
Euzosteria
    metallica 48
    tuberculata 48
exoskeletons 7, 9, 44, 82, 134
Extatosoma
    buforium 89
    tiaratum 82, **89**
eye disease of mantids 178

F
False Garden Mantis 76
Fastosarion brazieri **153**
'Feeder Roaches' 170
fibreglass 186
Ficus
    carica 95
    macrophylla 60, 86
Fiddler Beetle **26**
fig 95
flies
    blowflies as food 170
    parasitic 180
    vinegar 171
Flinders Ranges Scorpion 129
Fluon 159
fluorescent lighting 163
foods 167–75
    and health 177
    artifical 167, 172–4
    emergency 183
    natural 167–71

forceps feeding 169
forest mantids 79
Formicidae 13–19
frass 32, 45
fresh foliage 168
freshly killed insects 169
fruit 168
fun displays 186
fungal disease, Spiny Leaf Insect 178
funnelwebs 107
    Sydney 101, **107**, 176, 182

G
Garden Wolf Spider **116**
Gardenia species 57
gastropods 145
Geoscapheus species 47
Giant Burrowing Cockroach 43, 44, **47**
giant grasshoppers **70**
Giant Green Mantid **77**
Giant Green Slantface **71**
Giant Panda Snail **149**
Giant Rainforest Centipede **136**
Giant Sand Cockroach 45
Giant Water Spider 122
glass jars 157
glass tanks 155–6
Glochidion ferdinandi 39
Glorious Cockroach 49
glossary 194–6
glucose solution 174
    as emergency food 183
Gminatus
    australis 91, 92
    wallengreni 92
Golden Orb-weaver **117**
Goldengreen Stag Beetle **27**
Goliath Stick Insect 82, **85**
Goniaea
    australasiae **72**
    species 72
gonopods 139
Gordian worms 180
Gossypium hirsutum 93
grape 95
Grass Mantis **78**
grasses 166, 168
grasshoppers 8, 51, 65–73
    bark mimicking 72
    displaying 66
    eggs 65
    giant **70**
    Gumleaf **72**
    handling 66
    Lesser Mountain Spotted **73**
    moulting times 181
    orthopteran mix 172
    sexing 65
    Spur-throated 70
gravel-filled water dish 175
Great Yellow Slug 150
Green Carabid Beetle **28**
Green Jumping Spider 6, **118**
Green Metallic Cockroach 45
Green Tree Ant 13, **17**, 159–60, 186
Grevillea species 55, 60
groundcover plants 166
Gryllodes sigillatus 53, 170
Gumleaf Grasshoppers **72**
gumleaf katydids **56**
gypsum cement 188
    case study 189
Gyromantis species 79

H
Hadra webbi **151**
Hadrogryllacris species 62
Hadronyche species 107
haemolymph 181
handling
    and health 177

and stress 182
    see also under specific types,
    e.g. phasmids
Harlequin Bug **95**
    Cotton 91, **93**
Harmonia conformis **25**
health 176–83
    deficiencies in captivity 182–3
    diseases 178–9
    effects of ageing 184
    emergency food 183
    euthanasia 184
    importance of observation 176
    moulting problems 181
    parasites 179–80
    physical injuries 181–2
    quarantine 177
    record keeping 176
    stress 182
    why is my bug sick? 177
heat lamps 160
heat mats 160
heating 160–1
Hedleyella falconeri **149**
Helea
    castor 30
    scaphiformis **30**
Helena Gum Moth 38
hemimetabolistic development 8, 9, 44, 51, 66, 75, 82, 91
Hemiptera 91–5
Hemisaga species 61
Hemithynnus species 98
herbivores 52, 66, 83, 146
Hercules Moths **39**
hermaphrodites 145
Heteropoda species 115
hide boxes 166
Hierodula
    atricoxis 77
    majuscula **77**
Holconia
    immanis **115**
    species 115
holometabolistic development 9, 22, 35
Hooded Horror **77**
House Centipede **137**
household heaters 161
housing 155–66
    enclosure fit-out 165–6
    enclosures 155–8
    escape prevention 159–60
    humidity 161
    lighting 161–3
    substrates 164–5
    temperature 160–1
humidifiers 161
humidity 161, 177
huntsman 114, 115
    Badge **114**
    Banded **115**
    Social **120**
Hydro Stone 188, 189
Hymenoptera 97–9
Hypolimnas bolina nerina 34, **37**

I
Indian House Cricket 53, 170
Inland Robust Scorpions **129**
instars 9, 44
invertebrate blood 181
invertebrates 7
    hemimetabolistic development 8, 9
    holometabolistic development 9
    observation 176
Iridomyrmex 15, 18
    glaber **15**
    purpureus **18**
Isometroides vescus **131**
Isopedella species 116

J
jars 157
Jumping Jack 13, 16

K
katydids 51–63, 65, 168
    Alpine 59
    Common Garden **55**
    feeding habits 52
    gumleaf **56**
    handling 52
    Leaf-winged **57**
    moulting times 181
    Mountain **59**
    Queensland Palm 60
    Rainforest Tree **60**
    reproduction 51
    sexing 51
    Spiny-legged 55
    Spotted Predatory 7, **61**
king crickets 63
Knobbly Cockroach 48

L
ladybirds, Common Spotted **25**
Lampona
    cylindrata **123**
    murina 123
Lamprima
    aurata 27
    latreillei **27**
larvae
    ants 13
    beetles 22
    butterflies and moths 35
    wasps 97
Latrodectus hasseltii **119**
Laxta
    friedmani 46
    species 43
leaf insects 81–9
    Spiny 80, 81, 82, **89**
leaf litter 165, 166
Leaf-winged Katydid **57**
leg shedding 181
lemon 40, 70
Leopard Slug **150**
Lepidoptera 35–41
Leptomyrmex species 19
Lesser Jollyweed 37
Lesser Mountain Spotted Grasshopper **73**
Lesser Wanderer Butterfly 41
lethargy, and stress 182
light emitting diodes (LEDs) 162, 163
lighting 161–3, 177
Lily Pily 55, 60
Limacus flava 150
Limax maximus **150**
Liocheles waigiensis 126, **130**
Liquidambar species 38
Litter Cricket **58**
live food 169–71
    blowflies 170
    cockroaches 170
    crickets 170
    forceps feeding 169
    mealworms 170
    methods of feeding 169
    other backyard invertebrates 171
    prey size 171
    vinegar flies (*Drosophila*) 171
Living Stones 69
Lord Howe Island Melaleuca 86
Lord Howe Island Stick Insect 82, **86**, 166
Lychas species 131
Lycosidae 116

M
Macropanesthia rhinoceros 43
Mallee Mantis 78

mandibles 16, 97
mantids 74, 75–9
  bark 79
  body structure 75
  Common Green **76**
  compound eyes 75
  eye disease 178
  forest 79
  Giant Green 77
  handling 75
  moulting times 181
  Netwinged **79**
  parasitisation 180
  reproduction 75
  sexing 75
mantis
  False Garden 76
  Grass **78**
  Mallee 78
  Purple Winged 78
mantis eye disease 178
mantispids 180
Mantodea 75–9
marbled scorpions 131
Margin-winged Stick Insect 82, **87**
Mastigaphoides species **57**
mealworms 170
Meat Ant 14, **18**
Megacephala australis **33**, 165
Megacrania batesii 81, 82, **88**
Megadolomedes australianus 122
Megazosteria patula 45
Melaleuca howeana 86
mercury vapour lamps 163
mesh enclosures 156
metal halide lamps 163
Metallic Cockroach 48
Metallic Shield Bug 95
Mictis profana **94**
Milkweed 41
millipede food 173
millipedes 139–43, 168
  Australian rainforest 138, **141**
  broad groups 139
  defensive response 139
  displaying 140
  feeding 140
  handling 140
  moulting 140
  pill 139–40, **142**
  Portuguese **143**, 186
  reproduction 140
  sexing 139–40
Missulena
  occatoria **106**
  species 106
mist spraying 161, 175
Mitchell's Cockroach 43, **48**
Mitchell's Rainforest Snail 149
moats 159–60, 186
modern spiders 111–23
  body structure 111
  displaying 113
  egg laying 112
  feeding 112
  handling 112, 113
  moulting 112
  moulting times 181
  reproduction 111–12
  venom 112
moisture in substrates 164, 175
mollusc mix 173
Monistria
  pustulifera 65, **68**
  species 68
Morton Bay Fig 60, 86
Moth Plant 41
moths 35–41
  Emperor Gum **38**
  food preferences 35, 36
  handling 36

hatching problems 35
Helena Gum 38
Hercules **39**
  moulting times 181
  sexing 35
moulting 9, 22, 44, 91, 112, 126, 134, 140
moulting problems 181
moulting times 181
Mountain Katydid **59**
mouse spiders 101
  Red-headed **106**
Mastachilus species **29**
Mutillidae 99
Myrmecia
  pilosula 16
  species **16**

N
Native Gardenia 57
native grasses 166
Native Mulberry 89
natural displays 186
  case study 187
natural foods 167–71
  fruit and vegetables 168
  live food 169–71
  plants 167–8
  pulpy (decomposing) wood 168
Nauphoeta cinerea 170
Neomantis australis 79
Neosparassus
  diana **114**
  species **114**
Nephila
  edulus **117**
  maculata 117
  plumipes 117
Netwinged Mantids **79**
New Zealand Mirror Bush 70
newspaper (as substrate) 164
no lighting required 162
no specialised lighting required 162
nocturnal species 162
Northern Goliath Stick Insect 85
nuclear polyhedral viruses (NPVs) 178
nymphs 43, 51, 66, 82, 91

O
observation of invertebrates 176
Oecophylla smaragdina **17**, 159
oil coating, for escape prevention 159
Olearia species 59
Ommatoiulus moreleti **143**, 196
omnivores 44, 52
ootheca 43, 75
operculum 126
Opodipthera
  eucalypti **38**
  helena 38
orange 40
orb frames 157
orb-weavers 157
  Golden **117**
Orchard Butterfly **40**
Omalanthus nutans 39
Orthodera ministralis **76**
orthopteran mix 172, 183
Otway Black Snail 147
ovipositor 51, 97

P
palms 60
Pandanus Cockroach **49**
Pandanus tectorius 88
Panesthia species 47
paper daisies 69
paper wasps 97
Papilio aegeus **40**
Paracaedicia serrata 55
parasites 179–80
parasitic flies 179

parasitic wasps 180
Paratemnopteryx couloniana 46
parthenogenesis 82
Partula Snail 173
passalid beetles **29**
Passalidae 29
Passiflora species 57
Passionfruit Vine 57
Peace Lily 58
pectines 125
pedipalps 101, 111, 125
Penalva flavocalceata **63**
Peppercorn 38, 84, 85, 87
Peppermint Stick Insect 81, 82, **88**
Phalacrognathus muelleri **31**
Phasmatodea 81–9
phasmids 80, 81–9
  defence mechanisms 81
  eggs 82
  feeding 83
  handling 83
  parthenogenesis 82
  reproduction 82
  Ringbarker 84
  sexing 81
  Spur-legged 84
  Tessellated 87
  see also leaf insects; stick insects
pheromones 15, 112
Phlogius species **105**
Pholcus phalangioides 123
Phricta
  species 60
  spinosa **60**
physical injuries 182
  leg shedding 181
  stopping bleeding 182
Pie Dish Beetle **30**
pill millipedes 139–40, **142**
pink winged stick insects 87
Pipturus argenteus 89
placement of artificial foods 172
plants
  as food 167–8
  as shelter/decoration 166
  fresh foliage 168
  fresh grass 168
  potted 168
plastic containers 166
Platyzosteria species 46
Podcanthus species 84
Poecilometis species 94
polystyrene and epoxy resin 190
  case study 191
Polyzosteria
  limbata **45**
  magna 45
  mitchelii **48**
  species 44, 48
Portuguese Millipede **143**, 186
potted plants 168
praying mantids see mantids
presentation of artificial foods 172
prey size (live food) 171
primitive spiders 100, 101–9
  blister disease 179
  body structure 101
  displaying 103
  egg laying 102
  feeding 102
  handling 103
  moulting 102
  moulting times 181
  moving 103
  reproduction 101–2
Pristhesancus plagipennis 92
proboscis 36, 91
pronotum 91
Prostanthera species 68, 73
protein deficiency 183
Prunus species 38, 95

Pseudomantis albofimbriata 76
Pulmonata 145–53
pulpy (decomposing) wood 168
pupation 35
Purple Winged Mantis 78
pyrgomorphs
  Australian Grass 71
  Blistered 64, 65, **68**

Q
quarantine 177
queen 14
Queensland Apple 39
Queensland Palm Katydid 60

R
radula 146
Rainbow Stag Beetle **31**
rainforest millipedes, Australian 138, **141**
Rainforest Scorpion 126, **130**, 183
Rainforest Snail **151**
  Mitchell's 149
Rainforest Tree Katydid **60**
Randia fitzalani 57
Raniliella testudo 69
raspy crickets 82
record keeping 176
Red Assassin Bug 92
Red-headed Mouse Spider **106**
red light 162
Red Triangle Slug **152**
Redback spider 112, 113, **119**
Reduviidae 91
responsible bug keeping 11
Rhaphidophoridae 54
Rhinoceros Beetle 22, **32**
Rhinocricidae **141**
ringbarker phasmids 84
rocks 165
Rosa species 70, 85, 89
roses 70, 85, 89
rostrum 23
Rubus fruiticosus 89

S
St Andrew's Cross Spider **121**
Salticidae 118
sand 164
Schinus molle 38, 84, 85, 87
Scolopendra morsitans **135**
Scolopendrids 133
Scorpiones 125–31
scorpions 124, 125–31
  behaviour change 176
  Black Rock **128**
  body structure 125
  collecting 127
  desert 129
  displaying 127
  feeding 126
  Flinders Ranges 129
  fluorescence 127
  habitats 126
  handling 126, 127
  Inland Robust **129**
  marbled 131
  moulting 126
  Rainforest 126, **130**, 183
  reproduction 126
  sexing 125–6
  Spider Hunting **131**
  venom 126
  Wood 128
Screw Pines 88
Scutigerids 133
Scutiphora pedicellata 95
Segestidea queenslandica 60
semi-slugs 145, 153
Shield Bug 94
  Metallic 95
sick invertebrates, checklist 177

Sida 37
Sida rhombifolia 36
silicone spray 159
silty clay 165
Silver Birch 38
Sipyloidea species 87
Slantface, Giant Green **71**
slugs 9, 144, 145–53
　　body structure 145
　　displaying 146
　　eggs 146
　　Great Yellow 150
　　Leopard **150**
　　mollusc mix 173
　　Red Triangle **152**
　　reproduction 145
　　Spirulina flakes 173
snails 9, 144, 145–5
　　Black Carnivorous **147**
　　body structure 145
　　Common Garden 146, **148**
　　displaying 146
　　eggs 146
　　Giant Panda **149**
　　Mitchell's Rainforest 149
　　mollusc mix 173
　　Otway Black 147
　　Partula 173
　　Rainforest **151**
　　reproduction 145
Snugs **153**
Social Huntsman Spider **120**
soft-bodied bugs 9
soil 164
sources of bugs 6
Spathiphylum species 58
specialised lighting 162–3
Speckled Cockroach 170
spermatophores 51, 81, 126, 134, 139
Sphaerospira species 151
Sphaerotheriida 139, **142**
sphagnum moss 165
Spider Ant 19
spider crickets 58
Spider Hunting Scorpion **131**
spiders
　　Black House 123
　　blister disease 179
　　Enamelled 121
　　Garden Wolf **116**
　　Golden Orb-weavers **117**
　　Green Jumping 6, **118**
　　mouse 101
　　Red-headed Mouse **106**
　　Redback 112, 113, **119**
　　St Andrew's Cross **121**
　　Social Huntsman **120**
　　Trapdoor **108**
　　Water **122**
　　White-tailed **123**, 185
　　Wishbone **109**
　　Wolf 110
　　see also funnelwebs; huntsman;
　　　modern spiders; primitive spiders
Spinifex Cockroach 49
spinnerets 101
Spiny Leaf Insect 80, 81, 82, **89**
　　fungal disease 178
Spiny-legged Katydid 55
spiracles 111, 133
Spirulina flakes 173
Spotted Predatory Katydids 7, **61**
Spur-legged Phasmid 84
Spur-throated Grasshopper 70
stag beetles 22
　　diet (adults and larvae) 173
　　Golden 27
　　Goldengreen **27**
　　Rainbow 31
Stanwellia species **108**
stick insects 81–9

Children's 82, **84**
fungal disease 178
Goliath 82, 85
Lord Howe Island 82, **86**, 166
Margin-winged 82, **87**
moulting times 181
Northern Goliath 85
Peppermint 81, 82, **88**
pink winged 87
Titan 81, 85
sticks 165
strawberry plants 95
stress 182
stridulation 51, 105
Striped Desert Cockroach 49
substrate depths 164
substrate moisture 164, 175
substrates 164–5
sugar ants 12, **19**
sugar diets 174
　　as emergency food 183
Sydney Funnelweb 100, **107**, 176, 182
Syzygium species 55, 60

T
tarantulas 101
　　Australian 102, **105**, 165, 191
Lycosa godeffroyi **116**
Tectocoris diophthalmus 91, **93**
Teleogryllus commodus **53**
temperature 160–1, 177
Tenebrio molitor 170
Tenebrionidae 24, 30
Tenodera australasiae 78
Terpandrus
　　horridus 56
　　species **56**
　　splendidus 56
terrariums 155
Tessellated Phasmid 87
Theraphosidae 105
Thersites mitchellae 149
Thick-legged Raspy Cricket **62**
thorax 13, 43, 97
tibial spurs 102
Tiger Beetle 20, **33**, 165
timers 161–2
Timonius rumphii 39
Tinzeda species 59
Titan Stick Insect 81, 85
toadhoppers 186
　　Common **69**, 187
toolboxes 158
trade with other bug keepers 6
trapdoor spiders **108**
Tree Lucerne 86
Triboniophorus graeffi **152**
Tropidoderus childrenii 82, **84**
true bugs 91–5
　　displaying 91
　　handling 91
Typostola species 115

U
ultraviolet (UV) deficiency 183
ultraviolet (UVB) lights 163
Urodacus
　　armatus 129
　　elongatus 129
　　manicatus **128**
　　novaehollandiae 129
　　yaschenkoi **129**

V
Valanga species **70**
vegetable oil, for escape prevention 159
vegetables 168
vegetation 166
　　as food 167–8
velvet ants 96, **99**
ventilation 161

vials 158
Victaphanta
　　atramentaria **147**
　　compacta 147
vinegar flies, as food 171
Vitis species 95

W
Wanderer Butterfly **41**
wasps 97–9
　　body structure 97
　　paper 97
　　parasitic 180
　　wingless flower 98
water 175
　　and health 177
　　gravel-filled water dish 175
　　mist spray 161, 175
　　moisture in substrates 175
water spiders **122**
　　Giant 122
water sponge 175
wattle 23, 85, 89
weevil, Botany Bay **23**
Weigela species 57
Westringia fruiticosa 68, 73
White-kneed King Cricket **63**
White-tailed Spider **123**, 185
wine cooling cabinets 161
wingless flower wasps 98
wishbone spiders **109**
wolf spiders 111, 116
　　Garden **116**
Wood Scorpion 128
'Woodies' 170
workers 14
Wuelling's Stick Insect 85

X
Xylotrupes ulysses **32**

Y
Yarrow 59

Z
Zonioploca flavocinta 49